Steam, Steel & Shellfire

Steam, Steel & Shellfire

The Steam Warship 1815 –1905

Editor: Robert Gardiner
Consultant Editor: Dr Andrew Lambert

CONWAY
MARITIME PRESS

Series Consultant DR BASIL GREENHILL
CB, CMG, FSA, FRHistS

Series Editor ROBERT GARDINER

Consultant Editor DR ANDREW LAMBERT

Contributors DAVID K BROWN
N J M CAMPBELL
DENIS GRIFFITHS
ANDREW LAMBERT
DAVID LYON
JOHN ROBERTS
WILLIAM N STILL
MICHAEL WILSON

Frontispiece: Two British ships symbolising the radical changes that warships were to undergo in the nineteenth century. In the background is Windsor Castle, *last in a line of sailing three-deckers that could trace their ancestry back to the* Sovereign of the Seas *of 1637; she was converted to steam screw propulsion in 1857 and is seen here in later life as the gunnery training ship* Cambridge *at Devonport. In the foreground is the coast defence turret ship* Hydra. *Low freeboard monitors like this were the first warships to abandon an auxiliary sailing rig completely.* (CMP)

© Conway Maritime Press Ltd 1992

First published in Great Britain 1992
by Conway Maritime Press,
an imprint of Brassey's (UK) Ltd,
33 John Street, London WC1N 2AT
Reprinted 1994

British Library Cataloguing in Publication Data

Steam, steel and shellfire: warships 1815–1906
I. Gardiner, Robert J., and Lambert, Andrew D.
623.82509

ISBN 0 85177 564 0

Designed by Tony Hart
Typeset by Inforum, Rowlands Castle, Hants
Printed and bound by The Bath Press, Bath

Contents

Preface

THIS is the fourth title in an ambitious programme of twelve volumes intended to provide the first detailed and comprehensive account of a technology that has shaped human history. It has been conceived as a basic reference work, the essential first stop for anyone seeking information on any aspect of the subject, so it is more concerned to be complete than to be original. However, the series takes full account of all the latest research and in certain areas will be publishing entirely new material. In the matter of interpretation care has been taken to avoid the old myths and to present only the most widely accepted modern viewpoints.

To tell a coherent story, in a more readable form than is usual with encyclopaedias, each volume takes the form of independent chapters, all by recognised authorities in the field. Most chapters are devoted specifically to the development of ships, but others deal with more general topics like 'Guns and Armour' or 'Machinery' that relate to many ship types, thus avoiding repetition and giving added depth to the reader's understanding of the factors influencing ship design. Some degree of generalisation is inevitable when tackling a subject of this breadth, but wherever possible the specific details of ships and their characteristics have been included (a table of typical ships for each relevant chapter includes a convenient summary of data from which the reader can chart the evolution of the ship type concerned). Except for the earliest craft, the series is confined to seagoing vessels; to have included boats would have increased the scope of an already massive task.

The history of the ship is not a romanticised story of epic battles and heroic voyages but equally it is not simply a matter of technological advances. Ships were built to carry out particular tasks and their design was as much determined by the experience of that employment – the lessons of war, or the conditions of trade, for example – as purely technical innovation. Throughout this series an attempt has been made to keep this clearly in view, to describe the *what* and *when* of development without losing sight of the *why*.

The series is aimed at those with some knowledge of, and interest in, ships and the sea. It would have been impossible to make a contribution of any value to the subject if it had been pitched at the level of the complete novice, so while there is an extensive glossary, for example, it assumes an understanding of the most basic nautical terms. Similarly, the bibliography avoids very general works and concentrates on those which will broaden or deepen the reader's understanding beyond the level of the *History of the Ship*. The intention is not to inform genuine experts in their particular area of expertise, but to provide them with the best available single-volume summaries of less familiar fields.

Each volume is chronological in approach, with the periods covered getting shorter as the march of technology quickens, but organised around a dominant theme – represented by the title – that sums up the period in question. In this way each book is fully self-sufficient, although when completed the twelve titles will link up to form a coherent history, chronicling the progress of ship design from its earliest recorded forms to the present day.

With *Steam, Steel and Shellfire* the series enters waters which, if not entirely uncharted, have never been the subject of a complete or thorough survey using modern methods. Therefore this volume is necessarily based on a greater proportion of entirely original research than its predecessors, and its conclusions suggest that earlier interpretations must be subject to major revision.

To even the most casual observer the nineteenth century was a period of radical technological advances. In naval warfare, these included shell guns and rifled ordnance, the steam paddle-wheel and then screw propulsion, iron followed by steel construction, and the protection of hulls with armour plate, not to mention the perfection of underwater weapons like the mine and torpedo and the first steps towards practical submarines. As a result, earlier histories tend to concentrate on the technology, often making Victorian inventors and engineers the heroes of simple morality tales, with navies and their administrators cast in the role of arch-conservative, bigoted villains who refuse to support their ideas. Given the Victorian concept of Progress, so many developments seemed inevitable with hindsight, and any opposition to even the most visionary scheme was condemned as reactionary. Thus was born the great myth of nineteenth century naval history that the Royal Navy, the dominant navy of the period, was wedded to the past and very resistant to change.

As this book demonstrates, navies were not slow to adopt new technology as long as it was proven, but they were naturally cautious with the public purse, leaving most of the costs of research and development to what today we would call the private sector. There were also many other factors bearing on decision-making, ranging from the evaluation of the importance of sea power to individual nations, to the strength of their industrial base. Without an understanding of this complex strategic, political and economic background, a history of technology alone is less than half the story.

However, the progress of the technology itself is also complex, and in the case of steam propulsion and iron shipbuilding, the division between warships and merchantmen is an artificial one. *Steam, Steel and Shellfire* has confined its coverage to naval aspects of the story, but the reader who desires a fuller understanding of the nature of nineteenth-century ship development will find the subjects covered in greater depth in the companion volume *The Advent of Steam* to be published next in the series.

Robert Gardiner
Series Editor

Introduction

THIS book is a study of the impact of technology on nineteenth-century naval design. It follows the development of warships from the first application of steam machinery to a seagoing warship through to the revolutionary British battleship *Dreadnought* of 1906.

The role of technology

Throughout the nineteenth century the capital ship was the most complex and expensive machine constructed by man. It was unrivalled as the symbol of national power and, after 1860, of industrial maturity and economic stability. Although the battleship employed the latest advances in technology it did not stand alone; it was merely the pinnacle of industrial achievement. The technological revolution that transformed warship design between 1815 and 1905 can only be understood as an integral part of the wider revolution that affected every aspect of society in the same period. Warships are built by societies, crewed by men and employed for political ends. If this point is ignored it is hard to explain why some societies demonstrated a greater level of commitment to naval power, and proved more successful in shipbuilding innovation.

Existing studies of technological development, as it influenced warship design in the nineteenth century, have only served to obscure the real impact of change. In adopting a technology-led approach historians have ignored the fact that critical decisions were made by politicians and naval officers, not by engineers. Too many accounts of this period take the view that progress was inevitable and opposition absurd. This reflects the large body of contemporary material critical of the official view, both within and without the world's navies. By contrast this study attempts to support the official line, following the evolution of warship design from the perspective of the policy-makers. Those responsible for national security were wise enough to base their decisions on the proven capabilities of any new technology, rather than the optimistic prog-

noses urged by the projectors of successful developments, not to mention the legion of chimaerical schemes. The dominant navy of the period, the Royal Navy, adopted new technology when, and only when, it could demonstrate an ability to outperform existing systems. Because Britain depended on sea power to a far greater extent than any of her rivals it should come as no surprise to find that the Royal Navy took the lead in pioneering new systems, from steam and the paddle wheel fighting ship to the turbine engine. The fundamental technological changes were revolutionary, not evolutionary, and did not fit the Darwinian mould imposed on them by twentieth-century analysts more interested in patterns and themes than the manner in which the major navies responded to new developments. There are no straight lines of progress linking the warships of 1815 with those of 1905, and this book does not attempt any such artificial exercise.

By contrast, the role of navies remained constant, so that changes in detailed design reflected the impact of technology and not the introduction of new tasks. If the tactical system of Tsushima (1905) was the same line of battle that Nelson had employed, the object of the battle was also one that he would have understood – to prevent the enemy gaining the safety of a fortified base from which he could threaten sea communications. It should be no surprise to learn that the early naval strategic thinkers – Captain Mahan, Admiral Colomb and Sir Julian Corbett – relied explicitly upon case studies from the age of sail. Steam, steel and shell guns did not introduce new roles for navies, nor did they revolutionise strategy. However, these developments did make sea power more effective, and more powerful. In every area, from coastal bombardment to logistic support of armies, the fleets of 1905 were far superior to those of 1815.

The influence of tactics on design

One major problem for any study of warship design between 1815 and 1905 lies in the shortage of significant battles of the classical pat-

tern. In consequence the four major navies, all with experience of war at sea before 1815, attempted to integrate new technology and strategic options into the existing pattern between 1815 and 1860. It is worthy of note that many developments of this period were adopted, employed and passed out of service without ever being used in combat.

The major technical developments of the century, the shell gun, the steam engine, the screw propeller, the iron ship, armour plate, breech-loading artillery, the turret and later barbette system of gun mounting and underwater weapons, are all examined in detail in the chapters which follow. In order to make sense of their appearance in the world's warships they will be placed in context: the success of such specific concepts was entirely dependent upon the ability of the engineering community at large to build the new equipment and the policy-makers to conceive a role for them. The former point helps to explain the large role of non-maritime innovators in the nineteenth century, men such as Paixhans, Ericsson, Smith and Brunel.

Before discussing the revolution in naval design that took place between 1815 and 1905 it is first necessary to understand the nature of naval warfare in the last days of the sailing navy. The standard view is that nothing changed after Trafalgar (1805) until the steam ship burst onto the scene at some unspecified date in the 1830s, rendering the sailing ship obsolete overnight. The reality is at once more complex, and less revolutionary. Individual elements of the navy did undergo significant change, but the overall effect was limited by the materials and technology of the wooden warship. Consequently, the capital ships of 1815 were still the dominant element in naval warfare in 1850, although repairs and modifications to such ships as the British 120-gun *St Vincent* ensured that they were structurally stronger and benefited from improved guns, magazines and rig. The great three-decked sailing battleships of 1850 could throw at least double the broadside weight of those of 1815 and were better sailers, but they were in many

When designed in 1844 the three-decker Royal Albert *was the largest warship of the time. Early paddle steamers, even armed with shell guns, were little threat to such vessels, despite an apparent superiority of manoeuvre. With the advent of the propeller, this ship, like many battleships, was fitted with screw machinery, and gained the advantages of mobility without any loss of firepower.* (IWM)

cases the same ships. New vessels were built on improved models, but offered no critical advantage. No steam warship in service in 1850 posed a serious threat to such a floating fortress, for even becalmed her all-round fire would disable any steamer that had the temerity to approach, while her massively built hull could absorb far more punishment than the exposed machinery and upper deck batteries of contemporary paddle frigates. Between 1815 and 1850 the sailing line of battleship with muzzle-loading smooth bore guns reached something approaching perfection as a weapons system. Shell guns, steam engines and the screw propeller were all introduced into a sailing battlefleet dominated by the material, the men and the philosophy of the sailing navy. This remains critical to any understanding of the decisions that were taken, and therefore of the nature of warship design and the use made of the new technology.

Only when the screw propeller reduced the impact of steam power on broadside-armed wooden warships could steam achieve primacy at sea. It is important to note how far the lessons of the sailing ship period were carried over into the steam era, and then the gradual falling away of experience as a base for future thinking after 1860 as the unlimited opportunities of iron and steel promised to resolve so many strategic and tactical problems.

In the 1860s new technology opened up a plethora of possibilities, and allowed naval architects to create alternative designs for specific functions to a far greater extent than had ever been possible with wooden ships. However, this only served to create confusion, to which the policy-makers responded by ac-

cepting those features of the design that could be quantified as the bases for design, rather than attempting to rethink, or even understand the conceptual side of the design process. The parameters of design were now fixed by speed, endurance, armament, armour, size and cost. As the number of guns borne by capital ships fell from 120 to 2, with no corresponding improvement in fire control, the possibility of hitting the target was necessarily reduced. The idea that only a gun capable of penetrating the thickest armour plate yet manufactured (which was of necessity fitted to the ship in question) was fit to be carried aboard a first class warship took hold to such a degree that all else was compromised. Here the lack of serious combat experience tended to reinforce the mistaken conception of the ships. Without a fleet action on the open oceans designers were left with the American Civil War, a one-sided coastal campaign that spawned the monitor; and the Austro-Italian engagement off Lissa, a clash of the ill-armed with the ill-led that served only to mislead an entire generation into an overvaluation of the ram. A variety of technical developments in the 1880s resulted in a degree of standardisation with the pre-dreadnought battleships, the typical example displacing 12,000–14,000 tons, armed with four 12in and twelve to fourteen 6in guns and capable of up to 18kts. Finally, the Sino-Japanese War of 1894, the

The Battle of Lissa in 1866 appeared to show the ram to advantage, since the Italian ironclad flagship was dispatched in this fashion (albeit while virtually stopped at the time). In fact, analysis of the battle could support some surprising conclusions – unarmoured wooden ships had been considered banished from the line by ironclads, but the Austrian Kaiser *(seen here repairing damage after the battle) proved less vulnerable than expected and in action had actually rammed an Italian ironclad.* (CMP)

Spanish-American War of 1898 and Russo-Japanese War of 1904–5 provided the information that supported the dreadnought concept and a more rational approach to naval design.

The political and strategic situation, 1815–1905

Warships are built to meet specific requirements, which can most simply be stated as a national strategy. Before dealing with the history of warship design in the century of the naval revolution it is well worth considering why the powers built warships, and how they chose from the myriad of designs that were available after 1860. National strategy, and not technology dominated those decisions.

Between 1815 and 1905 the Royal Navy maintained a maritime preponderance that was essential to the defence of Britain's vast imperial and economic empire. Her strategic position was ably summarised in 1890 by Captain Alfred T Mahan in his seminal work, *The Influence of Seapower Upon History, 1660–1782*. Mahan asserted that the commitment to maintain naval supremacy in battle had been the key element in the rise of Britain to world power. While this American officer was less than scrupulous in his use of historical example, and has been subject to criticism and revision ever since, the basic threads of his argument hold true. Britain sustained her world empire by meeting any challenge to her naval preponderance, in peacetime by outbuilding her rivals, in wartime by destroying their fleets. In addition, and outside the scope of Mahan's thesis, Britain used diplomatic links, quasi-wars and alliance policy to reduce the threat. The battlefleet strategy conditioned every aspect of British naval policy, from the design of the ships to the development of the dockyards.

British strategy

In the period under consideration in this book the Royal Navy fought only one major war, one in which her opponent would not take the risk of naval battle. However, her strength at sea was used throughout the period to deter conflict and support British interests. With sea power secure the Royal Navy was free to oper-

ate world wide with small vessels both to police the seas against pirates and slave traders, and to impose Britain's view on countries from Algiers and Zanzibar to China and Japan. Because the handful of major engagements – Algiers, Navarino, Acre and Alexandria – were embarrassingly one-sided, the nineteenth-century Royal Navy has been seen as a colonial gunboat force which had little or no influence in Europe. The failure of the Palmerston Government to act over the Schleswig-Holstein Crisis of 1863 has been used to 'prove' the point. This distorted perception has been adopted uncritically as part of Correlli Barnett's thesis advanced in his book *The Collapse of British Power* published in 1972. Subsequently, historians have been competing among themselves to find the earliest date from which to begin the decline of Britain. In *The Rise and Fall of British Naval Mastery* of 1976 Paul Kennedy argued that sea power, and with it British strength, was a wasting asset in the nineteenth century. Having adopted Sir Halford Mackinder's 'Heartland Thesis', Kennedy claimed that the era in which sea power was decisive had ended by 1900, in favour of land powers, and in particular that the land power in control of the Eurasian Heartland would control the world. As the 'Heartland' has always been identified with the Russian Empire the events of the past two years would suggest Mackinder was if anything less prescient than Mahan. In truth Mackinder's thesis was little more than a pseudo-scientific excuse for Russophobia.

Attempts to play down the power of the Royal Navy in international politics reflect a widespread ignorance of the impact of sea power during the one major war Britain fought in the period, the Crimean War of 1854 to 1856. In contrast to the popular image of the Charge of Light Brigade, neglected soldiers and Florence Nightingale, this conflict was one

of only two successful invasions of Russia in the modern age and, furthermore, crippled the power of the Russian state for ninety years. British sea power carried an allied army to the Crimea and sustained it there for eighteen months, starved the Russian army out of Sevastopol, ruined the Russian economy through a strict blockade, destroyed a series of Russian fortresses and finally posed a threat to Cronstadt, the most powerful sea fortress in the world and the seaward defence of St Petersburg, capital of the Czarist state. Faced with this threat Russia accepted allied terms that destroyed her preponderant influence in Eastern and Central Europe and removed her from the lists of the major naval powers for forty years. The ability of the Royal Navy to create extemporised fleets of steam gunboats, armoured batteries and mortar vessels, to experiment with submarines and underwater demolition, impressed the Russians far more than the British.

The offensive employment of sea power

The lessons of the Crimean War, together with the new design freedom provided by iron, steam and heavier artillery, was first evident at the bombardment of Kinburn when, on 17 October 1855, French floating batteries played a significant part in the destruction of a Russian fortress. Until the 1890s this aspect of naval warfare held the attention of the three major sea powers. The French were quick to commit the idea of a 'Floating Siege Train' to paper, although they were unable to turn their ideas to effect in 1870. British policy-makers accepted the concept and kept up the forces for coastal attack, although their success in this area has long been neglected. The turret ship, which combined low freeboard, heavy armour

The British fleet's freedom of action in the Baltic was a significant factor in bringing Russia to the conference table at the end of the so-called Crimean War. The bombardment of Sveaborg in August 1855, seen here in a lively painting by J W Carmichael, was regarded as a dress rehearsal for coastal assaults that would culminate with an attack on St Petersburg itself. (NMM)

and the heaviest possible guns, provided a weapons system that was of limited value for combat on the open oceans, but, as John Ericsson pointed out in the case of HMS *Devastation*, would prove perfect for assaulting deep water harbours (he was particularly concerned for the security of New York). In 1863, 1878 and 1885 the threatened appearance of a British fleet in the Baltic was enough to reduce the Russian government to a state of panic. Naval power was, if anything, more significant in the nineteenth century than it had been hitherto. It proved crucial in the Crimean War, the American Civil War and the Russo-Japanese War, and it was no coincidence that the alliance with preponderance at sea was victorious in both World Wars. The real threat to Britain was that posed by a superior force at sea, be it another battlefleet, or a fleet of cruisers to prey on her commerce. Mahan's book appeared just as many of the major powers were building or rebuilding their navies. His battlefleet strategy was adopted without question by Germany, Russia, Japan and finally by the real target for the book, the United States. This sudden explosion of battleship construction forced the Royal Navy to abandon the turret ship, a class which it adopted in the absence of any serious naval threat, and develop the high freeboard battleships with their heavy guns mounted in barbettes. The *Royal Sovereign* class of 1889 were the first class of large open-ocean battleships built since the mid-1860s.

However, battlefleets were not the universal panacea that Mahan suggested. In 1904–5 Russia was taught a very hard lesson in strategy, when her battlefleet, divided by half the world, was unable to concentrate in time to deal with a smaller, but centrally placed Japanese fleet. At a more profound level it should have been clear to the Russians that they did not require a battlefleet, for the territory over which the war was fought was part of the Eurasian Heartland, and had a rail link with St Petersburg. The inefficiency of the single line Trans-Siberian Railway should have served notice to those strategists who supposed that iron roads could

replace the sea as the great highway of commerce, and of large-scale warlike movements. Japan, another island empire, and the United States, effectively a continental island, were the two powers with most to gain from following the British model. Germany, Russia and France all had more pressing demands for defence funding on their land frontiers, and in consequence they could not follow a truly Mahanian programme. Not one of them found sea power to be a positive asset.

Alternatives in sea power

In the nineteenth century Britain's naval rivals were France, Russia and the United States. All three had to create maritime strategies which reflected the pre-eminence of the Royal Navy. Only France and the United States possessed the maritime industrial base to mount a serious challenge to Britain, but neither could sustain the necessary level of expenditure or construction. France alternated between a battlefleet to challenge the Royal Navy and cover an invasion that would exploit her superiority in troops, and a *guerre de course* programme that would harrass British commerce. Early naval programmes attempted to combine these two elements, but the Syrian Crisis of 1840 demonstrated the futility of a fleet that could not mobilise the battlefleet numbers of the Royal Navy, and this forced the French to look for more radical solutions. The first had been proposed by an artillery officer, Colonel Henri

Paixhans, in his *Nouvelle Force Maritime* of 1822. Paixhans suggested that a force of small steam boats armed with shell-firing guns of his design would be the best counter to the British sailing battlefleet. Shell guns proved tolerably effective, but problems with the fuses made them less successful thans Paixhans had hoped. In addition the steam boat as a warship did not come of age until a later French innovator, Dupuy de Lôme, completed the steam screw battleship *Napoléon* in 1851. Early steam ships were inefficient, unreliable and poor gun platforms. In consequence thirty years elapsed before they had any serious impact on the manner of fighting at sea.

French innovation did not end with Paixhans: twenty years later Admiral the Prince de Joinville, younger son of King Louis-Phillipe, urged the preparation of a steam navy for the invasion of Britain, and his collaborator Dupuy de Lôme suggested an ironclad warship, more than a decade before *Gloire*. Joinville was instrumental in ordering the first wooden screw steam battleship, de Lôme's *Napoléon* of 1851. The success of this ship encouraged the Second Empire of Louis Napoleon III to build a wooden screw steam battlefleet after 1852 to threaten Britain. Louis-Napoleon hoped to increase the necessity of a French alliance, and therefore of co-operation with French policy, to Britain. The British responded by outbuilding France in this category of ship. The French then forced the pace again with the first seagoing ironclad, *La Gloire*. The British once again outbuilt the French in numbers of ships and used the new freedom of design provided by iron hulls to add a significant measure of individual superiority with *Warrior* of 1861, the first iron-hulled seagoing armoured battleship. The French challenge faltered after 1865, with the rise of the Prussian army, and collapsed after defeat in the Franco-Prussian War of 1870–71 in which French preponderance at sea had been utterly useless. Only in the 1880s did France begin to rebuild her navy, and this time her programmes were crippled by the competing claims of the battlefleet and the *guerre de course*. Only at the very end of the period did France, now in alliance with Russia, mount a serious challenge to the Royal Navy. Once again the military threat of Germany ensured that this rivalry was short-lived, ending with the *Entente Cordiale* of 1904. The fundamental flaw remained, French policy-makers failing to understand that Britain would not surrender her maritime preponderance. France failed, as Tirpitz's elaborate 'Risk Fleet' policy failed in the twentieth century, because British policy-makers would pay any price to retain their freedom from entangling alliances.

In their search for a response to British maritime preponderance after 1815 the French were regularly forced back onto the oldest alternative to contesting control of the sea, the *guerre de course*. In addition they considered that the potential offered by new technology for altering the nature of war at sea could be made to work in their favour. This philosophy had more influence on the development of marine technology in the period 1815 to 1890 than any other. It encouraged the French to believe that by changing the rules they could overthrow the Royal Navy. This exposed a fatal flaw in French reasoning. It presupposed that the superiority of the Royal Navy was based upon tradition, a superior maritime population and long years of victory when, in fact, the real foundation of British supremacy lay in the continuing willingness of the House of Commons, under any government, to find the funds necessary to maintain the world's most powerful fleet. Tradition and victory flowed from secure funding, based upon a vast maritime trade that required the protection of the navy. A nation dependent upon trade for its survival would pay any price to retain command of the sea in wartime, including the impressment of its seamen.

The Russian navy was the most backward of the four major sea powers in the nineteenth century. Her sailing battlefleet was large, if outdated and badly built, but the shift to steam and iron widened the gap. Russia lacked a domestic engineering base, and was forced to turn to her rivals for help. Between 1830 and 1906 Britain, the United States, France, Germany, Sweden, Denmark and even Belgium built warships and machinery for the Imperial Navy, while the strength of the domestic base was largely composed of foreign-owned firms. In Russia's one major war with European powers, the Crimean War of 1854 to 1856, the fleet was placed at a critical disadvantage by the lack of steam battleships. It should be noted that it is doubtful if the Russians would have ventured to sea against the British and French fleets even if all three had been under sail or steam. After 1856 the Russian navy adopted a coast defence and *guerre de course* programme, a choice given emphasis by the danger of British operations in the Baltic in 1863, 1878 and 1885. In the 1880s a new battlefleet was built, only to be destroyed in the Far East (half of it still tied up in harbour, just as the Black Sea Fleet had been in 1855); the remainder perished at Tsushima, the most complete naval victory of the modern age. Russia learnt little from this experience, and was building another fleet of capital ships when the First World War broke out. Both battlefleets were utterly dependent upon foreign assistance for both design and specific areas of construction.

The United States Navy developed along lines that reflected her isolation from her major rivals. The small peacetime navy was configured for trade protection and local policing, relying in the years before 1861 on the latent capacity of the maritime sector for rapid wartime expansion. Thereafter the demands of the continental frontier absorbed the greater part of American effort until the last decade of the century, when the new politics of expansion and the message of Mahan led to the creation of a major battlefleet from the remains of an obsolete wooden cruising fleet. American designs reflected the peculiar circumstances under which the US Navy operated, and exhibited a marked preference for indigenous sources of supply throughout the century. During the Civil War, 1861 to 1865, the Federal Government created a powerful coastal assault force, backed by fast cruisers to attack the vulnerable Southern ports and rivers while imposing an effective blockade. However, the origins and objects of the epochal *Monitor* have been ignored. The type was always configured for coastal operations against batteries, lacking the seakeeping qualities to survive in the wide ocean, let alone to fight under such conditions. Similarly the technology behind this new fleet was far from novel. In 1865 the swollen war fleet actually possessed very few effective warships. The monitors were only suitable for local defence, while the fast cruisers of the *Wampanoag* type could only offer a limited threat to the British or French, as the Secretary of the Navy had admitted when ordering such expensive weapons. After the war the cruisers were deprived of their speed and equipped with masts and yards of unequalled size. The United States Navy was not a major force at sea until the late 1890s and in consequence her greatest contribution to the development of naval technology came from the inspirational writings of Alfred Mahan, the apostle of the battlefleet.

The minor naval powers were forced to rethink their programmes in response to the rise of technology that they would be hard pressed to match. Older maritime nations such as Sweden, Holland, Spain, Denmark, Naples

At times of tension naval power can be applied persuasively but with less provocation than land forces. When various disputes between Britain and the Federal side in the US Civil War threatened to become serious, Britain reinforced its fleet on the North American station. This is Bermuda harbour in 1862; the main lines of battleships at anchor are the Nile *(foreground),* Aboukir, Edgar *and* Conqueror. *(NMM)*

and Turkey had three choices. They could accept that they were no longer capable of meeting the vessels of the major powers; they might buy their ships, engines or weapons from the major powers, creating a dangerous degree of dependency; or they could attempt to create a small-scale version of the naval industries that supplied the major powers, largely by government investment. Sweden adapted the most suitable elements of the new technology and relied upon her domestic engineering base; Holland and Denmark accepted a minor role, and split their procurement between the major powers and the domestic base. Spain and Naples attempted to create an indigenous paddle wheel steam navy, but thereafter accepted the inevitable dependence on Britain and France, at least in the latter case until Italy was united. Turkey made little pretence at domestic engineering expansion, purchasing the majority of her iron steam ships from Britain.

Of the new sea powers, Japan and Germany began by purchasing abroad, but always intended to establish a large domestic industrial base, and by 1905 both were effectively self-sufficient. Austria survived a series of disasters and ended the century with a domestic industrial base and a clear role.

The spread of new technology

The technical innovations of the nineteenth century had a marked impact on the ability of even the most wealthy powers to sustain the domestic engineering base of their fleets. The first breakthrough, the steam engine, played into the hands of the British. From the first commercial use of steam – Fulton's Boulton & Watt engined *Clermont* in 1807 – the superior quality and availability of British engines gave the Royal Navy a major edge. Her competitors had two options: to purchase their machinery in Britain, with the consequent problems of wartime supply; or to attempt to create a domestic source. The United States, isolated by distance and import tariffs, managed to develop an individual school of design, but the rest of the world, including the major powers of Europe, were all at one time or another forced to rely on British suppliers. At the height of the steam battlefleet construction race of the late 1850s, France had to buy ma-

chinery from Robert Napier's Glasgow works, which were also producing engines for Russia and Turkey. Russia never escaped from her dependence on imported machinery, despite attempts to create an indigenous base with foreign assistance. The minor powers were placed at a particularly severe disadvantage by their limited requirement for naval machinery. Although Holland, Sweden, Spain and Naples did create their own government engine plants, these could never compete on price or availability, and only rarely on quality, with the British system of ordering from the private sector. Further advantages accrued to Britain from her burgeoning maritime trade, and the quality of South Wales steam coal. Many of the critical advances in naval engineering were pioneered by the mercantile community, where potential profit provided an incentive for progress. Among these were oceangoing paddle wheel and screw propelled vessels, the compound and triple expansion engine, condensers and iron hulls. As the leader of the technical revolution of the nineteenth century Britain was uniquely positioned to exploit progress. However, the response of British policymakers was cautious and closely aligned to the defence of both maritime supremacy and low naval estimates. When the French pioneered any new system, from the shell gun to the torpedo boat, the British response was to outbuild, improve and restore a healthy degree of superiority. The classic statement of this approach was provided by the Surveyor of the Navy, Captain Sir Baldwin Walker, on 22 June 1858 in response to the ironclad *La Gloire*.

Although I have frequently stated it is not in the interest of Great Britain, possessing as she does so large a navy, to adopt any important change in the construction of ships of war which might have the effect of rendering necessary the introduction of a new class of very costly vessels until such a course is forced upon her by the adoption by Foreign Powers of formidable ships of a novel character requiring similar ships to cope with them, yet it then becomes a matter not only of expediency but of absolute necessity. This time has arrived. France has now commenced to build frigates of great speed with their sides protected by thick metal plates, and this renders it imperative for this country to do the same without a moment's delay.

This was Walker's approach, but before 1848 the Royal Navy pioneered almost all the important technical developments that led to the modern warship, from steam and the screw propeller to iron warships. The Royal Navy could not afford to ignore any new development; in contrast they were studied from inception to introduction and where they appeared promising they were subjected to experiment. This was the case with the paddle wheel steamer, the screw propeller, armour and much else. However, where the private sector would bear the cost parsimonious politicians were always happy to leave the role of pioneer to others.

The shell gun and the development of modern artillery

Following the pioneering work of Colonel Henri Paixhans in the first decade of peace after 1815 the shell gun was gradually adopted into the French, American, British and Russian fleets. At first a few pieces replaced the 68pdr carronades in the bow ports of the lower deck on British ships. By 1852 British and French battleships were designed for a lower deck battery of thirty 8in shell guns, increasing their close range destructive power. Shells proved to be less accurate than solid shot, while contemporary artillerists were divided as to the efficacy of the new armament. After the futile bombardment of Sevastopol on 17 October 1854, Sir Howard Douglas considered that the effect of British fire would have been much increased by arming the ships with heavy solid shot guns, the 95cwt 68pdr and the 56cwt 32pdr. These were the only guns he believed equal to the task of shattering masonry. Despite the claims of Paixhans and others, the shell gun did not have the profound effect on naval warfare in the era of the wooden ship that has so often been ascribed to it. Problems with fuses ensured that the successes at the proving ground were not repeated at sea, while lower rates of fire and loss of accuracy limited the value of these guns. Shells were also dangerous to handle and peacetime accidents made them unpopular.

By contrast new and heavier solid-shot firing guns were largely successful. The British 68pdr, an 8in gun weighing 95cwt, also proved to be the outstanding armour-piercing piece of the early 1860s, a combination of heavy powder charge and improved projectiles enabling it to break through the 4½in wrought iron plates of *Warrior*. Armour, first used aboard coast attack craft in 1854, was initially developed to keep out exploding shells. Only after the artillerists had driven a shell through the early plates was it necessary to increase the thickness. Outsize American guns, up to 15in, were admirable for smashing the structure upon which the Confederate armourclads carried their low grade laminated plating, but they were inaccurate, slow to reload and impossible to cast loose in any sort of seaway with the carriages and handling systems available. As a weapons system the heavy gun monitor was ideal for coastal and riverine operations, although it lacked the volume of fire to subdue well served earthworks. Out of sight of land, or in a storm it was incapable of combat and, on occasion, of staying afloat. They were adopted by the coast defence navies, Sweden, Holland and particularly Russia, as an antidote to the rising cost of large ironclads. The Americans admitted the failure of the super heavy gun before the end of the Civil War, shifting to large broadside batteries of medium calibre weapons in all their cruisers.

The shift to breech-loading guns, a vital concomitant of rifled artillery, took some time to mature. The initial British heavy breech-loader, the 100pdr Armstrong, first issued aboard HMS *Warrior*, was a great disappointment. Metallurgical problems with the breech restricted the powder charge and left the gun with an inferior armour-piercing performance to the old 68pdr smooth bore. Returning to muzzle-loading was by no means as retrograde a step as it might appear. Only with the development of improved, slow-burning powders did the barrels become too long for ease of reloading, and by that time new steels were capable of sealing the breech reliably. Although the heavy naval gun made great strides in the 1880s, it remained the prisoner of short range fire control systems until the turn of the century. However, the QF (quick-firing) medium calibre gun, in service from the mid-1880s, dispelled the torpedo boat threat for two decades. Once the concept of fire control had caught up with the performance of the guns, battle ranges were opened out, just in time to preserve the battleships from the danger of torpedo attack.

Underwater weapons

The submarine, mines and torpedoes offered a new way of sinking ships, and an ideal leveller for the underdog. From David Bushnell's *Turtle* of 1776 this approach had been seen as the key to humbling the dominant battlefleet, usually that of Britain. As with the early shell gun, these weapons did not live up to their publicity until the very end of the period under review, the sinking of *Blanco Encalada* in 1891 being the first significant success for a self-propelled torpedo, and even then the target was at anchor.

Conclusion

Despite the remarkable advances in naval and maritime technology that followed the industrial revolution the battlefleet remained the dominant element of naval power throughout the nineteenth century. The challenge of new weapons, and new strategies, was countered by equally innovative use of technology. It was within the framework of the battlefleet that the nineteenth-century naval technological revolution took place. It should be recalled that in order to use the sea it is first necessary to secure a working control of the relevant areas. This is as true today as it was in 1815 or 1905.

Andrew Lambert

Anglo-French naval rivalry finally disappeared in the face of a more dangerous mutual opponent, Germany. Symbolic of the Entente Cordiale *is this visit of French pre-dreadnoughts (of the* Liberté *class) to Malta about 1910.* (CMP)

1

The Introduction of Steam

THE steam engine was the first major manifestation of the industrial revolution to have a profound effect on warship design. By 1830 the steam warship had been accepted in the major fleets, and by the mid-century naval strategy moved at the pace of steam. However, early steam warships did not make the sailing battleship obsolete, or increase the danger of a French invasion of Britain. Wooden ships could not sustain the weight and volume of simple paddle wheel engines and the full armament of a regular man of war of similar size, so steam was only a peripheral force until the screw auxiliary engine, which had a more limited impact on the design of new ships, was adopted. In addition wooden warships could not be built significantly larger. Consequently steam only came to dominate naval warfare when steam engines

The first practical steam warship was Fulton's Demologos, *a catamaran with a paddle-wheel between the hulls; the single-cylinder engine was in one hull with the copper boiler in the other, marked by four funnels in a square configuration. The hull form protected the paddle and allowed a full broadside armament, but would have been too stiff in a seaway. Although perfectly practical for Fulton's harbour defence battery, this made the catamaran form unsuitable for a seagoing warship, and* Demologus *did not point the way forward.* (Smithsonian Institution)

were installed in battleships, while the perfect antidote to steam powered invasions were flotillas of defending steamers. Steam merely assisted naval forces to carry out their age-old tasks more efficiently. Only when further technological advances were combined with steam could warship design escape from the limits imposed by wooden hulls.

The paddle wheel warship, 1815–1830

This study of the early history of the steam warship may appear to be largely based on British sources. This reflects the fact that between 1815 and 1850 the Royal Navy led the world in the conceptual, tactical and technical development of steam warships. The naval administrations of the major powers were interested in the potential of steam, and kept abreast of the latest thinking. In practice this ensured that the development of the steam warship was dominated by Britain, the nation with the most powerful engineering, shipping and naval infrastructure and, for many of the same reasons, the largest commitment to the

sailing warship. Quite simply, Britain had too much to lose to lag behind in this field, and too many domestic engineering and shipbuilding assets to do so from ignorance. France, although the second strongest naval power, and largely aware of the potential of steam, was forced to rely on British machinery, design expertise, engineering and even good quality steam coal. Russia made no effort to keep up with the new developments, resorting to foreign purchases and foreign owned engineering works. The United States built so few steam warships before 1840 that her domestic base was dominated by mercantile experience. The reasons why Britain should have taken the lead are numerous, and would require far more space to elucidate than is available here. Suffice it to say that Britain was the only world power of the period, a power based on economic, imperial, industrial and commercial supremacy, supported by the Royal Navy, a navy that was paid for with the profits of the British trade and was configured for the defence of sea communications and insular security with a superior battlefleet. Policy-makers at Whitehall did not take risks with new technology. They kept abreast of the best practice, took advice from qualified engineers, particularly those who were not trying to sell them anything, and moved into the various aspects of steam tech-

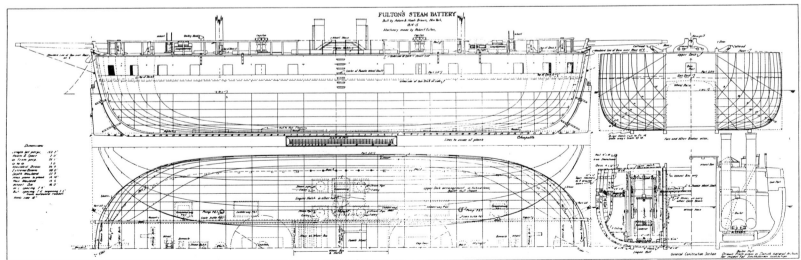

nology as and when they were required. This process was not dictated by the progress of foreign fleets, despite the efforts of alarmists to create an illusion of inadequacy. By contrast the Admiralty created the structures to oversee and administer the new system as it came to fruition, matching engineering expertise to naval advice until such time as the Royal Navy accepted the end of the sailing warship. With a secure structure, change could be assimilated. This was particularly important for the conceptual aspects of ship design. The key questions concerned the role of the new ships, for if many argued that steam would change the nature of naval warfare, few had anything concrete to offer, and fewer still cared to reflect on the limits imposed by contemporary technology. The greatest success of the Royal Navy came in this area, with a conscious decision to avoid the errors of over-ambition. In most cases the Navy stood back and allowed the private sector to make the running in engineering and design, with only occasional and limited government intervention. As the largest market for new systems the Admiralty could afford to keep a watching brief. The only significant error of the period resulted from a combination of political pressure and a rare case of technological over-ambition, not undue caution or blind conservatism.

The limitless horizon

Steam and the industrial processes that were associated with it opened up new avenues for warship development. Unfortunately, historians have concentrated on the ultimate success of the iron steam warship, and employ hindsight to create the illusion of an inevitable line of progress from *Charlotte Dundas* through *Clermont*, *Comet* and *Demologos* to the latest generation of warships. This is altogether too simplistic to be taken seriously. The world of marine technology was never closed to sideways fertilisation, as the role of non-specialist engineers such as the Brunels demonstrates, nor can such an approach explain the dead ends, missed opportunities and technical problems that litter the history of the steam warship. Navies were interested only in practical results and naval policy-makers rejected the visionary, the imperfect and the impracticable. Warship design, as a compromise between the desires of the user and the availability of funds and technology to meet them, became infinitely more complex with the destruction of old certainties between 1815 and 1860.

In the first two decades of steam shipping there were many who argued that the Admiralty should take the lead in developing the steam ship. These projectors almost invariably required funds, and saw the government as a provider. If the Royal Navy had no interest in leading the development of steam at sea, it could not afford to stand back and allow any other power to take the lead.

Early contacts between the Royal Navy and the steam ship, up to *Congo* in 1816, did little to encourage further interest. The constant drip of advice from respected engineers, particularly Sir John Rennie and Marc Brunel, provided both a stimulus to action and the basic information on which to form a policy. For the practical aspect of steam ships the Admiralty, led by the most experienced naval administrator of all, Lord Melville, turned to the Navy Board, a subordinate body charged with the civil administration of the Navy.[1] The Navy Board consulted Rennie on every new project concerned with any branch of engineering. They made less use of Brunel, who had fallen out with the influential Surveyor of the Navy, Sir Robert Seppings. In addition the Navy Board had their own expert on steam machinery, Simon Goodrich, the Mechanist at Portsmouth Dockyard. If there was any opposition to steam it came from the Navy Board, which tended to be more conservative than the Admiralty.

A policy for steam engine vessels

Before we can make any sense of the early steam warship it is necessary to consider the purposes for which they were designed. To this end the approach of the Admiralty and the Navy Board in Britain can be contrasted with the concepts being advanced in the United States and France.

The most important aspect of early steam ships lay in the limited capabilities of the machine. The Admiralty were well aware of steam, from the earliest efforts down to the first practical vessels. Following the success of *Comet* on the Clyde in August 1812 Henry Bell approached the Admiralty with 'his observations on the utility of applying small, portable steam engines to vessels'. The letter was endorsed in the normal manner: 'Their Lordships will not give him any further trouble.' By a curious coincidence the House of Lords called for the papers relating to the Earl of Stanhope's *Kent* four days later.[2]

The sad case of *Kent* was hardly the precedent to encourage further interest in a system capable of no more than five miles per hour. Rennie was rather better received when he advised, in concert with Sir Joseph Banks, doyen

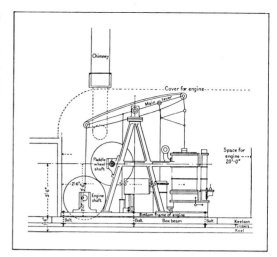

Paddle-wheel engine for the Congo, *1815. (From Smith's* History of Marine Engineering*)*

of the British scientific community, and Sir John Barrow, Second Secretary to the Admiralty, that the exploration vessel for the Congo river should be equipped with a steam engine. *Congo* was duly ordered on 13 September 1815. It should be noted that Rennie was not trying to sell anything, even if he was the London agent for Boulton & Watt, one of whose 20hp beam engines was installed. *Congo*'s trials, in late 1816, proved that steam could propel vessels and that this particular vessel had not been designed for the engine. *Congo* went off to her eponymous river under sail. The engine joined the growing number being used in the dockyards for pumping and power.

Steam entered naval service in Britain long before 1816, aboard dredgers. The first steam dredger was ordered in 1802, having been suggested in 1800 by General Samuel Bentham, the Inspector General of Naval Works. A second dredger was built at Deptford in 1806. Both craft were designed by Goodrich. Although humble the dredgers had an immediate impact on British naval policy, allowing the Admiralty to dispense with plans to build a new dockyard at Northfleet to replace those of the Thames and Medway, which had become clogged with mud. Steam came into naval service ashore soon after, Brunel building his blockmaking establishment at Portsmouth in 1807. Soon after, all yards were investigating the use of a pumping engine for emptying the docks. This was significant, since pumping was

1. Robert Saunders Dundas, Second Viscount Melville: First Lord of the Admiralty 1812–1827 and 1827–30.

2. Bell to Admiralty, 2 April 1813, PRO Adm 12/161. House of Lords to Admiralty, 6 April 1813, *loc cit*. A W Skempton, 'A History of the Steam Dredger, 1797–1830', *Transactions of the Newcomen Society* 47 (1974–76), pp97–115.

the role in which the steam engine first reached maturity. After Bentham was dismissed in 1812 naval interest and expertise were sustained by Goodrich, who remained in service at Portsmouth until 1830.

Just before *Congo* was completed Marc Brunel called the attention of the Admiralty to steam. Admitting the imperfections of existing ships, he stressed their manoeuvrability and freedom from the influence of wind and tide. He warned that these qualities made them ideal for smuggling. Now that the wheels were strong enough for sea passages, steam ships would soon be capable of many important tasks. He was critical of the American steam battery *Demologos*, which he suggested would soon be destroyed by smaller, mobile steamers. He also suggested the use of steam in the Packet Service. Lord Melville, while impressed by this confident approach, considered it unnecessary to discuss steam navigation in general. Sensibly he identified a specific task, calling for Brunel's opinion on 'towing ships of war out harbour in the Thames & Medway, & at Portsmouth and Plymouth'. After conducting his own experiments Brunel favoured two moored steamers, using their machinery to drive capstans. He advised hiring the Margate packet *Regent* for trials. The Admiralty directed the Navy Board to communicate with Brunel.[3]

Melville's response was entirely correct. While later commentators have derided him for timidity the *Regent* trials suggest that, if anything, he had been over-ambitious, for the small packet ship was incapable of stemming the tide at the entrance to Portsmouth harbour with a large vessel in tow. Steam could not yet carry out the first, and most basic task for which it was offered, that of short range prime mover for large sailing warships. Until it could do this it was no more than a novelty. Brunel was 'dismayed' by the results, and the far from helpful manner of the Navy Board. He would not be the last to make such observations. In 1817 and 1818 Rennie pressed individual members of the Admiralty Board to employ steam for towing, to little avail.[4]

After the failure of *Regent* the Board sponsored further work by Brunel and others, particularly experiments combining steam and sail. The Admiralty were well aware of the limitations of contemporary engines, and were content to follow the technical lead of the commercial sector.

The two firms patronised by the government for all marine engines before 1830, Boulton & Watt and Henry Maudslay, were the leaders in the experimental and practical use of steam at sea in the first decade of peace. This reflected

an understandable anxiety on the part of the Navy Board to restrict orders to proven contractors, proven in the general engineering field in the case of Maudslay, and the market leader for steam engines in the case of Watt. This policy was often criticised, but rarely wrong. Other contractors had to prove their worth before securing any offers, and price was never the final determinant. Boulton & Watt's were invariably the most expensive engines and Maudslay's only slightly cheaper. Only after 1830 did the new Admiralty spread their list of approved contractors, with mixed results. Up to that time Maudslay dominated the market, having superseded Boulton & Watt in the role of leading marine engine builder after 1817, building larger sizes and pioneering fundamental improvements. The most significant was the water changing apparatus for boilers; before the level of salinity became harmful the brine could be partly drawn off without shutting down the engine. This was demonstrated on the first steam passage to India, that of *Enterprise* in 1825.[5] This work offered the possibility of long range steaming, and as such was of particular interest to the Navy, which had more demanding requirements of its vessels than the mercantile sector. Commercial steamships were employed on specific routes where speed and regularity were at a premium, but the Navy could never be certain where it would have to act, and the consequences of mechanical failures would be more serious. Naval and mercantile development began to diverge at an early stage, and despite spectacular individual examples of cross-fertilisation they rarely coincided again. Once naval steamers mounted heavy guns at the bow and stern they could never match the speed and economy of mercantile designs.

In 1819 Rennie persuaded Melville to repeat the towing experiment. On 4 June *Eclipse* (104ft × 16ft 9in; 70hp Boulton & Watt) owned by the General Steam Navigation Company, took six hours to tow the 74-gun *Hastings* from Woolwich to a point beyond Gravesend.[6] Pressure was also applied from within the Navy. In August 1819 the Commissioner at Deptford Dockyard, Captain Robb, suggested that the Navy Board should build a steam vessel, of secondhand timbers after the style of a common lighter, for towing and transporting stores in the Thames and Medway.

On 10 November 1819 the Admiralty ordered a steam tug. The Navy Board called on Rennie for help, and the advice tendered included the outline design of an 80hp steam vessel. The Navy Board admitted their own lack of experience in the matter, but expressed con-

cern over the exposed paddle wheels. They were also far from anxious to begin work; one year later the board submitted a plan, based on Rennie's suggestions, but requested permission to delay until the new Post Office packet had been completed. The Admiralty ordered the vessel to be built 'as expeditiously as possible'. Well aware of the progress being made in every aspect of ship design, Rennie stressed the need to learn by experience. While he derived some satisfaction from the decision of the Admiralty to adopt steam, he was disgusted by the attitude of the Navy Board.[7]

Although Rennie's design had been adopted, both the Admiralty and Simon Goodrich inspected the two Post Office steam packets. These were good enough sea-boats, although the arrangement of the machinery was not to Goodrich's taste. The Navy Board made little progress with the new vessel. In December 1821 the Admiralty sent a sternly worded minute, both to complain of slow progress with the steam vessel, and to order another pair. These ships, *Lightning* and *Echo*, were later enlarged to take engines of 100hp, with frames 'of the strongest description'. In addition, the Navy Board was instructed to build steam packets for the Post Office, adding to their design and construction experience.[8]

The first naval steamer to be completed, the

3. Brunel to Admiralty, 29 August 1816 and 11 October 1816 & Admiralty Minutes, PRO Adm 1/4384.

4. R Beamish, *Life of Sir Marc Brunel* (London 1862). S Smiles, *Lives of the Engineers* (London 1862), vol 2, pp266–8.

5. J Tann, 'Fixed Capital Formation in Steam Power, 1775–1825: A Case Study of the Boulton & Watt Engine', in C Feinstein & S Pollard, *Studies in Capital Formation* (Oxford 1988), pp166–181. G N von Tunzelman, *Steam Power and British Industrialization to 1860* (Oxford 1978), pp52–3, 85–88, 91. Maudslay Society, *Henry Maudslay and Maudslay, Sons & Field Ltd.* (London 1949). List of all Maudslay engines. J P Muirhead, *Life of James Watt* (London 1858), pp442–45. J Tann (ed), *The Selected Papers of Boulton & Watt* (London 1981), vol I, pp11, 276 & 375–385. E C Smith, *A Short History of Naval and Marine Engineering* (Cambridge 1937), pp23–26.

6. Smiles, *op cit*, p268; D K Brown, *Before the Ironclad* (London 1990), p212.

7. Robb to Navy Board, 6 August 1819, PRO Adm 106/3443. Admiralty to Navy Board, 10 November 1819. Navy Board to Surveyor, 13 and 28 November 1819. Navy Board to Admiralty, 15 May and 29 November 1820, PRO Adm 106/2279 and 2280. Admiralty to Navy Board, 15 May 1820. Rennie to James Watt 30 May 1820, Smiles, *op cit*, p268.

8. Admiralty to Navy Board, 8 January 1822 and reply of same date. Post Office to Admiralty, 22 April 1822, PRO Adm 12/210.

One of the Royal Navy's first steamers was the Lightning of 1823. She enjoyed a long and successful career between the Algiers expedition of 1824 and war service as the Baltic fleet's survey ship in 1854. This model depicts the ship equipped for this latter duty but the changes were minimal. (NMM)

gesture. Clarence was a capable administrator and a largely positive force during his brief tenure of office. He employed Lightning as a royal yacht for his tour of the Dockyards, and demonstrated a solid appreciation of the advantages of steam. However, the most important step in the development of the steam warship taken in 1827 – the decision to order Dee, a 700-ton vessel of 200hp – was taken a month before he took office, and must therefore be credited to Melville. Dee was more than twice the size of any previous naval steamer, with double the horsepower. She was the first steamer capable of carrying a significant armament: as completed in 1830 this was settled as two long 32pdrs and four carronades. The design was heavily influenced by large merchant steamers, particularly those on the Edinburgh – London route, which was used by Melville and other Scots members of the Board. Captain Charles Napier believed that she was 'nearly a copy of the Queen of Scotland, a vessel intended for passengers only'. Certainly Lang, the purported designer of Dee, was hardly civil when reporting to the Navy Board on Napier's observations.[11]

Once the steam ship had established a reputation for quick and reliable short sea passages it was inevitable that the Foreign Office would employ them to carry dispatches. During the 1828 crisis in Portugal Echo was sent to Lisbon, as foul winds were delaying the regular Mediterranean sailing packet. Within two years the Navy was running a packet service through to Corfu, and purchased two large vessels from the General Steam Navigation Company for the purpose. These proved to be a bad bargain, suffering from poor quality machinery and earlier inadequate maintenance. However, the service continued until 1837, when it was put out to private tender. The Packet service has been largely ignored by historians of the steam

Rennie-inspired Comet, was launched on 22 May 1822 at Deptford. The design was largely based on that of the contemporary brig-sloop. Her first employment in her design role came in September, when she towed the 44-gun frigate Seringapatam from Woolwich to the Nore. The following year a fourth steamer was ordered, African, largely at the behest of the Colonial Secretary. However, the real function of the steamer remained towing, and once the service had established itself there were never enough steamers available to tow every ship that called for help. Consequently the General Steam Navigation Company was often called on 'to send a steamer to tow the [. . . .] to Sheerness immediately'. The cost of this service, up to £150 from Woolwich to Sheerness, encouraged the Navy Board to call for further naval steamers. They had a marked preference for building in the Royal Yards, as opposed to purchasing merchant vessels. Experience with the first steamers was already filtering back to influence new designs, notably on the position of the wheels. However, the steamer was merely a harbour auxiliary, it was not entered on the list of the Navy, or placed under the command of a commissioned officer. Towing was not restricted to harbours and rivers. Echo at Plymouth was sent as far abroad as Milford Haven with a dockyard hoy, while Lightning from Portsmouth went to Algiers in 1824, to support the mortar vessels that were intended to attack the city if the Dey proved uncooperative.[9]

The construction of these vessels did not imply an acceptance of the steam warship. In 1822 the Treasury passed on a letter covering improvements in the application of steam to vessels of war. The Board suggested that the author submit his model, 'but they beg at the same time to state that they are not at all anxious to give any encouragement to the application of steam to ships of war'.[10] Put quite simply, the Board was not interested in speculation on the subject of steam warships. The tugboat had been accepted, but until there was concrete proof of the requirement for steam in other roles there was no point in wasting money.

The decision of the Duke of Clarence, as Lord High Admiral, to include steamers on the Navy List on 4 December 1827, under commissioned officers, has often been cited as a breakthrough. Possibly this over-values the

9. Commissioner Brown to Navy Board, 27 March 1826 and Marginalia, PRO Adm 106/1799 and Digest entries 1824–6.

10.Treasury to Admiralty, 25 August 1822 (endorsed 25th), PRO Adm 1/4300.

11. Admiralty to Navy Board, 4 April 1827. Woolwich Dockyard to Navy Board, 22 August 1828 and 14 October 1830. Napier to Sir John Pechell undated (pre 1830), C Napier, The Navy (London 1851), pp77–96.

warship, but it provided invaluable basic experience in the operation of a steam fleet, along with lessons to guide the development of machinery and hull forms.

The first ten years of steam in the Royal Navy can be summarised as the 'Tug and Packet Boat' phase – tactical mobility and strategic communications were the areas in which steam could outperform sail. This was the only justification for the cost of operating new and expensive technology. Steam tugs allowed heavy sailing ships to leave harbour in almost all states of wind and tide, without exhausting the crew by towing or kedging. In addition they transformed the relationship between naval commanders and their political masters, imposing a timetable on communications. Once a regular steam packet service had been established into the Mediterranean commanders knew that a reply would be available within the month.[12]

Maintaining a steam fleet

Once steam had been accepted into the fleet the Navy Board was obliged to consider the question of maintenance and repair. The pioneer steam ships had been built in the Royal Dockyards on the Thames and Medway, and sent to one of the London Docks where the contractors would install the engines, boiler and wheels. Early powerplants were subject to frequent breakdowns, largely with defective boilers and wheels, the engines themselves being generally reliable, although the piston packing was soon destroyed by sustained hard work. Before 1830 anything requiring repair would be sent back to the manufacturer. The Controller, Admiral Byam Martin, despite a personal dislike of steam, was professional enough to lay the ground work for the first Naval Steam Factory, which grew up piecemeal at Woolwich. To this end he consulted the preferred suppliers of the late 1820s, Maudslay, Son & Field of Lambeth, only two days after steamers were first placed on the Navy List. Following their advice he recommended that boilers in particular should be repaired in the Dockyards, largely to save time. By 1829 he had also ordered the erection of a

HMS Rhadamanthus *was one of four steamers built to competitive designs in 1831–32 (based on the* Dee *of 1827) and plainly intended as genuine warships. This model shows the long guns fore and aft on pivotting slide mountings and the pair of carronades abaft the boats. This ship was very seaworthy and became the first British steamer to cross the Atlantic, although a large part of the passage was completed under sail. (NMM)*

boiler factory at Portsmouth. The steam engine was now an integral part of the naval service, even if it was entirely as an auxiliary to the sailing fleet. The Treasury took care to stress 'that this should be a pure repair facility, the construction of engines or even parts should not be considered.[13]

In 1831 the whig Admiralty pressed the manufacturers to provide service contracts with the engines, but met a predictable refusal. Boulton & Watt stressed the hard nature of naval service and the commercial impossibility of meeting the Admiralty's request.[14]

By 1830 the steam ship had reached a level of development which made it a regular element in the Navy. The design of naval steamers was still dominated by existing sailing ship designs, although modified by mercantile practice in such areas as paddle wheel design and finer bow lines. The success of the Royal Navy can be judged from the longevity and reliability of the pioneer steam ships. None was a conceptual failure, and the majority served on in subsidiary roles for many years. This was testimony to the solidity of their hulls, and the basic good sense of relying on low pressure condensing engines.

The French navy and steam, 1815 to 1830

Only one other navy made any serious commitment to steam in the 1820s. French policymakers saw, if only dimly, that the new power might overturn the inbuilt superiority of Bri-

tain in sailors and maritime resources. However, French experiments with steam had not resulted in the creation of a steam marine – indeed the first successful steamboat in France was Fulton's effort of 1803 while the first commercial service was started by an American in 1817. After initial interest in the *Demologos* concept the French navy realised by 1822 that the type was severely limited. The first French naval steamers, and also the first truly French steamers, *Africain* and *Voyager*, were built for service on the Senegal river in 1818. In 1819 a mission was sent to the United States to gather information, and this helped to shape future policy. The resulting *Coureur* of 1824 could be considered a useful prototype, but as with most French ships of the period she relied on British-owned companies for her engines. The British expedition to Algiers in 1824 created some alarm, and realising that Britain had a healthy lead in the new technology the French made considerable efforts to catch up. The Council of the Admiralty favoured arming steamers along the lines of a galley, with one or

12. C Dandeker, 'Patronage and bureaucratic control – The case of the naval officer in English Society 1780–1850', *British Journal of Sociology* 29 (1978), pp300–20.

13. Byam Martin to Maudslay, 21 October 1828, BL Add 41, 397.
Navy Board to Admiralty, 7 November 1828.
Admiralty to Navy Board, 6 November 1829, PRO Adm 106/1908.
Treasury to Admiralty, 10 April 1829, PRO Adm 1/4304.

14. Boulton & Watt to Admiralty, 7 October 1831, PRO Adm 1/4390.

two heavy guns bearing over the bows, and using steam to tow ships out of harbour when the blockading British would be blown off station by adverse winds. *Caroline* was placed on the list of the navy in 1824, three years before the British *Lightning*, and was intended to be armed with the new Paixhans shell gun.

French design was dominated by fear of Britain, her advanced engineering and mercantile steam sectors being viewed with an envy tinged by admiration. Only in 1828 was an effective naval steamer, *Sphinx*, built. Her hull was a copy of the English merchant steamer *Leeds*, while her 160hp machinery was provided by Forrester of Liverpool. Of the seven steamers intended to take part in the invasion of Algiers in 1830, only *Sphinx* and *Nageur* actually arrived with the fleet. *Sphinx* proved particularly useful, supporting the landing and then carrying the despatches back to Toulon. Her type became the standard for all future French ships; the engines were copied and the hull repeated.[15]

Pioneer steam warships

In contrast to the steady, unspectacular progress made by the Royal Navy, and followed by the French, there were several isolated steam warships that gave a misleading glimpse of the future. Although they dominate histories of the steam warship the majority of them had no impact on the development of the type. They demonstrate both the vision of their constructors, and the limits of the available engineering and shipbuilding technology. The pragmatic and visionary strands of development were largely reunited around 1830, with *Dee*.

Early attempts to create a true steam warship were bound to end in disappointment. The technology of the era was incapable of producing a suitable combination of firepower, mobility and structural strength. Therefore pioneering efforts were crippled by the necessary element of compromise; some aspects of their design had been emphasised at the expense of others. Those that were intended to be anything more than lightly armed merchant vessels were confronted with insuperable difficulties. The Earl of Stanhope's *Kent Ambinavigator* of 1793, often described as a warship, was only an experimental steam ship, built with help from the Admiralty. She was later converted into a sailing privateer, but never carried engines and guns at the same time. In 1805 the Cornish engineer Richard Trevithick offered a steam fireship, and later a steam ship to tow fireships for an attack on Boulogne harbour,

but the Admiralty never made their intentions clear. Trevithick's promising compact high pressure non-condensing engine was available as a portable powerplant or as a prime mover on road, rail or water. The advantages of this unit were obscured by a boiler explosion, and hostile advertising by Boulton & Watt.[16]

The limited endurance and performance of the early marine steam engine, using the Watt system, restricted the impact of steam on warship design to the tactical sphere. The outstanding examples from the period before 1830 rationalised this dilemma in different ways. The American Robert Fulton's *Demologos* of 1814 was conceived as a large mobile battery. With seven years' experience of commercial steam navigation behind him, Fulton was well aware of the limited capabilities of contemporary engines. Therefore he restricted his vessel to a specific function, the defence of New York harbour and the prevention of a close blockade of Long Island Sound. To protect the paddle wheel Fulton used two half hulls separated by the wheel race. With a 5ft thick hull *Demologos* would have been a formidable opponent for any warship of the period. However, she was not intended for sea service; initially she had no sails and made only 5½kts under ideal conditions. Several nations expressed interest in *Demologos*, France, Holland and Denmark having good reason to look for a blockade breaker and coast defence ship. Yet her rapid reduction to storeship duties after the end of the War of 1812 reflected the restricted role for which she was conceived, the limited capabilities of her machinery and a general lack of interest in such special types.[17] Furthermore her utility has been exaggerated. Despite her mobility and great structural strength Fulton had included in the design the seeds of destruction, and it was perhaps fitting that she should be destroyed by fire, albeit by accident in June 1829, for red-hot shot was the best antidote to such a mass of timber. In late 1814 the British Dockyard at Halifax, Nova Scotia, fitted the gunbrig *Sharpshooter* with a furnace to heat 24pdr shot. This vessel offered only a small target for *Demologos*'s powerful broadside. Further furnaces were ordered from Portsmouth Dockyard in 1815. Had the war continued another year it is probable that the first steam warship would have ended her career in flames; her massive hull offered a perfect lodgement for incendiary shot.[18]

At a more fundamental level the design of *Demologos* revealed that the world's youngest navy saw steam as the answer to a strategic dilemma. The Americans would not provide any form of naval defence for their own har-

bours beyond the range of shore based guns. Consequently the only interest shown by the US Navy in steam warships in the period before 1840 lay in the field of harbour defence. Plans were prepared to build further steam batteries, both in 1814–15 and throughout the following twenty years. In consequence it should hardly be a surprise that the second United States war steamer, the battery/frigate compromise *Fulton II* of 1837, was a complete failure as a seagoing steamer, and little better suited to harbour defence.

It required a naval officer with a technological background to achieve a better balanced design. Lord Cochrane's *Rising Star* of 1821 combined the endurance of a full sailing rig with the tactical power of steam and an effective, unencumbered battery. The air-tight wheel chambers were open to the sea, with a further pair of keels outboard. While existing accounts claim she achieved speeds up to 12kts this would appear highly unlikely, in view of the poor performance of the Thames packet steamer *London Engineer* which employed the same drive arrangement, and the bluff, flat-bottomed hull. The first trials on the Thames credited her with 5–6kts, a more plausible figure. The armament was mounted conventionally, each broadside being pierced for ten guns. *Rising Star* reached Chile too late to take part in the War of Liberation against Spain, spending the last eight years of her brief career in the service of British merchants in South America.[19] Under an officer of Cochrane's ability and enterprise a successful campaign by *Rising Star* might have influenced the future design of steam warships, by emphasising the need to subordinate the propulsion system to military qualities.

Cochrane did command steam ships in his last combat role, as Admiral of the Greek Navy during the War of Independence (1825–29). However, the famous *Karteria* was inferior to *Rising Star* in almost every respect. Unlike her precursor she was powered by Elijah Galloway's high pressure machinery, which proved a constant source of disaster, unlike the engines built by Maudslay. The ship, and her disap-

15. Stephen S Roberts, 'The Introduction of Steam Technology into the French Navy: 1818–1852', unpub Ph D Thesis, University of Chicago (1976), pp41–125.

16. Dickinson & Titley, *Richard Trevithick* (Cambridge 1934), pp77–80.

17. D Canney, *The Old Steam Navy: Frigates, Sloops and Gunboats, 1815–1885* (Annapolis 1990), pp3–4.

18. Admiralty to Board of Ordnance, 5 April 1815, PRO WO 44/498.

19. H P Spratt, *The Birth of the Steamboat* (London 1958), pp110–113.

One of the steamers employed in the Greek War of Independence was the Epicheiresis, *ex-*Enterprize. *Although not as famous as the* Karteria, *the ship is better documented and this modern model by Steve Kirby is based on extensive research.* (John Bowen)

pointing sisters were largely conventional paddle wheel steamers armed with four 68pdr guns. The only noteworthy aspects of their design were the use of a solid frame and the installation of largely water-tight compartments around the engine space. Under Captain Frank Abney Hastings, RN, *Karteria* proved a dangerous opponent for the ill-organised Ottoman navy. This was in spite of her unreliable machinery and limited performance. Her sisters arrived late, while after the death of Hastings the limited value of *Karteria* was revealed. However, she had been used in action, exploiting the advantages of steam at the tactical level, and had been seen by the Royal Navy.[20]

The reasons for the failure of the early steam warship are not hard to find. The technical shortcomings of the paddle wheel, and of early steam machinery are well known; the conceptual failure is less obvious. Until the impact of the steam engine on warship design could be reduced, and the engine had the power, reliability and economy to replace sail as the prime mover of the world's battlefleets it would have to be satisfied with an auxiliary role, both in ships and fleets.

The military use of steam ships before 1830

The first successful use of a steam ship in warfare came when General Andrew Jackson employed the Mississippi steamer *Enterprise* to move men, stores and messages during the New Orleans campaign of January 1815. In 1822–25 the East India Company used *Diana* and later the pioneer oceanic steamer *Enterprise* (a very common name, along with 'Comet', 'Meteor' and 'Lightning') in the Burma War. The former worked in the Irrawaddy river while the larger vessel provided a regular despatch and transport link with Calcutta. The United States Navy hired *Seagull* in 1822 for service against pirates in the West Indies, but these ships were unarmed and provided mobility for regular forces. Hastings's *Karteria* was the first purpose-built warship to see service.[21]

The paddle wheel fighting ship, 1830–1850

By 1830 steam propulsion had reached a level of development that permitted serious consideration of steam warships. The responsible administrations were forced to consider the functions that these expensive units could fulfil. Lacking significant practical experience, and in the face of considerable cost, it took a great deal of faith to launch into new technology. It was already clear that paddle wheels could not be employed on regular warships, and that the existing small tug and packet boats could only carry a few guns on the upper deck. Attempts to combine steam and a broadside battery were largely responsible for the increase in the size of steam warships, but did little to clarify their role. The history of the paddle warship after 1830 for the major navies was merely a long process of accepting the obvious, that war steamers, however large, were still auxiliaries for sailing warships.

The introduction of steam encouraged speculation on the way in which it could alter the nature of war at sea. In the main these proved chimaerical; but among the most durable illusions were those concerning the use of steam to change the balance between the weak and the strong, steam ships as a knock out weapon and the convertability of merchant steamers into powerful warships. All three ideas would feature throughout the nineteenth century. In fact

steam merely emphasised the degree to which sea power was a function of financial strength and political commitment. Nations that had to be strong at sea took up steam, and only powers with limited interest in, or understanding of, sea power such as Russia and Austria, suffered through the introduction of steam.

In view of the limited space available aboard early steamers for guns, particularly a broadside battery, the naval role for steam was profoundly affected by the introduction of large calibre shell guns following the work of the French artillerist Henri Paixhans. Paixhans's exploding shells were only one aspect of his 'system', the other being a mosquito fleet of small steam ships armed with these guns, to destroy the British sailing battlefleet. After 1822 the steam warship was, curiously enough, seen as a great leveller. However, this result was only achievable if the entire package worked as Paixhans had envisaged. In the event the guns were of dubious utility, shells proving unreliable and inaccurate, while French steam engines did not match those of Britain for many more years. The French navy adopted the new shell guns, but made little progress with the remaining elements of his system until 1840. Where there was no opposition at sea, merchant steamers made an acceptable substitute for warships, but they were not built to carry heavy weights, nor to sustain the prolonged hard use of war service. Their major contribution came in the field of transport and logistics. The Anglo-French invasion of the Crimea in 1854 was made possible by steam shipping, while the year-long campaign of attrition was won by the regularity of steam.

In Britain the more progressive naval minds quickly grasped the implications of steam. The most significant contributors to the debate before 1830 were Admiral Lord Cochrane, and Captains Hastings, Ross and Napier. These officers anticipated a new order at sea, and one that worked to the advantage of Britain. Hasting's work in the service of Greek Independence provided a practical demonstration. Ross's book of 1829 followed the technical and tactical scheme of Paixhans, added a call for high pressure machinery to minimise the space required and the exposure of machinery to gunfire, while reversing the strategic implications suggested by the French artillerist. Cochrane spent the 1830s developing a rotary engine to meet these requirements, but with little success. Captain Charles Napier (1786–

20. C Lloyd, *Lord Cochrane* (London 1947), pp176–189.

21. D L Canney, *op cit*, p3.

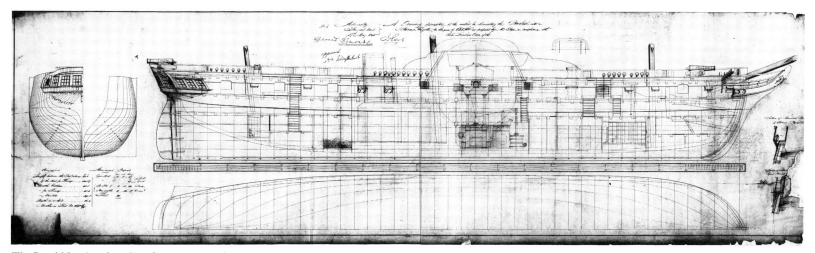

The Royal Navy's only sailing frigate converted to paddle was the Penelope *of 1828. This drawing shows the original scheme for conversion in 1843 but the ship was eventually lengthened by 65ft. She was the prototype First Class paddle frigate, and as converted carried a main deck battery of eight 68pdr/65cwt long guns and two 68pdr carronades, plus two 42pdr pivot guns and ten 42pdr carronades on the spar deck.* (NMM)

1860), the most dynamic figure in the steam navy, followed the subject from the first decade of peace down to the introduction of the iron-clad. His experience began with a pioneer iron steam ship service on the Seine, and continued with an unsuccessful request to command *Lightning* despite his seniority, when she was commissioned as a Royal Yacht for the Lord High Admiral. In addition Napier provided well argued suggestions for improved designs, which received the attention of the whig Board after 1830; he tried to use steam while serving in the Portuguese Civil War, succeeded during the Syrian Campaign of 1840, developed his own design for the steam frigate *Sidon*, ended his active career commanding the first fleet dominated by steam to be employed in a major war and wrote almost his last letter on the subject of ironclads. From the outset Napier was convinced that steam ships would work to Britain's advantage, simplifying blockades, completing victories, defeating invasions and facilitating the attack of fortified harbours and

amphibious operations. In battle they would play a specific role, similar to that of cavalry. His suggestions emphasised light draught, protection for the machinery and the need to integrate the design of the hull and machinery with an appreciation of the service for which naval steamers were required. Such opinions, forcefully expressed, made him few friends, but he was not without influence.[22]

The strategic impact of steam

Three years before any steam vessels were placed on the Navy List the First Lord of the Admiralty was expressing fears about French exploitation of the new force. He was not concerned by the danger of invasion, because 'if we are tolerably alert, and with our command of machinery and fuel, we ought to *out steam* all Europe'. However, it would be difficult to protect the entire coast with steam vessels, particularly against the most dangerous possibility, a steam raid on the Royal Dockyards. He was worried that the likely response – fortification adequate to repel such a raid – would, by 1860, be a serious competitor with the battlefleet, the real guarantor of insular security, for limited defence funding.[23]

The true antidote was to meet the invasion force at sea with war steamers. In 1847 Captain Lord John Hay considered that five steam frigates would defeat an invasion of any size, from their ability to disable the transports and create a panic among the troops. Twenty frigates would turn defeat into disaster. The old rules were unaffected by steam: without a working command of the sea, invasions were still impossible.[24] Fears of invasion, raised by alarmist politicians, nervous publicists and self-serving officers from both services, exercised the attention of many, but there was never a serious danger of a French invasion. Steam made interception almost certain, while the effect of

heavy gunfire on lightly built mercantile steamers crowded with troops was too horrific for any sane man to contemplate. French soldiers were nervous enough crossing the Black Sea to the Crimea in 1854, protected by a fleet double the size of the Russian force, for them to have attempted the Channel. The raid remained a threat, but old strategies were more than adequate to counter any such danger. Until the advent of the submarine, the Royal Navy remained wedded to the close blockade of enemy harbours as the best method of deterring invasion. The construction of the coaling base on Alderney in the 1840s, although called a 'Harbour of Refuge', was intended to facilitate a steam blockade of Cherbourg.

Steam and naval tactics

The tactical role of steam ships before 1840 was strictly limited to towing and conveying messages. The unreliable and exposed machinery, combined with a lightweight armament ensured that the pioneer steam warships had no place in a fleet action, in particular not within 2000yds of a battleship. These ships reflected the failure of policy-makers to understand the value of mechanical power. Underarmed, vulnerable and costly to run, they proved to be a dead end. Paddle wheel warships were merely added to the list of naval types in which Britain felt obliged to maintain equality with France. In war their role would be restricted to scouting, despatch service and towing. As warships they were of some value in combating their own type, but otherwise could never come to grips with a sailing warship, as their qualities were entirely dependent upon their vulnerable machinery. They could support the sailing battlefleet, but even the boldest officers only intended to use them to tow heavy ships into action.

The one role in which they were superior to

22. J Ross, *A Treatise on Navigation by Steam: and an Essay towards a System of Naval Tactics peculiar to Steam Navigation* (London 1828).
C Napier, *The Navy*, pp42–64. Letters to the Lord High Admiral and the Admiralty, 1827–28. The letters to the Admiralty were consulted in 1831 by Admiral Pechell, a Lord of the Admiralty, and an advocate of improved gunnery.

23. Lord Melville to the Duke of Wellington, 3 July 1824, BL Add 38, 296, f36–7.

24. Lord John Hay to Lord Auckland, 16 January 1848, Russell MSS, PRO 30/22/7A, f143–6.

The Royal Navy's big paddle frigates were generally 'one-offs' rather than series buildings, in the hope that competing designs would sponsor improvement. Design expertise was not confined to the dockyards, and the Admiralty occasionally looked outside the Surveyor's department. One such venture was Captain Sir Charles Napier's Sidon, *a powerful ship with main deck battery of sixteen guns with six more on the upper deck. She reflected Napier's experience in amphibious and coastal warfare.* (NMM)

existing types, amphibious operations, depended on gaining control of the sea with conventional forces, as in the Black Sea campaign of 1854. The large paddle wheel ships had the deck capacity to carry 1000 troops, and for short distances over 2000. In addition they were fitted with paddle box boats – large double-ended boats that were inverted over the upper run of the wheel, these could carry up to 100 men and were particularly useful for landing horses and artillery. Napier realised this, and designed his war steamer, *Sidon*, accordingly. The lack of any major fleet action, in combination with the innumerable punitive operations against third world states, for which steam warships of the most modest armament were ideal, has distorted the historical perception of naval development. It is worth noting that during the First Opium War of 1841–43 the British, for all their reliance on steam, had to bring up two old 74s to deal with Chinese forts. Weight of fire was the only reliable method of overcoming shore batteries.

The steam warship

In 1829 HMS *Columbia* was armed with two long 24pdr guns on pivot carriages designed by Captain Marshall. This was a significant measure, as it was the first time that a Royal Navy steam vessel had carried anything more than light saluting weapons. The following year *Dee* was fitted with two long 32pdrs, after the Admiralty had rejected the alternative battery of twelve 6pdrs. Armed in this manner the ships had no place in the existing order of broadsides and lines. New tactics were required.

In December 1830 the long period of Tory government ended. The new Whig regime was committed to political and economic reform, including a reduction of the naval estimates, and the abolition of the Navy Board. To discredit the Navy Board, which was held in high regard by William IV, Sir James Graham, First Lord of the Admiralty, claimed that the Navy Board had left the country dangerously short of steam vessels. Arguing that steam would change the character of any future naval war, he emphasised the danger of allowing the French to gain a superiority in the new type. Byam Martin pointed to the number of vessels already built, the level of arming ordered, and the large reserve of merchant steamers available as a war reserve. He concluded by warning against an unnecessary rush into expensive and unreliable ships, particularly as 'the means of this country, and the skill of our manufacturers, cannot fail to give us a superiority over others in steam as we have had heretofore in vessels of a description more congenial to the habits of our practical seamen'. Graham ignored these sound arguments. Not troubling to consider the true state of the rest of the world's steam navies, he ordered four 800-ton war steamers, had magazines installed aboard all steam vessels and urged the rapid completion of the war steamers. Martin considered this a waste of Dockyard time, time which would be better spent on sailing battleships.[25]

On the advice of Sir Thomas Hardy, the First Naval Lord, the 800-ton vessels were armed with a purpose-built 84cwt 10in shell gun, which became the largest gun in the fleet. This one-gun battery suggested that the steamer would exchange the weight of each shell for the number of guns deployed by regular warships. With only one gun the ship could be manoeuvred to fight end on, to engage other steamers, harrass sailing ships and bombard coastal positions. The French had been quick to realise that steam ships followed the basic layout of the oared galley, and offered similar tactical opportunities. It should be noted that the large sailing warship with a powerful broadside had rendered the galley obsolete at the end of the sixteenth century; re-

placing men by steam would not alter the relationship. It should be stressed that *Dee* and the four larger units that followed her were pioneers, since no other nation had yet built such large and powerful steam warships.

The Admiralty first took control of design and purchasing away from the Navy Board, and in April 1832 the Board was abolished. This appeared to give greater clarity to the process of laying out a specification, and then designing the ship; in reality it left the new Surveyor of the Navy, Captain William Symonds, with the freedom to concentrate on his beloved sailing ships. The Admiralty often had cause to remind him that designs for steam vessels were outstanding. By 1835 steam had become sufficiently important to warrant a specialist Inspector of Steam Machinery, with terms and conditions equivalent to those of a dockyard Master Shipwright, the senior shipbuilding officers. The post went to Peter Ewart, a pupil of John Rennie who had been considered for a partnership by James Watt. In keeping with his experience and advanced years, Ewart proved to be a sound, cautious engineer. He selected engines from Thameside firms, and from Boulton & Watt, in preference to those from further afield, notably Liverpool and Glasgow. He also preferred tried and tested technology, leaving the private sector to pay for pioneering work. Two years later the reluctance of Symonds to co-operate on the design of steam ships forced the Admiralty to create the Office of Controller of Steam, under Captain Sir Edward Parry, a noted Arctic explorer. This triangular administrative structure would prevail until the end of the sailing navy in 1850, when the Admiralty merged the post of Controller of Steam with that of Surveyor. In the interval it proved to be a troubled and often wasteful arrangement. In addition Symonds' steam ships were roundly criticised by Napier and others for their limited armament and excessive draught, features

25. Graham to Martin, 22 January 1831; Martin to Graham, 27 January and 16 June 1831; Martin to Oliver Lang, 21 February 1831, BL Add 41, 399.

of the hull form adopted by the Surveyor for all his steamers.

Experience with *Dee* and her four half-sisters *Rhadamanthus*, *Medea*, *Salamander* and *Phoenix*, indicated that large steam warships were useful for towing, message-carrying and other auxiliary services. The first two proved particularly useful in blockading the coast of the Netherlands in 1832. However, if they were to be sent further afield than the Mediterranean it was vital that a steam factory be set up to keep them in order, and large stocks of coal provided. Steam warships were tied to their bases to a far greater extent than the sailing ships they supported, both for coal and maintenance, and consequently Britain, with a world-wide chain of bases, was the only power in a position to exploit steam. When he left the Admiralty in 1834 Graham called for ten more First and Second Class steamers (800 and 500 tons), but his successors were content to proceed slowly, watching British commercial developments, the area where real progress was being made.

The paddle frigate

In early 1835 the Surveyor was ordered to design a modified *Medea* class vessel for engines of 220hp by Boulton & Watt. The draught was ordered thirteen months later as *Gorgon*. She was followed by an order for a larger vessel, *Cyclops*. Seaward & Capel then persuaded the Board to fit engines of 350hp, intended for *Cyclops*, into *Gorgon*. The extra power of the new machinery, which was restricted by size and weight rather than power, was the result of using direct drive from the piston rods to the crankshaft, replacing the heavy and bulky side lever machinery originally planned. Machinery weights continued to fall during the 1840s, largely through competition among the British builders and the use of improved boilers. Higher steam pressures led to reduced coal consumption.

Gorgon proved a successful sea-boat, being large, stable under sail, and quite fast under steam. Despite her size and power she carried only six heavy guns, on the open upper deck. In

consequence they were hardly true frigates, but the term 'steam frigate' was first applied to *Cyclops*, and then to all subsequent large war steamers. This gave the large steamer an importance that could not be justified by results. While some argued that *Gorgon* could defeat a battleship, the captain of the gunnery training ship *Excellent* made it clear that no steam ship could approach within 3000yds of a battleship without risking the destruction of her machinery. After 1815 battleships possessed the capacity for all-round fire. In consequence the paddle steam warship was never a threat to the sailing battlefleet, merely a useful supplement. During the Syrian Campaign of 1840 the steamers were used to support an amphibious campaign, landing stores and equipment, and towing the fleet. When the fleet bombarded the fortress of Acre on 3 November, *Gorgon*, *Vesuvius*, *Stromboli* and *Phoenix* were available. The first thought of many, including Napier, then second in command, was for the fleet to be towed into position, but there were not enough steamers to move all the heavy ships at once, and in the event the wind shifted, allowing them to come in unaided. This left the steamers in support, firing at long range – a shell from *Gorgon* destroyed the Egyptian magazine and resolved the battle ahead of schedule. Admiral Stopford commanded the fleet from *Phoenix*.

After *Gorgon* two competing strands can be identified in British steam ship design. Some wished to make the steamer capable of carrying a full broadside on the main deck, to fight in the conventional manner. The principal reason for this was the limited protection provided to the guns and gunners by the upper deck bulwarks. These were normally constructed from larch or fir and offered little resistance to shot or shell. Furthermore the ports for the heavy pivot guns tended to be wide and high, to allow the guns to traverse and elevate. A main deck battery would avoid the danger of a steamer being disarmed by close range fire. Others recognised the futility of the attempt, and preferred to restrict the paddle warship to approximately 1000 tons, with an upper deck battery, high speed and considerable towing power. These two strands of thought were put into practice by successive governments.

The Tory ministry of Sir Robert Peel built a series of gun deck steam frigates, culminating in *Terrible* of 1845. *Terrible* was one of the largest paddle wheel warships ever built. Her designer, Oliver Lang, was the 'pet' of the Admiralty, and was given everything he requested – tubular boilers (rather too many in the event), a free hand on dimensions, and a powerful battery. The heavy guns were more powerful than the standard 32pdr of 56cwt. They gave *Terrible* an advantage in range and accuracy that came close to supporting the argument that steam ships could defeat sailing battleships. In addition her engines gave her the power to tow a large three-decker at up to 8kts. However, the type was enormously expensive to build and to run, and came into service just as the screw propeller offered a more satisfactory compromise between steam and sail. *Terrible* served with distinction in the Crimean War, taking part in the Bombardment of Odessa on 23 April 1854, when nine paddle frigates attacked the harbour defences. Later

The Gorgon *and* Cyclops *of 1835 and 1838 respectively formed the basis of development in the Royal Navy, the former as the prototype for many First Class sloops and the latter for Second Class frigates.* Gladiator *shown here was a more powerful derivative of* Cyclops *and one of three* Firebrand *class ships built in the early 1840s. A feature of British paddle warships was a boat carried upturned above each paddle-box, clearly seen here; these were particularly valuable for amphibious operations.* (NMM)

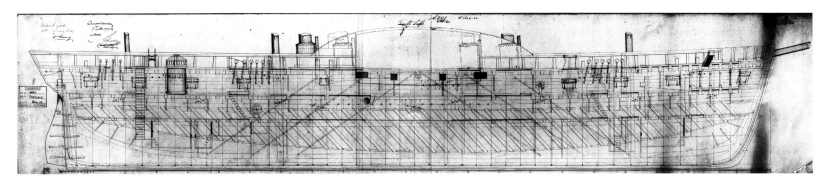

The largest British paddle warship was HMS Terrible *of 1845. This original profile draught shows the large amount of diagonal strapping necessary to keep rigid a hull that was also immensely strongly framed. Armament was eight 56pdr/98cwt and eight 68pdr/95cwt divided equally between main and upper decks, plus three 12pdr/6cwt on the main deck.* (NMM)

Terrible fought at the Bombardment of Sevastopol on 17 October 1854, when the lesser steam ships were employed as tugs, landed heavy guns for the siege of Sevastopol and demonstrated a prodigious capacity for transporting troops. Rebuilt in the 1860s she remained on the Navy List for many years.

Of the other paddle frigates, only Napier's *Sidon* warrants particular notice (1329 tons, 211ft × 37ft). She was primarily conceived for amphibious warfare. Napier modifed an existing design, based on limited draught, to keep all the machinery (apart from the paddle wheels and paddle shaft) below the waterline. Her bunkers were lined with iron, so that they could be filled with water when empty to preserve the proper immersion of the wheels. He also adopted wrought iron in place of cast in the engine, to reduce the risk of damage from gunfire, and emphasised the capacity to carry troops and the mounting of a truly formidable battery, comprising twenty-two guns (32pdrs and 8in shell guns on the main deck and 68pdrs and 10in guns on the upper deck). Both the concept and construction of *Sidon* did credit to Napier, who understood the impact of steam on warship design rather better than the architects who were responsible for the rest of her type. She was slightly less stable than other paddle frigates, which limited the value of her heavy rig, but her military qualities compensated for this defect.[26] The other large steamers were less satisfactory: *Terrible's* low and cramped stern prevented the effective use of her guns, while *Retribution* could not carry any main deck guns until her 800hp engines had

been replaced by a new set of only 400hp. In 1852 Oliver Lang junior submitted a proposal for a new paddle frigate. Essentially an enlarged *Terrible*, some 260ft long, with engines of 1000hp and thirty-six guns, (thirty-four 68pdr 95cwt, two 68pdr 113cwt) on a tonnage of 2540, she would have been as heavy as a two-decker steam battleship, and slightly faster, but quite unequal to facing a broadside of 45 guns.

Alongside the steam frigates the Royal Navy built a series of smaller steam sloops. The Committee of Reference on Naval Architecture, established in 1846 under Captain Lord John Hay, brought a degree of realism to the design process. They produced the design for a Second Class frigate, developed from the steam sloops of the *Sphynx* class, with a flat floor and ten guns on the main deck, exploiting the increasing power produced by marine engines by installing a plant with a nominal rating of 400hp, which provided adequate power for speed and towing capacity. The Whig administration of Lord John Russell left a free hand to Lord Auckland, and he elected to pursue the auxiliary screw steamer, while building the last Second Class steam frigates, the *Valorous* class

of 1849 (1257 tons, 210ft × 26ft). However, the paddle wheel warship died at the same time as the sailing battleship. In 1850 both were rendered obsolescent by the screw steam battleship.

Despite doubling the size and power of the steam warship in less than a decade, the tactical and strategic value of the type remained constant. The enormous engines of *Terrible* were ideal for high speed towing and high speed despatch duties, but cost a King's ransom to keep in full commission. By the mid-1840s the experienced officers of the Royal Navy recognised that the future of war lay in combining steam and battleships. From 1846 the major British fleets, the Channel Squadron and the Mediterranean Fleet paired each battleship with a steamer. The Mediterranean Fleet made considerable use of steam in June 1853 when it was ordered to Besika Bay, in November to pass the Dardanelles, and on 17 October 1854 when the fleet attacked Sevastopol. On the last occasion, the paddle steamers were lashed to the

26. Sir Baldwin Walker, Evidence before the 1859 Committee on Naval Engines, *Parliamentary Papers XV* (1859), p26.

Terrible after the removal of two boilers and their funnels (as completed the ship was over-provided with steam generating capacity). (CMP)

disengaged side of the battleships, to preserve their mobility. If steam was now vital for naval operations it made sense to fit it into major warships, rather than provide them with tugs.

The hull forms of naval and mercantile steam ships began to diverge as warship mounted heavy guns at the bow and stern. The earliest empirical work on steam ships, such as that of David Napier, pointed to fine lines of entry and a fine stern run as the keys to speed. This was particularly important when real power remained low. However, if a warship wanted to carry heavy guns fore and aft she could only do so, in a wooden hull, if the bow and stern had a sufficient reserve of displacement to support the guns. Increasing effective horsepower reduced the value of extreme lines, permitting the use of a hull form capable of supporting an effective armament. As an indication of the form of the large paddle warships the Indian Navy paddle frigate *Punjaub* of 1853 sailed for many years as the fast clipper *Tweed*.[27]

The difference in the strength and form of naval and mercantile hulls was a major reason why the latter were of only limited value for war service. The exception to this rule was provided by the Atlantic liners, notably *Great Western* of 1838, which was built to naval standards with high quality machinery. This ship demonstrated that steam ships could operate continuously for twenty days on end, which influenced French, American, and even British warship design. However, there were only ever a handful of ships of this class.

Paddle wheel warships were never satisfactory performers under sail. All were designed as full powered steam ships, in which the rig was restricted by the priority given to engines, boilers and wheels. In addition, the resistance offered by masts and yards when steaming into the wind reduced speed and increased coal consumption. The early steamers were fitted with low masts and lowering topmasts, providing a useful supplement when the wind lay in right quarter, or if the machinery failed, but otherwise offering the smallest resistance. The cost of steam operations ensured that steam warships, as opposed to packets, made long passages under canvas alone, or with the most limited working of the engines to give the ship

sufficient speed through the water for the sails to contribute. Unlike merchant ships, warships normally had the manpower to operate a large square rig. Furthermore, operating far from the regular shipping lanes, Royal Navy warships would cruise under sail to preserve their coal, not only to save money, but also to keep their bunkers for an emergency. American ships followed this practice, but the French, particularly in the Mediterranean, were operating on regular steam routes and could contemplate a light emergency rig.[28]

Attempts to provide the paddle frigate with a rig adequate to accompany the fleet with cold boilers were only of limited value. The machinery occupied the proper position for the main mast; the alternative was too far aft and resulted in a loss of efficiency. The lack of fore and aft sail area on the brig rigged *Gorgon* played a part in her running aground off Montevideo in 1846. Later, paddle wheel warships were fitted with an extra mast aft, which gave them a most ungainly aspect, and only a moderate improvement in sailing performance. Almost all paddle warships were under canvassed for their size, to reduce drag under steam in packet vessels, or for the want of space and stability in large ships. Only the very last paddle frigates, in particular Napier's *Sidon*, managed to carry a rig appropriate to their dimensions. Furthermore, the drag of the wheels could only be avoided by unshipping the paddle boards, a difficult and time-consuming process that rendered the ship next to useless as a steamer. Although the cost of coal was not the most serious weakness of the paddle warship, it did contribute to the decision to adopt the screw auxiliary.

From the compromise inherent in the exposure of the propelling machinery and reduced broadside fire, the paddle wheel warship was always an auxiliary. Once this was recognised the design process could be resolved. Large steamers were for towing and amphibious operations, small vessels for gunfire support, communications and the normal duties of small craft in any age.[29]

The French navy and the steam warship

After the success of *Sphinx* at Algiers the French navy reproduced this design for the next decade as an auxiliary for the sailing fleet. There was no attempt to build serious steam warships, such as *Dee* or *Gorgon*. Confined to transport duties, and short of domestic engine builders the French steam navy limped along building twenty-two ships to the same design. Only in 1836 was it decided to move up from the 160hp plant of *Sphinx* to a 220hp plant, to match the *Dee*, and even then the old designs

27. D MacGregor, *Fast Sailing Ships: 1775–1875* (London 1988), p254.

28. See Basil Greenhill and Peter Allington's forthcoming paper 'The Trouble with Sails'. The writer is indebted to the authors for permission to use this material before publication.

29. J Fincham, *A History of Naval Architecture* (London 1851), pp287–339.
D K Brown, *op cit*, pp61–72.
C J Bartlett, *Great Britain and Seapower, 1815–1853* (Oxford 1963) pp198–220.
C Napier, *op cit*.
Letter to Sir James Graham, 30 May 1832, pp97–99.
Letter to Lord Ellenborough, 10 April 1846, pp135–8.
Letter to Lord John Russell, 17 June 1849, pp138–145.
Letter to *The Times*, 7 March 1850.

Early French interest in naval steamers was compromised by lack of an industrial infrastructure to build the machinery. For its first paddle frigates the French navy was forced to order 320nhp and 450nhp engines from Britain and the Netherlands. The paddle frigate Descartes, *of 20 guns, was the largest of a batch laid down in 1840. (Marius Bar)*

The French aviso *or dispatch vessel* Souffleur *of 1849. This small ship of 700 tons was rated as a corvette, but was usually employed as a tug.* (Marius Bar)

were merely scaled up. *Veloce*, significantly with engines by Fawcett of Liverpool, was the first of the larger design. The smaller *Phaeton* and *Meteore* were particularly useful during the punitive bombardment of the Mexican fortress of St Juan d'Ulloa in 1838, but both proved unreliable. Reports of *Gorgon* in 1837 resulted in a quick decision to build a 300–400hp ship, but the French were unwilling to adopt direct acting engines. Two years later the success of Brunel's *Great Western*, a 400hp ship, encouraged further expansion of the new design. Larger ships could carry more coal, and hence steam further. Unable to contract with Maudslay, the French employed Fawcett for their first large engines.

The Syrian Crisis of 1840 exposed the weakness of the French navy, and its complete reliance on Britain for engines. In response the French adopted an ambitious programme for the indigenous construction of 450hp Atlantic packets, intended to act as warships when required. These ships were technically successful, although they clogged the list of the French steam navy for years after they had

been proved to be a conceptual failure. From this base the French naval engineering industry was able to make up much of the ground lost to Britain, although by no means all. Inspired by the Prince de Joinville, French ideas on the tactical and strategic employment of steam took shape in a programme once more aimed at overthrowing British preponderance with technology. Tactically the steamer was to be employed end on, with bunkers arranged fore and aft to protect the machinery and minimise the danger to the wheels; they would be armed with the largest shell guns. By 1845 Joinville accepted that the screw propeller would replace the paddle wheel, and began work on a

large full powered screw frigate, *Isly*, alongside the paddle frigate *Mogador*, both of 640hp. By 1847 it had become clear from experiments that the concept of end-on combat did not work, even paddle steamers finding it very difficult to maintain their position relative to a stationary target, let alone one capable of manoeuvring, and the small number of rounds that could be fired over the bow would not prove decisive. The French had made the greatest intellectual commitment to the paddle warship as a means of changing the old order, and they were ultimately disappointed by the inherent weaknesses of the type. Because they had expected more from the paddle warship they were the first to abandon it, three years before the British, in favour of another new concept, the screw battleship. The Royal Navy never considered the paddle frigate to be anything more than an auxiliary, and as such they were content merely to outbuild the French.[30]

The United States

Despite a burgeoning merchant marine and large riverine steam fleet, the United States demonstrated very little interest in steam warships after the brief commission of *Demologos*. There were good reasons for this. Steam was an expensive technology, and the US Navy had small budgets. In addition the chances of any hostile steam ships operating on the American

30. S S Roberts, *op cit*, pp123–400.

The first American seagoing steamers were the Mississippi *(depicted here) and the* Missouri, *launched in 1841. For comparative purposes they had different machinery, the former testing British-style side lever engines whereas the latter had inclined engines. They were large vessels, and the longest US warships built up to that time. Rated as frigates they carried a powerful armament of eight 8in shell guns on the broadside and two 10in shell guns on traversing mountings forward.* (By courtesy of D L Canney)

coast were almost non-existent before 1840, and little greater thereafter from the lack of bases and the short range of contemporary ships. Consequently there was little pressure for a steam force. The second American steam warship, *Fulton II* was conceived as a harbour defence battery in 1835. Configured for high speed, from high pressure non-condensing engines, with a riverine type shallow draught hull and heavy fore and aft fire, the ship proved to be a complete failure as a seagoing vessel. This was despite the shift to low pressure condensing machinery of 720hp in 1836. She was incapable of operating at sea, could not fire her guns ahead or astern and although fast spent most of a five year commission being modified. However, this ship marked the beginning of the American steam navy, her Chief Engineer being the first ever appointed. Only in 1842 was a Steam Engineering Corps established.

In 1839 Congress authorised two 'sea steamers', avoiding the conceptual disaster of *Fulton II*. The design parameters for the new vessels were drawn up by a group consisting of three architects, two engineers and Captain Matthew Perry, USN. They called for vessels mounting ten guns, with coal for twenty days' steaming and able to cruise under sail alone. One would employ the British style side lever engines, the other the American inclined type. It is probable that *Great Western*, which arrived in New York in April 1838, had a considerable influence on the design. *Missouri* and *Mississippi*, launched in 1841, were very large vessels, the longest warships yet built in the United States and as such a costly investment. The hull form was conventional, although they were among the first American warships to employ iron diagonal trusses to reinforce the frame, which was built solid. *Mississippi* also adopted four water-tight iron bulkheads. The armament was dominated by the bow battery. Using segmented lowering bulwarks 20ft long, it was possible to provide converging fire from the two 10in guns 112yds ahead of the ship. The main deck guns were a useful supplement, but these ships were intended to fight end-on. Like her European contemporaries, *Mississippi*'s war service involved coastal and riverine work. She took a

leading role in the Mexican War of 1845–48, carried Commodore Perry's flag on the mission to Japan in 1853, and served in the opening campaigns of the Civil War (1861–65) only to be destroyed by fire in the river for which she had been named on 15 March 1863. *Missouri*'s career was shorter, being destroyed by fire at Gibraltar on 23 August 1843. These ships were typical of the era, combining a mighty appetite for coal with the poor sailing characteristic of all paddle frigates. In one respect the Americans did create their own individual style. While *Mississippi* employed British type side lever engines, thereafter the Americans persevered with their own inclined design.

After a series of experiments in auxiliary propulsion and delays caused by the politically damaging 'Peacemaker' gun explosion in 1842 Congress finally sanctioned further steam warships in 1847, eight years after the first steam frigates, and four years after the loss of *Missouri*. The motivation would appear to have been the utility of steam in the Mexican War, when the Americans were forced to rely largely on purchased merchant steamers. Three more paddle frigates were built before 1850, *Susquehanna*, *Powhatan* and the smaller *Saranac*. All three proved strong, and like their precursor the first pair were heavily upgunned during the Civil War.[31]

The United States Navy did not possess a significant steam fleet until 1850, made only a limited investment in the paddle warship and was always interested in cruising under sail, in view of the vast distances over which it had to operate. Only large steamers could carry the coal to operate overseas, and all were masted for a reasonable, if unspectacular, performance

under canvas for strategic mobility. However, by 1850 there could be little doubt that steamers were vital to the American strategic picture, and that the United States Navy would become a steam fleet, albeit a screw steam fleet capable of cruising on cold boilers.

The rest of the world

Despite being the world's third naval power, Russia made little effort to develop a steam navy. Although a steam boat had been built at St Petersburg in 1815, and the navy purchased *Skorij* in 1817, these were small river craft. Russian engineering facilities were dominated by imported expertise and capital throughout the nineteenth century. Furthermore, the regime of Czar Nicholas I (1822–55) was more concerned with the appearance of naval power than the advance of technology. As late as the outbreak of the Crimean War the Russian navy had less than thirty paddle wheel warships, only four or five in the Baltic were of the class termed steam frigates by the British and French, and almost all were equipped with foreign engines, or of entirely foreign construction. The best steamer in the Black Sea, the 1500-ton *Vladimir*, had been built by C J Mare on the Thames in 1848, with engines by George Rennie. She mounted five 8in guns on her upper deck and was rated at 11kts. Five more 800-ton vessels built by Pitcher, with engines from Maudslay were also in the Black Sea. In the Baltic *Olaf* of 1850 was equivalent to the British *Valorous*, mounting guns on her main deck, but fitted with foreign machinery.

31. D L Canney, *op cit*, pp7–16 and 31–37.

Among the last, and certainly the largest, American paddle frigates were the Powhatan *(seen here during or after the Civil War) and* Susquehanna. *Officially referred to as frigates, they had no main deck armament but carried fourteen to twenty guns on the upper deck: in 1865, for example,* Powhatan *mounted three 100pdr Parrott rifles, one 11in and sixteen 9in Dahlgren smooth bores.* (Naval Historical Centre by courtesy of D L Canney)

A British intelligence report of 1852 credited the northern fleet with eight frigates and five small steamers, and the Black Sea with six and fifteen respectively. None approached *Terrible* in scale or concept, despite the acquisition of British plans by Russian diplomats. Russia made little attempt to create a steam navy, lacking the domestic base and the strategic programme to employ such ships. The Czar had only two uses for his fleet: to overawe his weaker neighbours, Turkey and Sweden, and to assist in the defence of his coasts and harbours against the British. Neither role required large, modern steam warships. In 1850 Grand Duke Constantine began to update the fleet, with outside assistance, but his programme was cut short in 1854.[32]

The smaller maritime powers demonstrated more real interest in steam than Russia. Although none can be said to have influenced the design of steam warships, being largely content to follow the major powers, Holland, Spain, Sweden, Denmark, Sardinia and Naples all built or purchased steam warships. Most were restricted to the occasional new unit by economic limits, but Spain, Sardinia and Naples in particular put in place serious programmes to create a steam fleet. The Neapolitans copied British designs, and purchased British machinery, while building up domestic capacity. Sardinia was content to purchase ships and engines on the Thames, and hire engineers as part of the package. Spain had acted with more haste, purchasing several ex-merchant steamers to serve during the Carlist War of the 1830s, notably the pioneer Atlantic steamer *Royal William*, which served as *Isabel Segunda*. Later British and American built warships were acquired, and the first Spanish steam warship was completed in 1843, but many more years would elapse before Spain broke free of her dependence on British engineering. Holland expressed interest in the *Demologos* concept, beginning the conversion of a frigate to carry engines in 1826, but ran out of funds. Despite having a major marine engineering industry, which supplied both the French and Russian navies, the Netherlands lacked the funds to move into steam. In addition the division of the naval requirement between two sections, Europe and the East Indies, further compro-

mised naval policy-making. Sweden also possessed a strong marine engineering sector, but her strategic position after 1812 emphasised defence against Russia, a role in which the paddle warship acted as a support for the oared gunboat fleet and the battleships. In consequence only three were built. The Danish navy acquired a royal steam yacht in 1819, James Watt junior's *Caledonia*, but made only limited progress thereafter. By 1848 the Danes had four steam warships. Two took part in the Battle of the Eckernfjorde on 5 April 1849, during the Schleswig-Holstein War. After damage to their paddle wheels, *Hekla* and *Gejser* lacked the power to tow the battleship *Christian VIII* and frigate *Gefion* clear of Prussian batteries. The former was destroyed by red-hot shot; the latter surrendered. Both steamers escaped. After so painful a lesson the Danes quickly moved to a screw auxiliary fleet. The same decision was reached by almost every one of the minor maritime powers. Those with a less well developed engineering sector were forced back to Britain for screw machinery, just as Naples in particular had built up her own machine shops. Dependence on external sources for machinery was a point of distinction between the second rank powers. It also demonstrated that Britain was the world leader in the export of warships, marine engines and technology.[33]

The Indian Navy, 1837–63: The first steam fleet

The first all-steam fleet was the Indian Navy, the title accorded to the old Bombay Marine in 1830. In 1836 the sailing ships of the Indian Navy were configured for a variety of tasks, primarily cruising in defence of trade, but the service was under attack on grounds of economy. The Governor of Bombay proposed to

replace the entire fleet with a steam flotilla, which would carry the mail to and from Suez, transport troops and operate on the major rivers of the region in support of Indian interests, behind the strategic screen provided by the Royal Navy. With no other significant naval power in the Indian Ocean the Directors of the East India Company were at liberty to create the first all-steam navy. Within a very short space of time the Court of Directors in London had ordered a number of suitable ships in British yards, and followed these with a series of teak built but British engined vessels constructed at Bombay. From 1837 the Indian Navy was reduced to little more than a mail service, with a serious impact on morale. However, the Indian Navy and the separate Bengal Marine did have an opportunity to use its steamers in action. The First Opium War of 1841–43 saw *Enterprise*, *Madagascar*, *Atalanta*, *Seostris* and *Queen* used to tow and generally support the heavy ships of the Royal Navy in their operations against Canton and Chusan. The prominent part played in this campaign by the iron *Nemesis* has tended to overshadow the outstanding contribution made by the Indian Navy in general. Until its abolition in 1863 the

32. C de St Hubert, 'Main Shipyards, Engine Builders and Manufacturers of Guns and Armour Plate in the St Petersburg area up to 1917', *Warship International XXII* (1985), pp333–361.

33. For the navies of Denmark, Sweden and the Netherlands see papers in the *Proceedings of the International Commission for Military History* Conference at Athens 24–31 August 1987.
L Sondhaus, *The Habsburg Empire and the Sea: Austrian Naval Policy, 1797–1866* (Louisiana 1989).
A Formicola and C Romano, 'L'Industria navale nel Regno delle Due Scilie sotto Ferdinando II', *Rivista Marittima* (April 1986), pp69–86.
C de St Hubert, 'Early Spanish Steam Warships', *Warship International XX* (1983) and XXI (1984).

Valorous, the last paddle frigate built for the Royal Navy, was launched in 1851. She was one of a number of paddlers damaged in action (in her case, off Sevastopol); analysis of these engagements suggests that paddles could still be effective when damaged so the vulnerability of the paddle warship may have been exaggerated. (NMM)

Indian Navy continued as a steam force, serving in the Second Burma War of 1852, the Persian War of 1857 and the Indian Mutiny. Only in 1854 did the P & O company take over the entire mail service, having operated alongside the Indian Navy for the previous ten years.

The warships of the Indian Navy were a compromise between the regular types used by the Royal Navy and the packet steamers employed on the longer mail routes. They were armed on the upper deck with 68pdr shell guns and 32pdr cannon, which proved particularly effective against forts and stockades. It was indicative of the relative lack of interest of the Indian Navy in firepower that they should have persevered with the faster paddle wheel warship right up to 1853. Unlike the world's other navies the Indian service relied on the Royal Navy to deal with any major opposition, and under that protective screen it was content to operate an auxiliary navy. Similarly the paddle wheel warship could only operate within a strategic environment conditioned by the sailing battlefleet.[34]

Andrew Lambert

34. C R Low, *The History of the Indian Navy*, 2 vols, (London 1877), vol 1, pp532; vol 2 pp55, 61, 65, 135–158, 301.
G S Graham, *The China Station: War and Diplomacy 1830–1860* (Oxford 1978), ch v–viii.
J Sutton, *Lords of the East: The East India Company and its Ships* (London 1981), pp126–154.

Paddle Warships: Typical Vessels 1814–1850

Ship or class [Type]	Nationality	Displacement (tons)	Dimensions (loa × breadth × draught) (feet–inches) (metres)	Armament	Machinery	Speed (max, kts)	Launch dates	Remarks
DEMOLOGUS	American	1450	153–2 × 56–0 × 13–0 *46.7 × 17.1 × 4.0*	26–32pdr	1–cyl VSL, 120ihp; internal paddle	5.5	1814	The first steam warship; never commissioned
RISING STAR	Chilean (British-built)	428bm	123–6 × 27–0 × 13–0 *37.6 × 8.2 × 4.0*	20 guns	2–cyl Maudslay DA, 70nhp; internal paddles	5–6	1821	Ordered by Lord Cochrane
COMET	British	239	115–0 × 21–3 × 7–6 *35.1 × 6.5 × 2.3*	2 guns	2–cyl Boulton and Watt SL, 80nhp	7.6	1822	Originally a tug; armed in 1831 to become first RN warship
EPICHEIRESIS	Greek (British-built)	450bm	150–0pp × 26–0 × ? *45.7 × 7.9*	4–32pdr	2–cyl, 100nhp	6	1826	Fought in Greek War of Independence
COLUMBIA	British	504	130–6 × 24–9 × 11–7 *39.8 × 7.5 × 3.6*	3–32pdr	2–cyl Boulton and Watt SL, 100nhp	8	1829	Based on 10-gun brig hull form
DEE	British	907	166–7 × 30–5 × 11–6 *50.8 × 9.2 × 3.5*	2–18pdr	2–cyl Maudslay SL, 200nhp	8	1832	Largest of early British steamers
SPHINX class [Steam aviso]	French	910	158–2 deck × 26–9 × 12–6 *48.2 × 8.2 × 3.8*	6–24pdr carr, or 2/4–16cm shell	2–cyl SL (various builders), 160nhp (30ihp)	8	1829–39	Successful class of 23 *avisos*
GORGON [1st Class paddle sloop]	British	1610	178–0 deck × 37–6½ × 17–3 *54.3 × 11.4 × 5.3*	2–42pdr pivot, 2–68pdr, 2–42pdr	2–cyl Seaward DA, 800ihp	9.5	1837	Prototype for later paddle sloops and frigates
CYCLOPS [2nd Class Paddle frigate]	British	1960	190–3 deck × 37–6 × 23–0 *58.0 × 11.4 × 7.0*	2–98pdr pivot, 4–68pdrs	2–cyl Seaward DA, 320nhp (1100ihp)	9.5	1839	First British 'paddle frigate'
ASMODÉE [Paddle frigate]	French	2736	238–8 deck × 40–10 × 18–2 *72.8 × 12.5 × 5.5*	12–30pdr, 4–22cm and 4–16cm shell	2–cyl Fawcett SL, 450nhp (900ihp)	11.7	1841	Typical large French paddle frigate
MISSISSIPPI [Paddle frigate]	American	3220	220–0 × 39–0 × 23–6 *67.1 × 11.9 × 7.2*	2–10in, 8–8in	2–cyl Merrick and Towne SL, 700nhp (685ihp)	8.7	1841	First effective US paddle frigate
PENELOPE [Paddle frigate]	British	1616bm	215–2 deck × 40–9 × 20–3 *65.6 × 12.4 × 6.2*	2–42pdr pivot, 10–42pdr carr; 10–8in pivot	2–cyl Seaward DA, 650nhp	11	1843	Converted from a sailing frigate of 1829
TERRIBLE [1st Class paddle frigate]	British	3189	226–2 deck × 42–6 × 19–10 *68.9 × 13.0 × 6.1*	8–56pdr, 8–68pdr, 3–12pdr	4–cyl Maudslay DA, 800nhp (2059ihp)	10.9	1844	Most powerful British paddle frigate of her day
LABORIEUX [2nd Class paddle corvette]	French	849	158–10 deck × 27–11 × 13–8 *48.4 × 8.5 × 4.2*	2 carronades	2–cyl Rochefort SL, 220nhp	8	1848	Small 'corvette' employed as a tug
POWHATAN [Paddle frigate]	American	3600	249–9 × 44–0 × 26–6 *76.1 × 13.4 × 8.1*	3–10in, 6–8in	2–cyl Mehaffy 800nhp (1500ihp)	11	1850	Largest American paddle frigate

Notes:
Tonnage abbreviation: bm=builder's measurement. Machinery abbreviations: (V)SL = (vertical) side lever; (O)DA = (oscillating) direct acting.

The Screw Propeller Warship

WITH the benefit of hindsight it is obvious that the paddle wheel could never be combined with the qualities expected of a regular warship. Therefore the screw propeller was the logical step. However, early steam ships were so encumbered by their machinery that they could not mount a significant armament, even if a screw propeller had been available. The marked decrease in weight and space per effective horsepower that took place between 1820 and 1850 was a major element in the success of the screw warship. Furthermore, the size of all ships was limited by the technology of wooden construction. Once iron had been accepted the old limits on size and shape were abandoned. To appreciate this point it is only necessary to con-

One of the most famous incidents of nineteenth century maritime history was the tug-of-war between the new screw sloop HMS Rattler *and the paddler* Alecto *in 1845. This was popularly supposed to have convinced a sceptical Admiralty of the value of the screw, but modern research has proved this to be a myth. The Admiralty was already keenly aware of the potential of the screw-propelled warship and the trials merely confirmed its practicality and provided much needed data for propeller development. (ScM)*

sider the brief period that elapsed between the success of the *Great Britain* and the exploitation of unlimited size in the *Great Eastern*.

Auxiliary power

These two caveats indicate that the true line of development for warships in the early steam era lay in making the new motive power subordinate to the fighting qualities of a conventional ship. There were two methods of achieving this result – building 'full powered steamers', the paddle wheel ships, to act as tugs, or to employ a power source sufficiently compact to be used in a regular warship. Pioneering efforts in this direction exploited a power source that was always available in large warships, the crew. Where the smaller warships of the eighteenth century had retained large sweeps for propulsion in a calm the success of pioneer paddle wheel steamers suggested an improved arrangement. As early as 1790 the steam boat pioneer Patrick Miller had sent a design for a twin-hulled paddle driven battleship to the King of Sweden, but without result. In 1819 Commander James Ryder-Burton (1795–1876) proposed using the crew, working at the cap-

stans, to drive a pair of collapsible wheels similar to those employed on the transatlantic passage of *Savannah* in the same year. After receiving a favourable report from John Rennie, the Navy Board ordered the machinery. On 12 May 1819 Ryder-Burton's machinery propelled the frigate HMS *Active* at up to 3kts. Later trials at Portsmouth and Halifax, Nova Scotia, demonstrated that the system worked, and that the wheels could be shipped and unshipped faster than boats could be got out to tow the ship, or to kedge with the anchors. Burton was awarded the Vulcan Gold Medal of the Royal Society in 1820.[1]

Despite the obvious success of the trials, the machinery was unshipped and stored at Portsmouth. In 1829 Napier, then fitting out the frigate *Galatea*, requested permission to try the wheels and a modified system of winches. The First Naval Lord, Admiral Cockburn, ordered the trial. With help from Simon Goodrich the

1. Letter from Miller: Sjöhistoriska Museet, Stockholm. Captain J Ryder-Burton, *On the Concentration of Force* (London 1841).
C H Ward-Jackson, 'Captain Burton's method of Propelling Ships of War in a Calm', *Proceedings of the Royal Society of Arts* (Sept 1988), pp740–1.

new system proved more efficient, making up to 4kts in a flat calm. The Admiralty ordered Admiral Sir Thomas Foley to report on the experiments, and possible uses for the system, in particular its applicability to larger vessels. Although the Navy Board were still far from impressed Napier used the gear throughout his commission, culminating in 1831 when he towed the 120-gun *Caledonia* out of Cork harbour at one mile per hour. Admiral Codrington recommended a trial in a battleship, 'in consequence of the difficulty as well as the expense of providing steam vessels with the fuel necessary for accompanying a fleet at sea'.[2] Napier called for another trial in 1839 when he fitted out the 84-gun *Powerful*, but was given no encouragement.

After his experience with steam on the Seine, Napier brought an informed mind to bear on the subject of steam. He realised the advantages that would arise, but accepted that steam could not be applied to major warships using the paddle wheel. The manual wheels could be rapidly dismounted and propelled a frigate at up to 4kts for over an hour. Such mobility was far superior to towing with boats, and little inferior to using steam tugs. More significantly it did not disable the ship for combat, since once dismantled the wheels would not be damaged in action. There is no explanation for the Admiralty's studied lack of interest in a successful and practical improvement in naval design. However, the recent improvements in steam must have suggested that the future lay in that quarter, and it made little sense to adopt man-power in time of peace, a point the Admiralty employed against auxiliary steam power in the same year, for the system could easily be installed in war.

Several of the early steam projectors argued that they were trying to combine steam with sail, but the limited power of the machinery and the drag of the wheels made such hopes premature. In 1839 the innovative engine builder Samuel Seaward returned to a theme he had advocated as far back as 1829, namely auxiliary steam engines for merchant ships. Seaward argued that the limited coal endurance of all true steam ships, then at a maximum of 20 days, precluded attempts to steam to India. Therefore it would be best to accept a low power, compact engine that could be used to push a sailing ship through calms. The East India ships *Lord Vernon* and *Earl of Hardwicke* made three return passages between them in this configuration, but proved only marginally economic. The 1000-ton Indiamen used 30hp engines weighing 25 tons with dismantling wheels. For naval use Seaward planned to fit a

60hp engine into the sail room of a *Vanguard* class 80-gun ship, which would drive paddle wheels for a speed of 5kts. The Surveyor of the Navy, Symonds, supported the proposal, but it was rejected by the Admiralty, who saw no requirement for such measures as they did not anticipate war. While Seaward was primarily anxious to add to his share of the Thamesside machinery market, his proposal had the merit of working within the limits of existing technology.[3]

Seaward demonstrated that a useful power unit could be fitted in regular ships without undue difficulty, making the steam auxiliary inevitable. His death in 1842 deprived him of the chance to see the screw propeller complete his concept.

The introduction of the screw propeller, 1837–1847

The Royal Navy dominated the early history of the screw propeller warship, for the same reasons that had conditioned the British response to steam. The now discredited view that the Admiralty deliberately hampered pioneering efforts to adopt the steam engine, and each successive advance in steam technology, ignored the gulf in practical engineering between first tests and effective exploitation.[4] Caution should not be condemned in those called upon to meet a new development, based on novel, unproven, technology, particularly with the advantage of hindsight. The policy-makers of the nineteenth century were experienced men, conscious of their responsibility for the defence of a maritime empire. Their reluctance to tamper with the fabric of sea power was understandable, their willingness to take up new ideas, once the technology was proven, while commendable, was no more than their duty. In no single instance did the Royal Navy fall behind its major rivals in responding to practical manifestations of technological change.[5]

While the French sought a 'Nouvelle Force Maritime' to overthrow British supremacy, the Royal Navy treated the steam ship as an auxiliary, primarily for towing. In 1838, when Napier urged the Admiralty to expedite the introduction of steam, the response of the First Secretary was at once cautious and far-sighted:

> Your points about steamers and paddle wheels I am not competent to give an opinion upon, but

I am strongly inclined to believe that neither the increased use of steam, nor that of shells and improved gunnery will diminish the advantages which this country has hitherto maintained at sea over other powers.[6]

The screw propeller

As the paddle wheel warship, even in its most powerful form, remained an auxiliary, the application of steam to the front line of naval warfare required a new form of propulsion. The critical advantage of the screw propeller was that it could make steam an auxiliary in broadside armed heavy warships. The Royal Navy initially adopted the screw propeller to create an auxiliary steamer, not as an alternative to the paddle wheel for 'full power' steam ships.

The screw propeller was developed into a practical form in the period 1836 to 1839 by two men, working independently. There had been at least five worthwhile and proven 'inventions' of the screw before 1836: those of Stevens in 1804, Owen in 1816, Ressel in 1827, Woodcroft in 1832 and Wilson in 1833. None had been able to secure the financial support required for extended trials, without which no navy would act. The Swedish engineer John Ericsson was the first to demonstrate a working screw vessel to the Royal Navy. His launch *Francis B Ogden* towed the Admiralty barge from Somerset House to Seaward's engine works at Limehouse and back in the summer of 1837. Aboard were the First Naval Lord, Sir William Symonds (the Surveyor of the Navy),

2. Admiralty to Navy Board, 17 January 1829, PRO Adm 106/1907.
Byam Martin to Admiral Seymour, 18 May 1829, BL Add 41,398.
Admiralty to Foley, 8 October 1830; paper given out to Admiral Sir Charles Adam in January 1839, PRO Adm 1/3472.
Admiral Codrington to Admiralty 6 October 1831, NMM COD 17/1 & 25 November 1831, NMM COD 17/2.

3. Samuel Seaward, 'Memoir on the Practicability of Shortening the Duration of Voyages by Adaption of Auxiliary Steam Power to Sailing Vessels, 9 February 1841', *Transactions of the Institution of Civil Engineers* III (London 1842), pp385–400.
Surveyor to Seaward Brothers, 9 October 1839, PRO Adm 91/9.

4. Briggs, Sir J, *Naval Administration* (1897), p9.

5. For a more detailed examination of this issue see A D Lambert, 'The Royal Navy and the Introduction of the Screw Propeller, 1837–1847', in S Fisher (ed), *Innovation in Shipping and Trade* (Exeter 1989), pp61–88.

6. H-J Paixhans, *Nouvelle Force Maritime* (Paris 1821).
Sir J Barrow, *An Autobiographical Memoir* (London 1847), p388.
Charles Wood to Napier 17 December 1838, Napier MSS, NMM NAP/20.

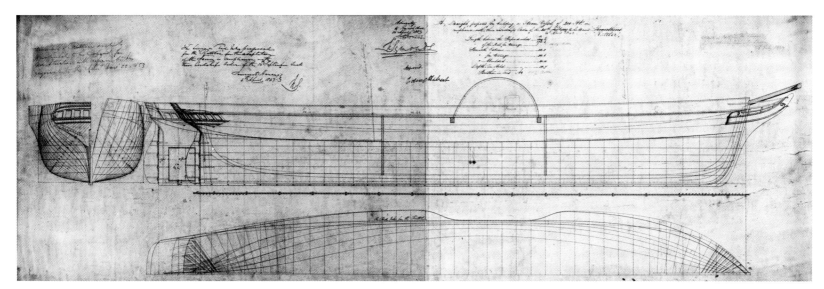

The original draught of the ship that became the Rattler, *showing the extended run aft and the large aperture for the propeller.* (NMM)

Parry, Captain Beaufort (the Hydrographer), and others. Experience with paddle vessels driven from aft of centre had demonstrated wayward response to the helm and Symonds declared that while the screw was a propeller any method of propulsion working at the stern would ruin the steering; the Admiralty barge had been towed to disguise this fatal flaw.[7]

Ericsson's screw, a pair of contra-rotating bladed drums aft of the rudder, was over-complex and, as the French discovered with the frigate *Pomone*, did have a detrimental effect on steering.[8] Certainly Ericsson's prospects improved when he removed one drum and placed a simple two-bladed propeller ahead of the rudder. His departure for the United States was not the end of his work in Europe, and his agent Count Rosen secured trials of his propeller in the tender *Bee*. Following the French order Rosen persuaded the Admiralty to install engines of Ericsson's design in the frigate *Amphion*.[9]

The Englishman Francis Pettit Smith never claimed to have 'invented' the screw propeller, confining his patent of 31 May 1836 to placing the 'Archimedean' screw between the sternpost and the rudder. Pettit Smith's most important contribution to the introduction of the screw into naval service lay in securing a group of backers, who formed the Ship Propeller Company in 1838 to exploit the commercial opportunities of the screw patent. The company built the 200-ton *Archimedes*, both in response to unofficial advice from the Second Secretary to the Admiralty and as a mobile advertisement. The company hoped to make money by licensing the use of the system.

The financial aspect of the history of the screw propeller has never been given due weight, but it should be emphasised that Ericsson, the Ship Propeller Company and a number of less well known screw patentees were interested in making money, not in the advance of theoretical science. The Admiralty, and the United States Navy, were well aware of this, and acted accordingly.

Archimedes, the beginning of naval interest

Archimedes was the first seagoing screw vessel, and a vital stage in securing naval interest. Built at Blackwall by Henry Wimshurst, the vessel was launched in November 1838. Significantly her first public trial, on the Thames on 16 October 1839, was laid on for the Admiralty. While no Lord of Admiralty attended, and the Company's request to tow a frigate was ignored, a party of naval officers, including Captains Parry, Symonds, George Evans, Francis Austin, William Shirreff and Basil Hall, the engineers Ewart, Miller, Charles Manby and Smith and a number of the company's shareholders, were aboard. *Archimedes* worked, but her underpowered machinery and bulky gearing were impractical. The propeller was geared for 127rpm, 5⅓ times engine speed. Parry, used to the relative sophistication of Seaward's direct acting paddle wheel engines, found the spur gearing bulky and noisy. His report emphasised the auxiliary nature of the invention. Observing that her best speed was only 7¾kts, far below that of the best paddle wheel vessels, he concluded, 'she is a nice little vessel, and a pretty model for sailing, which it seems to me they were anxious to combine with the screw experiment.'[10] This combination would be the key to success, rather than outright speed where paddle vessels would have an advantage for another twenty years, restricted by the lim-

ited knowledge of hull and propeller forms. George Evans, the first officer to command a Royal Navy steam vessel, ignored the technical shortcomings. He concentrated on potential, emphasising security from gunfire and the retention of the broadside, along with a standard rig, improved steering and reduced strain on the engines from the constant immersion of the propeller. He concluded, 'the screw will supersede every other means hitherto adopted for propelling vessels'.[11] *Archimedes* was then demonstrated to mercantile interests and sent on a round-Britain promotional tour, with important results.

Archimedes' impact on the Navy was increased by a series of cross-channel races with the Dover packets from May 1840. After modifications she proved a match for the regular paddle wheel vessels, once her relative size and

7. W C Church, *The Life of John Ericsson* (London 1891), vol i, p89.
The first screw propelled vessel to be given a successful trial was the *Little Julianna* of 1804, built by the American John Stevens and tried at Hoboken in May 1804. Although he continued experiments for another decade and obtained a British patent Stevens later transferred his attention to paddle wheel vessels. Spratt, *The Birth of the Steam Boat*, pp70–2.

8. HM Consul at Cherbourg to the Admiralty, 9 January 1847, PRO Adm 87/17.

9. Admiralty to Surveyor, 6 November 1843 & 18 June 1844, PRO Adm 83/30,–/32.
E C Smith, *A Short History of Naval and Marine Engineering*, p68.

10. Parry to Sir Charles Wood, 18 October 1839, in A Parry, *Parry of the Arctic* (London 1963), pp203–4.

11. Evans to Parker, 23 October 1839, in *A Record of the Services of Admiral George Evans* (London 1876), pp11–13.

power had been taken into account. Having established the validity of the concept, it only remained to decide how the new, and still largely experimental, development should be introduced into the Navy. There were several possibilities: further experiment with small vessels, or the construction or conversion of a larger ship. Given the level of technology, further experiment was vital to understand the potential of the screw. The decisions taken by the Admiralty must be viewed against this background.

Brunel, the *Great Britain*, and the Admiralty

Arriving at Bristol in May 1840, *Archimedes* created an immediate impression on the Great Western Steamship Company. Construction of their iron steamship was halted while Isambard Brunel, the company engineer, investigated the screw. *Archimedes* was chartered for a series of trials with different propeller forms and to compare her motion with that of *Great Western*. Brunel's report of 10 October 1840 was firmly in favour of the screw. He noted the compromise hull form of the trials vessel, but did not draw the same conclusion as Parry, because he was interested in the screw as a prime mover, not as an auxiliary. This basic point of departure between the naval policy-makers and the engineer has never been given due weight in explaining their different attitudes. Brunel was critical of the gearing, and considered the original screw inefficient.[12] The ship under construction, the *Great Britain*, was the largest merchant ship of the decade and the pioneer of many important developments. She was a full powered screw steam ship with auxiliary sail, designed for a specific role. The Navy would not build a full powered screw steam ship of her dimensions for almost two decades.

The importance of the *Great Britain* lay in the prestige she conferred on Brunel, which along with a copy of his report was largely responsible for his retention as the consultant engineer for the Navy's pioneer screw steam warship. Hiring Brunel ensured the Navy kept up with the experience that shaped his own project. In addition Brunel, unlike the Propeller Company, was not trying to sell the propeller. Uniquely Brunel had the vision and the courage to adopt the screw at once. No more large full powered screw steam ships were built in the 1840s, the reasons for this being primarily financial. The mercantile shipping community was, if anything, more cautious than the Navy. This was not surprising when many of them were dealing directly with their own

money, and had only recently become adjusted to the impact of the paddle wheel; Brunel, it should be noted, was neither a shipowner nor a naval architect. However, Parry was well aware of his success with *Great Western*, and recommended that he advise the Admiralty on the new system.[13]

Rattler and *Dwarf*

Before the Navy took any further interest in the screw it required a practical demonstration to supplement the acknowledged potential. Captain Chappell, liaising with the Propeller Company, proposed building a replica of any existing paddle wheel vessel to try the screw, and fitting a frigate for experiments on a larger scale. The Propeller Company objected to the use of a half-built paddle wheel vessel; both the First Lord and Symonds agreed, raising no objection to the screw during 1840. Parry advised constructing a replica of the 200hp packet *Polyphemus*, with her stern configured to allow modification and testing alternative screws. More immediately the Board sanctioned the modification of the 42-ton tender *Bee*, an instructional steam vessel for the gunnery training ship HMS *Excellent*, to carry a screw *and* paddles. Lord Minto's Board was prepared to spend money and appreciated the pioneering work conducted outside the Steam and Surveyor's Departments. It would be absurd to suggest that they opposed the introduction of the screw propeller.

Having decided to build a sister to *Polyphemus*, a model of her stern was sent to the Ship Propeller Company. Symonds was far from pleased by the reply, which required an opening 8ft long and 9ft 3in deep; this, he noted, 'tends to weaken the ship . . . particularly if she strikes the ground.'[14] The dispute between the Surveyor and the Steam Department must have had a bearing on Parry's decision to involve Brunel, who was invited to oversee the project after an interview with Minto on 27 April 1841. Brunel was given 'sole direction' of the installation of the propeller, without 'any interference'. This interference was, by inference, expected from Symonds, rather than Ewart, who was quite prepared to turn over the screw project. After visiting *Polyphemus* with Symonds, Brunel recommended a 200hp Maudslay 'Siamese' engine. At this stage Smith requested some elucidation of his position, and that of Brunel. Accordingly Minto, Adam, Symonds, Parry, Chappell, Brunel, Smith and Ewart assembled in Minto's room in late September. In view of Brunel's work for the Great Western Com-

pany and the Admiralty, Parry recommended that he be admitted to the 'conference' on the screw propeller.

At this stage the relationship between Brunel and the Admiralty was thrown into confusion by a change of administration. The Whig government was replaced by a Conservative ministry during September. The change broke up a team committed to large scale experiments, and removed from office Lord Minto, who had supported Parry in calling on Brunel for advice. The leading men of the new Board were the First Naval Lord, Admiral Cockburn, and the Political Secretary, Sidney Herbert. The First Lord, Lord Haddington, deferred to them in their respective areas of expertise. While the new team settled to their work Brunel's role was thrown into question, his understanding with Parry being unofficial. Within days of the new Board taking office the Commander in Chief at Portsmouth, Admiral Codrington, a leading radical Whig, wrote to Herbert. He advised fitting steam engines on the orlop deck of battleships and frigates, to prevent paddle steamers taking up positions to rake them when becalmed.[15]

On the first day of 1842 Brunel returned to the Admiralty for discussions with Parry and Symonds.[32] The new Board favoured a return to cheap screw experiments, using an existing vessel, the 180nhp steamer *Acheron*, with the engines already ordered. The vessel would be lengthened 4ft at the stern to incorporate an aperture 9ft 6in deep and 5ft long. Brunel criticised the selection of *Acheron*, arguing that her full stern lines would compromise the trial results.[16]

Herbert sent this letter to Parry and Symonds, demonstrating his interest. However,

12. E Corlett, *The Iron Ship* (Bradford on Avon 1975), p54–61.
I K Brunel, *Life of I K Brunel* (London 1870), pp539–558.

13. Parry to Claxton, 12 July 1838, thanking him for a copy of the published logs of the *Great Western*, and wishing him commercial success.
Parry to Claxton, 6 November 1840, acknowledging reports on the strength of the *Great Western* and asking for any information on 'the large iron ship, including the *Screw*', PRO Adm 92/4.

14. Surveyor to Admiralty, 16 January 1841 & 12 February 1841, PRO Adm 92/9.

15. Codrington to Herbert, 6 October 1841 and Herbert to Codrington, 24 October 1841, NMM COD 17/2 & COD 20/4.
L T C Rolt, *Brunel* (London 1957), p57.
Lady Bourchier, *Memoir of the Life of Admiral Sir Edward Codrington KCB* (London 1873), vol i, p349; vol ii, p523–4.
Codrington to Herbert, 4 August 1843, NMM COD 20/2, p112.

16. Brunel to Admiralty, 10 February 1842, PRO Adm 83/25.

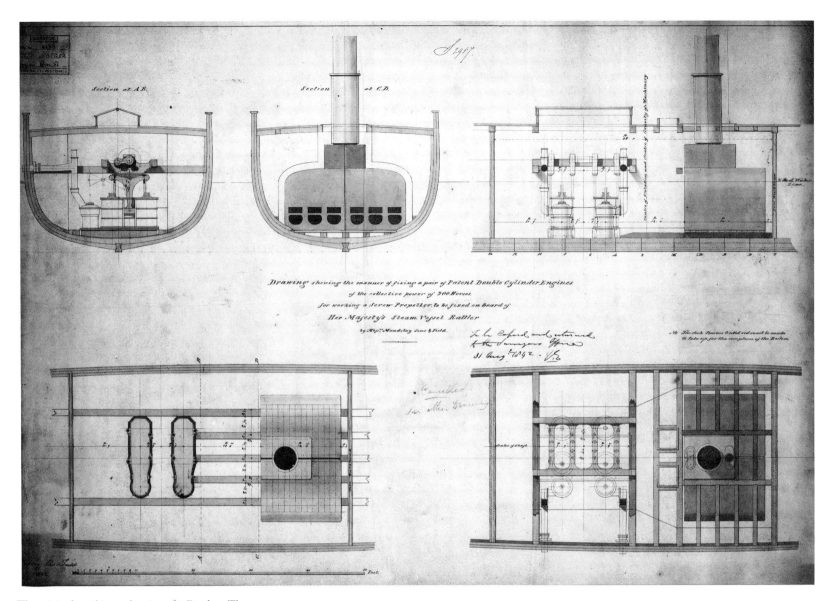

The original machinery drawings for Rattler. *The Maudslay four-cylinder Siamese engines are evident, but at this stage there is still no gearing, a large gear wheel being later fitted abaft the engines, for which the framework can be seen.* (NMM)

there was another side to the problem, and one which Brunel had not considered. The Admiralty was interested in the screw as an auxiliary for sailing vessels. In addition, any hull form they adopted had to support concentrated weights of heavy artillery at all points, including the bow and stern. Therefore the ideal fine stern run could not be achieved in a wooden warship without compromising the structural integrity of the vessel. As late as 1850 the ambition of the Admiralty in adopting screw propulsion for large warships was limited to a speed of 6kts.[17] The hydrodynamic requirements for such limited performance were very different from those of a full powered steamer. In proposing *Acheron* as a trials vessel the Ad-

miralty was not trying to spoil the experiment, merely demonstrating that their interest lay in the auxiliary use of the screw. At this juncture Brunel was the only proponent of the screw for use in full powered steamers. The Ship Propeller Company was more interested in auxiliary use. Symonds, observing that the steamers then building were too large for the 200hp engines, recommended a return to the plan of December 1840, constructing a replica of *Polyphemus* in place of the suspended paddle sloop *Rattler*. When the drawings were approved, Symonds was directed to proceed 'in communication with Mr Smith'.[18] The remaining drawings were sent to Sheerness as soon as possible. *Rattler* was a new design, built from seasoned timber prepared for a larger 280hp paddle wheel sloop of the *Styx* class. She was not converted from any existing ship.

On returning from Italy Brunel was informed that the work was in hand, with Smith advising the shipwright officers. Smith pro-

vided details of the screw aperture, the screw and the gearing required. Herbert confirmed the original intention of the Minto Board, that Brunel should oversee the installation of the screw in communication with Smith and Symonds.

Far from wanting to delay the ship, Symonds was annoyed to find that the construction of her after body was suspended, 'on account of the indecision of the Engineers who are to provide a screw propeller'.[19] Brunel advised that Maudslay's prepare the iron work for the stern, as it would have to fit accurately with the screw shaft. Hardly living up to the image of the apo-

17. A D Lambert, *Battleships in Transition: The Creation of the Steam Battlefleet: 1815–1860* (London 1984), pp31–2 on the 1850 Lisbon trials and the screw frigate *Arrogant*.

18. Admiralty to Surveyor, 6 April 1842, PRO Adm 83/25.

19. Surveyor to Admiralty, 3 September 1842, PRO Adm 92/10.

plectic First Naval Lord portrayed by Brunel's son, Cockburn sent Brunel's letter to Symonds for his 'information and guidance'.[20]

Launched in April 1843, *Rattler* received her engines in the East India Docks. She made a first proving run on 30 October, exceeding 8kts the following week. *Rattler*'s first trial was carried out immediately after the installation of her machinery, before she was docked at Woolwich for her copper. Far from showing the Surveyor's animosity to the ship, the early trial before coppering demonstrated the Admiralty's enthusiasm for the screw, and a desire to test it at the first opportunity.[21]

In June 1843 the Admiralty purchased the small iron screw steamer *Mermaid*, renamed *Dwarf*, as a trials vessel to complement *Rattler*. Built to test Rennie's conoidal propeller, *Dwarf* proved ideal; her size ensured she was easily docked and could run in the river, a useful quality for a ship based at Woolwich. In addition she had an excellent stern run. From early 1843 she tested many different propellers, while her stern was subjected to numerous modifications. The resulting data was used to modify *Rattler*, and to design later screw warships.

Technological progress, strategic problems and the practical steam warship

Rattler, for all her success as a steam screw auxiliary, was far from being a perfect warship. Her machinery was still exposed – because the 'Siamese' engine was configured for paddle wheels, the drive was taken just below the upper deck, well above the waterline. The Propeller Company, aware of the space wasted by the indirect drive, proposed a geared crankshaft in mid-1844 that would remove the need for the indirect gearing used in all previous screw steam ships, saving space and confining all machinery 'within a few feet of the kelson of any vessel'. The first such ship to enter service was the sloop *Niger*.[22] In many ways the placement of the machinery below the waterline was the crucial achievement of the screw, allowing it to fill the role of auxiliary power in sailing ships, as the projectors had hoped. *Rattler* remained an experimental vessel, being used as such for the remainder of the 1840s. Even before her famous cruise with Admiral Sir William Parker's squadron in 1846 she had proved the validity of the screw auxiliary, which was far more important than races and a tug of war with her half-sister *Alecto*. These came after the decision to adopt the screw, and can be seen as a public relations exercise. In

1844 and 1845 the Admiralty ordered the construction and conversion of several large screw steamers, from modified two-deckers to iron frigates. Cockburn, the most influential naval policy-maker between 1841 and 1846 was convinced, and took the opportunity to mock Napier for selecting the paddle wheel when allowed to build a war steamer of his own design: 'The proof we have lately had of the efficiency of the screw as a propeller on board of the *Rattler* convinced *me*, that it will be in future generally adopted & we are now adapting those building for that description of propeller.'[23]

There was a degree of urgency in the decision. Concern over relations with France led Sir Robert Peel's administration to sanction a large expenditure on steam ships, several of which were screw vessels. Reflecting the ambition of the Board, and the level of expertise available, these were auxiliary vessels with stern lines very different from those urged by Brunel. Believing Symonds's steamers were all failures, Cockburn called for alternative designs from the Surveyor's most bitter critics. Aware of the want of trust in the highest quarters, Symonds conducted a bitter rearguard action, alienating friend and foe alike. In large part this reflected political quarrels dating back to 1832. Symonds, although a permanent official, continued to support his Whig friends out of office. Such internal warfare did nothing to ease the development of the screw, or encourage objective analysis.

In the 1840s experiments were more important than construction, where other navies lagged far behind. Further, not one of the ships built before 1850 was entirely successful, resulting from a combination of poor machinery and limited hydrodynamic knowledge. *Rattler* and *Dwarf* provided the empirical data to build an auxiliary steam navy. Symonds was well aware of the new thinking on hull forms for the screw.[24] He objected to the effect the new form would have on sailing qualities, *because* he could not bring himself to treat steamers as front line warships, or rely on engines. Symonds saw the presence of so many sources of fire and heat as the principal disqualification of the steamer, of whatever type, as a warship.[25] Men in more poweful positions had different ideas: writing in 1848 Lord Auckland, the First Lord, stressed that the steam auxiliary was the warship of the future. Early trials with the three-masted screw schooner *Reynard* demonstrated the benefit of experience with *Rattler* and *Dwarf*. Launched on 21 March 1848, *Reynard* (516 tons, 148ft × 27ft 5in) carried eight 32pdrs. In the brig sailing trials of that

year, she proved almost equal to the purpose built sailing craft, without having resort to steam. Lord Auckland declared, 'I am satisfied that the whole theory of ship building will be directed from the old notions of sailing ships to the manner in which the screw auxiliary may be best combined with good sailing qualities'.[26] This meant abandoning Symonds's controversial wide beamed hull. Adding length to sailing hulls sacrificed manoeuvrability and speed to windward in favour of the effective use of the screw, but as a bonus the new hulls also provided improved sailing performance off the wind in favourable conditions, leaving steam to solve the problems of windward sailing that had long exercised the genius of shipbuilders and architects. This solution, of classic simplicity, made the steam auxiliary a far more effective warship than any that had gone before.

In Britain and America the rate at which the screw was adopted was conditioned by a clear reluctance to pay the cost of using a system that was protected by a patent. The Admiralty ignored several offers of 'exclusive rights' to the screw in the early 1840s, and deliberately set out to circumvent the rights of the Ship Propeller Company. The Arctic exploration vessels *Erebus* and *Terror* were fitted on a system devised by Oliver Lang.[27]

After 1845 the Propeller Company lost the strength to protect its rights, leaving the Admiralty to hire Smith as an individual consultant until 1850, when he was paid off with a final gratuity of £400. Other projectors were encouraged by the offer of trials at cost aboard *Dwarf*. By the time Smith secured a renewal of

20. Brunel to Admiralty, 17 September 1842 endorsed by Cockburn, 28 September 1842.
Brunel to Admiralty, 20 September 1842, PRO Adm 83/27.

21. Rolt, *op cit*, p286.

22. Ship Propeller Company to Admiralty, 11 June 1842, PRO Adm 87/14.

23. Cockburn memoranda in Haddington to Peel, 11 June 1845, BL Add 40,458, f55–64. In 1851 *Rattler* was sent to China, and on her return in 1856 was found to be defective and broken up.

24. Surveyor to Admiralty, 6 November 1846 & 12 January 1847, criticising the hull form of *Dauntless* and *Arrogant*, NMM Adm 92/12.

25. Symonds to Lord Auckland, 23 November 1848, NMM WWL/1 (Papers of Admiral Sir Baldwin Walker).

26. Lord Auckland to the Duke of Portland, 7 September 1848, Portland MSS PwH 611 (University of Nottingham Library).
Auckland to Rear-Admiral Sir Charles Napier, 7 September 1848, BL Add MSS 40,023, f278.

27. Admiralty to Solicitor, 11 June 1845, PRO Adm 12/449.

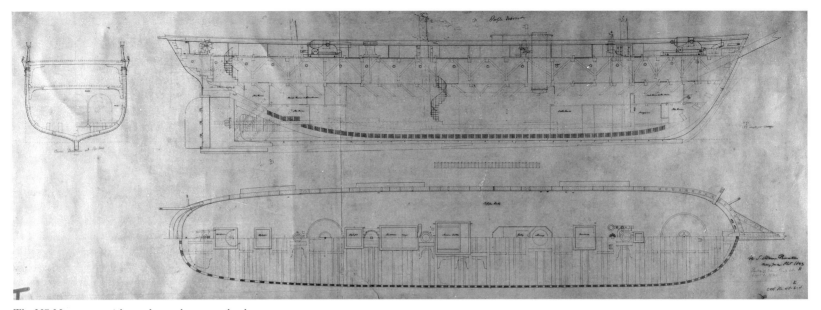

The US Navy was quick to take up the screw, the sloop Princeton *being completed in 1843. Since* Rattler *had a modified paddle steamer hull form, the* Princeton *may be regarded as the first purpose-designed screw warship. The screw could not be hoisted but could be uncoupled to feather when the ship was under sail. This official inboard profile shows another Ericsson innovation, the lowering funnel.* (US National Archives, by courtesy of Donald L Canney)

his patent, in 1850, the Admiralty was in a strong position. A final payment of £20,000 was made to cover the rights of all propeller projectors, in shares to be settled among themselves. Smith received around one-third of this fund. This was a paltry amount to offer to secure undisputed use of the system that was already the only method of propulsion used on new warships. That it was accepted reflected the skill of the Admiralty in its handling of both new technology and the private sector.

Ericsson in America

Ericsson's early backers, the American Consul at Liverpool, Francis B Ogden, and Captain Robert F Stockton, USN, anticipated the success of the new system in the United States. Following his experience with the Admiralty Ericsson designed a canal boat for Stockton and crossed the Atlantic. Stockton used his new boat, which arrived in April 1839, and the conversion of the merchant steamer *Clarion* to persuade the Navy Department to build a screw steamer. Begun in 1841 and launched on 9 September 1843 the sloop *Princeton* was the world's second purpose-built screw warship,

after *Rattler*. *Princeton*'s general layout was drawn up by Ericsson, and the hull lines and structure plans refined by John Lenthall. Heavily built of timber, without iron reinforcement, the ship proved a triumph as an auxiliary, notably during the Mexican War. Not only did she steam and sail well, she also proved quite economical, due in part to her advanced steam plant. The explosion of Stockton's 12in gun, the 'Peacemaker', in 1844 killed two major politicians. The Commodore unjustly blamed Ericsson for the disaster, having previously denied him any credit for the success of the ship. This soured relations between the Navy and the irascible engineer, and they were not improved by the Navy's attempts to get round Ericsson's patent rights. Lieutenant Hunter's horizontal paddle wheels were taken up with great enthusiasm, but proved a complete failure. The brief period of innovation in the Navy was associated with the tenure of Secretary of the Navy Abel P Upshur, for inspiration failed after Upshur, by then Secretary of State, was killed aboard *Princeton*.[28]

The second American screw warship was as great a failure as *Princeton* had been a success. *San Jacinto* of 1850 adopted a lop-sided alignment for the propeller and other contrived designs to avoid Ericsson's patent. Her first set of machinery was a collection of mechanical disasters; the responsible engineer was dismissed and the ship re-engined within three years.

The United States Navy was possibly the first to realise the full implications of the screw, employing the services of the most innovative marine engineer of the period, but still managed to be a long way behind the Royal Navy in 1850. The following decade did not recover the lost ground.

French policy

Lacking the innovative shipping and engineering basis of Britain and the United States the French navy had to take a larger role in the development of the screw. Frederic Sauvage's screw experiments in the 1830s proved inconclusive, largely from lack of financial support. The shipbuilder Augustin Normand brought Sauvage's patents and employed the English engineer John Barnes to develop them. The 120hp packet steamer *Napoléon*, ordered in December 1841 from Normand, was the first French screw vessel. Launched in 1842, she was employed on trials during 1843, reaching 10kts and sailing well. French constructors were well aware of the work being carried on across the Channel, paying particular attention to *The Great Britain*. In May 1842 *Pomone*, an experimental frigate, was re-ordered with a screw propeller. Lacking a body of scientific or empirical data of their own, the French Naval Ministry were particularly impressed when Count Rosen provided them with details of Ericsson's work in the United States. Consequently they adopted his entire machinery design, including the propeller and its placement abaft of the rudder, in preference to the Smith system. *Pomone* was launched in October 1845 and served as a trial for the auxiliary concept. In addition, several small steamers were ordered with the screw, including two royal yachts. By 1845 the French were ready to try their first large, full powered screw frigate, *Isly*, as a direct comparison with a paddle steamer, something the Americans would attempt in 1847 with *Saranac* and *San Jacinto*. However, the real opportunities of the screw were seen to lie in the auxiliary or *vaisseau mixte*. In 1846 the

28. D L Canney, *The Old Steam Navy*, pp21–30.

Dupuy de Lôme's Napoléon *(90 guns), the first purpose-designed screw line of battle ship, was launched in 1850 and ready for sea in 1852. Regarded as a highly successful ship, eight sisters were built to a basically similar design over a period of ten years.*

With limited space on the broadside they mounted a reduced battery of heavy calibre guns, with pivot guns on the upper deck. Tactically limited by its weak armament and exposed machinery, the paddle warship was condemned to an indecisive role at long range. The same heavy calibre upper deck battery was adopted for the pioneer screw frigates *Dauntless* and *Arrogant*, the 1845 blockships and the first draught of the pioneer steam battleship *James Watt* in 1847, although the lower decks were armed as sailing ships. Unlike the paddle steamer, the screw warship quickly adopted the normal broadside armament for line of battle tactics. With the funnel lowered only the greater length of the screw steamer betrayed the fact that it was not a sailing ship.

The rate at which the Royal Navy took up steam power, and later made it the principal method of propulsion, was determined by the progress of technology in relation to British strategic requirements. France built the full powered steam battleship *Napoléon* in 1851 to escort military convoys between Toulon and Algiers, reflecting limited strategic horizons. The Royal Navy converted four small steam battleships in the 1840s for local defence, but, like all British wooden steam battleships, these were auxiliary steam ships. The superior per-

French considered installing 100hp engines in four battleships and 60hp sets in the same number of frigates. This promised to resolve the sail-against-steam debate of the last decade, by subordinating steam to sail in seagoing warships. However, engines of this size would have offered no more than 2kts and barely the ability to manoeuvre. Influenced by the British blockships, the installed power was raised to 500hp and 250hp respectively before the designs were ordered in November 1846. The whole programme was running ahead of experience, with *Pomone* only available for trials in 1847. Following the 1848 Revolution, French naval programmes suffered from limited funds

until the *coup d'état* of December 1851. The first French steam battleship, converted from a half finished two-decker, *Charlemagne*, was completed in 1851, alongside the pioneer full power screw battleship *Napoléon*. To supplement their own work the French kept at least one engineer permanently in Britain to study the screw.[29]

Armament and tactics

Adopting the screw in large ships gave rise to important tactical implications. The armament of the paddle frigates emphasised their difference from the sailing ship of similar size.

29. S S Roberts, 'The Introduction of Steam . . .', pp351–447.

The internal profile draught of the prototype screw frigate HMS Amphion, *dated 1848. The main elements of the propulsion system are entirely below the waterline and do not interfere with the fighting qualities of the ship, compared with a similar sized paddle frigate.* (NMM)

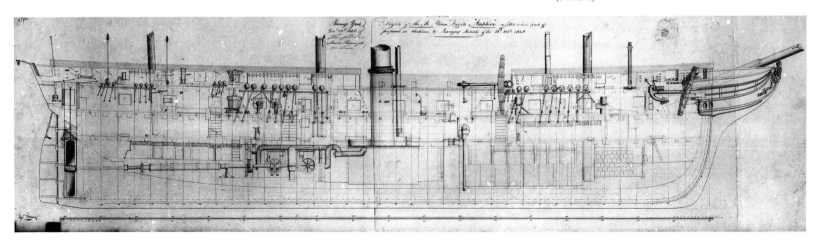

formance of British engines tended to obscure the point, but British ships were designed for world-wide operations, with cruising under sail a priority. Steam remained an auxiliary until the 1860s.

British policy-makers were anxious to exploit the screw propeller, to maintain, or improve, the ability of the Royal Navy to control the sea. This reflected the strategic position of Britain, an island state with a world-wide empire based on sea power. While they could not afford to ignore any development in their field, they were not interested in progress for its own sake, only in practical, proven systems. While private industry was prepared to make the running, and bear the cost of pioneering efforts such as *Archimedes*, there was no good reason for the Admiralty to duplicate their efforts. The Navy did have a role in the development of the screw propeller – to perfect it as a suitable auxiliary for warships, but the historiographical myth that the Admiralty were behind-hand, or positively hostile toward the screw is long overdue for revision. Steam was adopted and given an increasing role in naval affairs as technological progress allowed mechanical engineering to match the expectations of the pioneers.

The legend of obstructionism reflects the administrative problems of a weakened and divided Admiralty. This caused unnecessary confusion, most apparent in relations between Brunel, Smith, Parry and Symonds, all of whom favoured the screw, to different degrees.

Symonds did not obstruct Brunel: Brunel's real complaint was that the Tory Admiralty did not maintain a personal agreement made with the preceeding Whig board. At a personal level he was not alone in finding Symonds difficult; Parry was simply brushed aside, leaving his role to Herbert, who had the ear of Cockburn, and of the Prime Minister. The removal of Symonds and the redefinition of the Surveyor's duties ensured that the creation of a screw steam navy was carried through smoothly. Symonds was not, however, as is generally presumed, dismissed because of his opposition to the screw. The problems were administrative and personal. Furthermore he had reached the age of sixty-five. His successor, Sir Baldwin Walker, was appointed as a policy-maker, not a designer. He created the screw steam navy without the controversy that had surrounded Symonds.

The wooden screw steam warship

Between 1850 and 1860 the wooden screw steam warship was the dominant instrument of sea power, offering a hitherto unimagined combination of firepower, speed and manoeuvrability. These qualities made the battlefleet of the 1850s infinitely more powerful than

any that had gone before. However, this was a temporary stage in the implementation of industrial development at sea, a process that would be completed by the adoption of iron hulls, already attempted, but yet to be accepted.

The blockships of 1845

The pace of development in warship design has always been influenced by the international situation. In 1844–45 Anglo-French tension – particularly the Tahiti crisis, the publication of the Prince de Joinville's pamphlet *Notes sur l'etat des forces navales de la France*, and the French punitive attack on Morocco – created a situation in which the Anglo-French entente faltered and died. It was against this background that the Royal Navy made a rare error in the handling of naval technology, the iron frigate programme (see Chapter 3). In contrast, they made very good use of the screw in another area. The screw had been proved, albeit only as a satisfactory propeller. Therefore when the Royal Commission on Coast Defences reported in favour of improved fortifications, they added a requirement for mobile sea batteries. These would be quickly extemporised by converting some 1815–vintage 74-gun two-deckers and 44-gun frigates into screw steam ships with a jury rig. Initially only intended for local mobility, the ships were upgraded for Channel cruising, and by the time they had been completed (the first was *Ajax* in September 1846, only 13 months after being ordered) they were being considered as part of the Royal Navy's fundamental 'Cherbourg Strategy', a programme of ships, bases and reserves intended to facilitate an assault on the major French base.[30]

The conversions of the four 74s were simple: two merely had a 450hp engine placed in the after hold; the other pair were lengthened by 5ft or 8ft for an improved stern run, and their trial speeds ranged from 5.8kts to 8.9kts. The bluff sterns of all four ships made it hard to achieve any speed, and it is worthy of note that the better performers were the two ships with

---

30. A D Lambert, *The Last Sailing Battlefleet: Maintaining Naval Mastery 1815–1850* (London 1991).

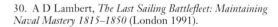

Besides new construction, both major naval powers converted ships that were on the stocks or even complete. Castiglione was a French 90-gun ship that had been in frame since 1835 and underwent a major conversion to produce a vessel nearly equal to the Napoléon in capabilities. She was launched in 1860. (Musée de la Marine)

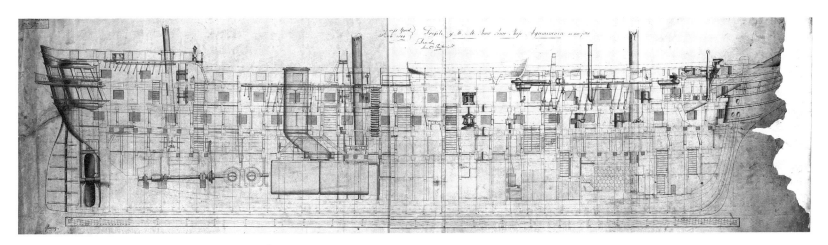

Britain had already embarked on a large programme of 'blockship' conversions when the news of the Napoléon *became public. In fact, a screw battleship had been designed as early as 1846 (as the* James Watt*), but the definitive design which became the* Agamemnon *was produced in response to rumours of the French ship; she was only ordered in 1849 but construction was rapid and* Agamemnon *entered service in 1853, shortly after* Napoléon. *The British ship was also very successful and formed the basis for future development. This is the original profile draught.* (NMM)

engines by Maudslay, rather than those that had been lengthened. The ships all lost their poop, but were armed with a powerful upper deck battery of two 68pdr 95cwt and four 10in 67cwt guns, a 'steamer' battery. The success of the blockship *Blenheim* on the coast of Ireland in 1848 had a profound influence on British policy. This should not be seen as surprising; British policy-makers were practical men, they were interested in results. However, the first new steam battleship had already been ordered in April 1847 as *Audacious*, later *James Watt*, to an inspired design by the Deputy Surveyor, John Edye. Uncertainty and a major overhaul of the Surveyor's Office resulted in the ship never being commenced. The conversion of *Sans Pareil*, ordered in October 1848, created a poor ship. She was too small, and crippled by poor machinery intended for one of the blockship frigates.[31]

The French progressed along a slightly different path. From the start of their domestic screw steam programme there were difficulties, largely brought about by the use of paddle wheel engines and geared drive to generate the

French efforts to compete with the Royal Navy were often hampered by a relatively poor industrial infrastructure and France was even forced to order machinery from her rival across the channel. These engines were built for the converted three-decker Louis XIV *by Robert Napier of Glasgow, who was proud to advertise the fact in this engraving.* (NMM)

desired propeller speed. The large engines built for the frigate *Isly*, and *Le Napoléon*, had to be replaced. By 1846 it was clear that the screw would work, and French policy-makers began to consider how they could exploit the new system. Joinville saw the low powered screw auxiliary as the best type for operations outside Europe. The initial plan was for 220hp engines in four existing battleships, but reports of the British blockships encouraged a shift toward full powered short range types for harbour defence. The result was a curious situation, in which parliament dictated that 500hp machinery be installed in the battleships. This wrecked the delicate compromise implicit in using the smaller engine. The engines were too large for the ships selected, leading some to call for extensive modifications; others preferred smaller engines, but the outstanding young engineer Dupuy de Lôme argued for a purpose-built steam battleship. This project was ultimately to result in the order for *Le Napoléon*,

on 14 July 1847. When the 500hp engines had been modified, removing two cylinders, they were installed in the almost complete sailing ships *Charlemagne*, *Jean Bart* and *Austerlitz*, which were launched in 1851 and 1852.

The rationale for the full powered steam battleship, which was originally conceived with only a light rig, was to protect steam powered shipping, either on the Toulon-Algiers axis, or for the invasion of Britain. The hull form was an expansion of that employed for the Transatlantic paddle packets, while coal was provided for forty days' steaming. Hastened to completion *Le Napoléon* was launched on 16 May 1850, to become the world's first true steam battleship. However, the French lost the opportunity to exploit their lead from a lack of funds available under the Second Republic; furthermore, what money was available was di-

31. D K Brown, *Before the Ironclad*, pp122–4.
A Lambert, *Battleships in Transition*, pp20–1, 139.

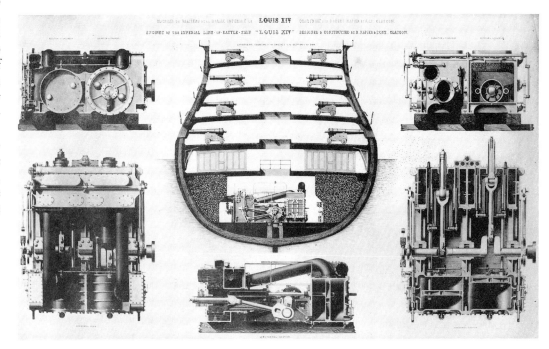

After four sister-ships of Agamemnon *had been ordered, a new more powerful design was developed, using the same midsection but a lengthened hull for finer lines. This became the* Renown *class, of which the* Revenge *(1859) was the second of four.* (IWM)

verted into further auxiliary steamers. Only in May 1852 did the Second Empire order a large class of full powered ships, along with further conversions. This was the central part of a new naval programme that looked to match Britain in numbers, to pressure Britain into supporting the ambitious programmes of Napoleon III. The ships were built, but the policy failed. Britain would not allow any rival to match her in battlefleet strength.[32]

The steam battlefleet

The British took longer to make a commitment to the purpose-built steam battleship, because the world-wide commitments of the service made it imperative to find a ship that

could operate under sail as well as steam. In July 1849 Edye's design was ordered as *Agamemnon*, to use a store of timber collected for a sailing ship of the same name. Fitted with 600hp trunk engines by Penn, *Agamemnon* proved to be an outstanding ship, being the basic design for the entire British steam battlefleet. Her design emphasised sail, while that of *Le Napoléon* was based on steam. Although the engines of *Le Napoléon* were rated at 900hp, *Agamemnon* was in fact a more powerful ship, and far more reliable. French claims to have exceeded 13kts should not be taken seriously. Later British ships with double the effective horsepower, notably the giant frigate *Orlando*, were only just capable of this speed. *Agamemnon* made 12kts, and it is possible that with her

sharper hull the French ship could have matched this, but early reports indicate that the vibration at full power was almost unbearable.

Aside from the single 95cwt gun bearing over the bow (a legacy of the paddle wheel era), the armament of *Agamemnon* was typical of the last generation of wooden battleships, both those designed with sail only, and the steamers. It emphasised that the wooden steam battleship was an amalgam of old and new. Only the addition of 25ft on the keel distinguished her from the last sailing 90-gun ship, *Aboukir* launched in 1848. Both ships were intended to fight as part of a fleet, normally in a line ahead formation to maximise firepower. Steam had finally come of age, by integrating itself into the existing order.

Agamemnon had a distinguished career. She carried the flag of Sir Edmund Lyons during the Black Sea campaign of 1854, taking the leading part in the attack on Sevastopol, and sustaining considerable damage. In 1855 she was present at the capture of Kinburn, and in 1857 laid the first, unsuccessful, Atlantic telegraph cable. Paid off from the North American Station in 1862, she was sold in 1870. By contrast *Le Napoléon* had to be given a new set of

32. S S Roberts, *op cit*, pp380–447.
A Lambert, *Battleships in Transition*, pp97–111, 140–143.

The largest British screw line of battle ships were the 121-gun three-deckers Victoria *and* Howe *(this is the as fitted draught of the former) laid down in 1856. They were very fast,* Howe *making 13.5kts on trials, and this was achieved by a unique outfit of eight boilers, four on either side of the machinery, giving the ships two funnels – the only British ships so fitted.* (NMM)

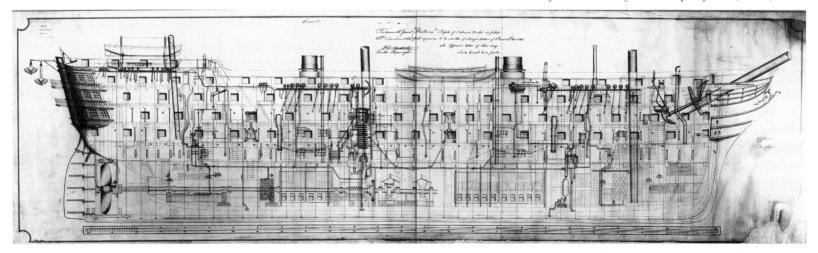

machinery in place of her complex and cumbersome four-cylinder geared powerplant in 1861. She missed much of the action in 1854 and 1855 through extensive periods undergoing repairs. France had still a little way to go to rival Britain in the availability and quality of large steam engines, and three French battleships were completed with British machinery.

In 1850 the Royal Navy had accepted that the sailing warship was dead. On the retirement of the Controller of Steam the opportunity was taken to combine his office with that of the Surveyor of the Navy, signifying that no more sailing ships would be ordered. In December 1852 the Surveyor secured a commitment from the government to find £100,000 for machinery to power a steam battlefleet. The French had already reached the same conclusions.

Britain and France were the only powers to create steam battlefleets, combining new ships with converted units. Britain completed eighteen new ships, forty-one conversions and nine blockships. France managed ten and twenty-

eight, ignoring the blockship. Russia, Turkey, Sweden, Naples, Denmark and Austria all built or converted at least one such ship. All were dependent upon British technical support, which in the case of all save Russia and Naples can be dated to the alliance politics of the Crimean War. The Austrian *Kaiser* had the distinction of being the only ship of her type to fight in a regular sea battle, at Lissa on 20 July 1866, where she was badly damaged by heavy shellfire, but survived to be rebuilt into an ironclad in 1870, and remained afloat until 1918.

The last and largest of the wooden steam battleships, the British three-decker *Howe*, was completed in 1860. Her 1000nhp machinery drove her at speeds in excess of 12kts. Measuring 260ft × 60ft × 25ft 10in, displacing 7000 tons and armed with 121 heavy guns, half of which were shell-firing, she combined great size with a tremendous weight of broadside. Because these great ships were never pitted against one another in a fleet action they have tended to be overlooked, but they should be

In 1854 America embarked on a programme of six very large screw frigates, generally referred to as the Merrimack *class, although the detailed designs varied. They carried a battery of unprecedented power (usually forty guns but sixty was sometimes claimed) and had a great impact on other navies. To the British, with memories of earlier 'super-frigates' of the* Constitution *type they seemed a particular threat, although they proved slow under steam and were far too large to be cost effective commerce raiders. Nevertheless, national pride in these ships is witnessed by this lithograph published in America in 1857. (US National Archives, by courtesy of Donald L Canney)*

seen in their true perspective, as a vital stage in the development of the modern warship, rather than dismissed as an aberration. While they had the firepower to destroy one another, it should be recalled that the wooden battleship proved a resilient antagonist, even for the stone batteries of Sevastopol.[33]

33. A Lambert, *Battleships in Transition*.
D K Brown, *op cit*, ch11 & 13.
F Bilzer, 'Kaiser, Linienschiff und Kasemattschiff der k (u) k Kriegsmarine', *Marine – Gestern, Heute* (1983), pp113–149.

The last of the six Merrimack type cruisers was the Niagara, *the largest of all. A ship of extreme lines, her original battery was confined to the upper deck, making her in effect the largest screw sloop of her day. She was later rebuilt as a 32-gun frigate (1862–63) and in this guise is shown here.* (Peabody Museum)

Frigates

The frigate was a natural candidate for auxiliary steam power. Those units intended for oceanic cruising would benefit from limited power, while cruising under sail. The first British screw frigate, *Amphion*, was ordered in response to the French *Pomone*, and provided several useful lessons. Of the four blockship frigates, only *Horatio* was completed, the old ships being too small for machinery, coal and the stores required for any serious cruising. Two new screw frigates ordered in 1844 and 1845 demonstrated the limits of contemporary scientific understanding. *Dauntless* was intended to be a full powered steam ship, but her stern run was too bluff to exploit her engines, and she did not benefit from an addition of 9ft. By contrast the auxiliary *Arrogant* made her speed easily with smaller engines. The auxiliary concept dominated the creation of the British screw steam fleet, all the new ships being fitted with a hoisting two-bladed propeller, sacrificing propulsive efficiency for speed under sail. Later frigates were converted from incomplete units laid down in 1847–49, and built to new designs that were little different from the conversions. In both cases a section was added amidships for the machinery, while water stowage was reduced, relying on the distilling galley to keep up a supply of drinking and feed water. The steam frigate was more widely adopted than the battleship, the Danish *Jylland* being a unique survivor from this era. Unable or unwilling to join the battlefleet building race, the United States and Russia turned their attention to very large frigates. The rest of the world was generally content with the 51-gun Fourth Rate, perhaps wisely so, as the larger units were of doubtful utility.

The large frigates also reflected an alternative approach to combat at sea, replacing large broadsides with a smaller number of heavier

The British response to Merrimack *and her sisters came in the form of the even larger, faster and more powerful* Mersey *and* Orlando, *launched in 1858. With very long hulls and heavy machinery their hulls were heavily stressed and consequently costly to maintain. It is arguable whether they were really necessary, but they added one more piece of evidence for the growing campaign in favour of iron hulls.* (NMM)

guns for increased range and striking power. These ideas were pushed to the limit in the United States. The original order for the large American frigates was given in April 1854, to use existing frame timbers from sailing Fourth Rates. From the outset they were intended to be sailing cruisers with tactical steam power. In the preceding four years Captain John Dahlgren, USN had developed a series of very heavy guns including 9in, 10in and 11in shot- and shell-firing pieces weighing one-third

more than the existing types, and firing a shell weighing up to 136 pounds. The new frigates mounted a broadside of 9in weapons.

The hull form was based on one developed in 1853 to rebuild the old two-decker *Franklin* as a steam frigate. The dimensions bore no relationship with the old ship. They should, by contrast, be compared with those of *Agamemnon* and *Le Napoléon*. The other ships employed slightly different dimensions, but the lines were identical. The real qualities of these ships

The French screw frigate Impératrice Eugénie *(3765 tons, 56 guns, 1856) was one of four First Class steam frigates that were to be in effect cruiser equivalents of* Le Napoléon. *They were fast under steam (12kts) but their seakeeping left much to be desired and as they had been built rapidly from poorly seasoned timber, their service lives were short.* (Marius Bar)

were obscured by a great deal of exaggeration. They were slow under steam, little more than 8kts being available from the first five, and despite the power of their guns they would have been no match for a two-decker, whatever they might have done with a European 51-gun frigate.

The sloop *Niagara* was built to more extreme lines, provided by George Steers, a noted builder of merchant clippers. The result was an auxiliary engined extreme clipper with an upper deck battery. While *Niagara* proved considerably faster than her frigate half-sisters, her battery was too heavy for safe use in a seaway, and was not improved when twenty 11in guns were placed on the gun deck and twelve large Parrott rifles on the upper deck. The gun deck battery had to be left ashore before she was safe to proceed to sea. As an attempt to create a cruiser reflecting the American tradition in clipper ships *Niagara* was an interesing experiment, but ultimately of limited utility. After laying part of the 1857 transatlantic cable and a number of other peaceful missions *Niagara* was rebuilt as a frigate, but like her half-sisters saw little service in the Civil War on account of her deep draught.[34]

In Britain the Surveyor, Baldwin Walker, was reluctant to go beyond the old standard broadside weapons, arguing that rate of fire at close quarters would still be decisive, even if the upper deck guns were ranging out to hitherto unheard of distances. Modern work on the problems of fire control and the accuracy of smooth bore muzzle-loading guns confirms the basic soundness of his views. Walker's essay into the giant frigate category came in response to an order from the Admiralty to match the American ships. His ships, *Mersey* and *Orlando*, were the longest and most powerful single-decked wooden steam warships, combining 1000nhp machinery with fine lines. The ships lacked structural strength, as

The so-called Crimean War offered the opportunity not only to test large steam powered warships but also to apply mechanical propulsion to the other end of the order of battle. In what was one of the earliest examples of mass production, Britain ordered over 150 gunboats for inshore duties. This is Magnet, *a member of the most numerous* (Albacore) *class.* (NMM)

might be expected, but they were the direct ancestors of *Warrior*, which was in many ways an iron hulled and armoured expansion of the concept that governed their design, and the lines they employed.

Smaller cruisers

After the successes of *Rattler* the Royal Navy was committed to an all-steam fleet below the Fourth Rate. Succeeding classes of corvettes and sloops were all steam auxiliaries, built to cruise under sail. High speed despatch vessels were built, but they used the paddle wheel up to 1860. The requirement for a large force of cruisers was based on the rapid advance of steam in the world's merchant services. These ships could easily be converted into raiders, posing a major problem as the Confederate raider *Alabama* would demonstrate. The small screw auxiliary ships were essentially diminutives of their larger contemporaries, employing the same technology.

The steam gunboat

The one area where steam made a significant difference in the potential of naval forces was in the projection of power ashore. At sea steam ships gained no advantage over other steam ships, but close inshore the mobility and speed of steam improved the tactical position of warships against forts. The vital instrument here was not the large and costly steam battleship, but the humble gunboat. Gunboats were not built for 'gunboat diplomacy', the use of limited force to overawe third world nations (which was actually the province of the smaller cruising ships), or to penetrate the great rivers of China. The true function of the steam gunboat was coastal assault against the forts and arsenals of major powers, in particular France and Russia. Once the screw had been proven it was possible to create a small vessel, capable of mounting one or two heavy guns, to bombard

34. D L Canney, *op cit*, pp45–59.

HMS St George (86 guns) was a conversion of an existing two-decker, originally launched in 1840 but modified in 1858–59. Such ships were not quite as effective as new construction but enabled a rapid increase in the strength of the steam battle line at a time of growing tension with France. (IWM)

from long range. The first prototype was the iron hulled royal yacht tender *Fairy* of 1845 (145ft × 21ft, 312 tons). Concurrent developments, including the blockships and a series of artillery trials intended to improve the range, accuracy and strength of all heavy guns were part of the 'Cherbourg Strategy', a programme to destroy the French arsenal by naval bombardment. The gunboats were not built in the 1840s; they were a wartime emergency type that could be prepared quickly when required. The requirement came in 1854, and the target was Cronstadt. The first order was placed in March 1854, for the *Arrow* class gun-vessels, slightly expanded wooden hulled versions of *Fairy*. They carried two 68pdr 95cwt guns, but proved too deep and rather unsteady gun platforms. The succeeding *Gleaner* and *Dapper* classes were smaller, drew only 7ft and carried the same armament (100ft × 22ft, 216 tons). They were cheap to build, and over one hundred were completed. The 60hp engines were mass produced by Penn and Maudslay, with a large degree of subcontracting. They were high pressure locomotive type non-condensing engines. Along with the rush-built hulls these engines were expected to be worn out by war service, and they did suffer from rapid boiler deterioration from a build up of salt. The British gunboats proved a great success, far more so than the equivalent French vessels, and excited the praise of many foreign observers. After the Russian War many gunboats were hauled out of the water at Haslar and preserved for a future emergency. Others were available to operate around the world, but it needs to be stressed that they were not originally built for colonial operations.[35]

In 1855 these new craft were employed in the Baltic and the Black Sea. Between 9 and 12 August the British and French bombarded Sveaborg, the island fortress complex astride

the fairway into Helsinki harbour. The use of mortars, rockets and heavy guns from small craft ensured that no allied lives were lost, while a great deal of damage was done to the Russian defences. In the Black Sea the gunboats served with distinction in the Sea of Azov campaign, cutting the logistics supply line of the Russian army in the Crimea, and at the capture of Kinburn on 17 October. Many more were ordered for 1856: they were to form the main body of a 'Great Armament' to bombard and destroy Cronstadt. The Russians, unwilling to stand the British attack, accepted the allied peace terms in March 1856, leaving the British to assemble their massive coastal assault force at Spithead for a Grand Review on St George's Day, 23 April 1856. This force was a complete armada for the Baltic, comprising battleships, cruisers, armoured batteries, gunboats, mortar vessels, support ships, and even a floating foundry. This can be seen as an all-time high point for the application of sea power against the shore. Within a few years the railway would redress the situation created by the strategic mobility of steam shipping, particularly the steam transports that carried the allies to the Crimea and sustained them throughout a year-long battle of attrition. In 1854 Russia did not have a single mile of railway track south of Moscow, and consequently most of her half-million fatal casualties were caused by disease, malnutrition and hypothermia on the road to war, rather than on the battlefield. The Crimean War was won by superior technology, using a maritime strategy

that wore down Russia and threatened an attack on the very centre of her power.[36]

Both Britain and France were impressed by the power of naval forces for coastal assault. The French created a doctrine for a 'Floating Siege Train', while the Royal Navy prepared suitable equipment and was still thinking in the same terms in 1877–78.[37]

The wooden screw steamship: some technical problems

Despite the success of the screw steam fleet of the 1850s it was clear to all intelligent naval constructors that the use of wooden hulls, however strongly reinforced, limited their freedom to exploit steam and new guns. Although the critical point came with the adoption of armour, the trend was already clear.

Wooden screw steam ships suffered from a number of disadvantages inherent in the material of which they were built. They could never be made strong enough to resist the inevitable deformation caused by the action of the sea on such heavily laden craft, along with the heat, damp, vibration and strains created by their engines, heavy guns and hard service. A wooden ship was still only a bundle of short timbers. The Anglo-French construction race and the Crimean War led to a shortage of suitable timber, with consequent price rises, and the temptation to use incompletely seasoned material. The combination of movement at the joint faces and green timber was the real cause

35. D K Brown, *op cit*, pp145–160.
A Preston & J Major, *Send a Gunboat* (London 1967).

36. A D Lambert, *The Crimean War: British Grand Strategy Against Russia: 1853–1856* (Manchester 1990). B Greenhill & A Giffard, *The British Assault on Finland 1854–1855. A Forgotten Naval War* (London 1988).

37. T Ropp, *The Development of a Modern Navy: French Naval Policy 1871–1904* (Annapolis 1987), pp16–19. Admiral Sir P Colomb, *Memoirs of Sir Astley Cooper Key* (London 1898), pp406–9.

The last generation of wooden screw ships were very long, and neared the limits of technology, despite iron strapping and all the other constructional advances developed since 1815. This view of the three-decker Marlborough *and the frigate* Phoebe *at Malta demonstrates that cruising ships had become as long as battleships – and* Phoebe *was not the largest frigate of her day.*

of dry rot. It would appear that the French used more green timber than the British in their battlefleet.

By the 1850s all nations were using the system of framing perfected by John Edye, combining parallel frames with substantial iron diagonal riders. The frames in most ships were very close together and were filled in solid up

The introduction of iron-hulled armoured ships in the 1860s did not spell the immediate end of wooden construction, which retained some advantages over iron for unarmoured hulls. Wooden cruisers continued to be built down to the mid-1870s, and even then there was a short-lived vogue for composite construction (wooden planking over iron frames). Typical of the ships that patrolled the sea lanes in the era of the 'Pax Britannica' was this wooden screw corvette HMS Wolverine, *one of a class of six launched between 1859 and 1863.* (CMP)

to the waterline, to form an inner hull. Edye chain-bolted the frames of British ships, extending the linkage and support. Despite this the form of ship was often altered during the launch; for example, the 91-gun *Caesar* hung on the ways and suffered considerable deformation, but even the smoothest launch resulted in some breakage. In consequence the critical alignment of the propeller shaft was rarely preserved for long, resulting in a loss of propulsive efficiency from increased friction in the bear-

ings and the stern gland. This was the cause of the startlingly rapid wear of the early bronze stern glands. The 120-gun *Royal Albert* nearly foundered in 1856 after her stern gland wore down. *Niagara* supported her propeller shaft at the driving end with three 2-ton bronze bearings. Pettit Smith and John Penn developed the *lignum vitae* stern bearing, which solved the problem of leakage at the stern, although it could do little to preserve the propeller shaft. The effect of vibration was particularly severe

at the stern, where most ships required a repair after their first trial, and all had to be re-caulked. The additional weakness caused by the hoisting propeller, used by the British and Americans in particular, merely exacerbated the problem. It should not be surprising that many ships began to decay at the stern; once the joints opened fresh water (from rain) could penetrate, promoting dry rot, the single greatest enemy of wooden warships.

While the screw allowed a reduction in machinery weights, from the smoother power delivery, wooden ships still required heavy engine foundations to prevent frame weakness damaging the machinery. The Austrian *Kaiser* suffered from poorly supported engines early in her career.

In conclusion

Through the instrument of the screw propeller the wooden steam warship became the only naval weapon that counted by the mid-1850s. Inside a decade it had entirely supplanted both the sailing ship and the paddle wheel steamer. In view of its limitations it can be argued that the most successful screw warships were those that retained the auxiliary concept of the British, even if later British ships were also capable of high speed under steam. This was an incomplete application of existing technology. Only when iron hulls were adopted could the modern warship be said to have come of age. Under the pressure of war this development came about within six years of the decision for a wooden steam battlefleet in Britain and France, and before any other power had really adopted the type.

Andrew Lambert

Screw Propelled Wooden Warships: Typical Vessels 1838–1860

Ship or class [Type]	Nationality	Displacement (tons)	Dimensions (loa × breadth × draught) (feet–inches) (metres)	Armament	Machinery	Speed (max, kts)	Launch dates	Remarks
ARCHIMEDES	British	232	125–0 × 21–10 × 10–0 38.1 × 6.7 × 3.0	None	2–cyl Rennie DA, 80nhp	9	1838	Pettit Smith's demonstration ship
RATTLER [Sloop]	British	1112	176–6 deck × 32–8 × 14–6 53.8 × 10.0 × 4.4	1–68pdr pivot, 4–32pdr carr	4–cyl Maudsay Siamese geared, 200nhp (519ihp)	9.1	1843	First RN screw warship
PRINCETON [Corvette]	American	1046	156–0 × 30–6 × 21–6 47.5 × 9.3 × 6.6	2–12in, 10–42pdr carr	2 Demicyl pendulum, 250nhp (c 330ihp)	8.7	1843	First US screw warship
POMONE [Frigate]	French	2010	179–0 deck × 43–8 × 20–3 54.8 × 13.3 × 6.2	18–30pdr, 8–22cm; 2–30pdr, 8–16cm	2–cyl Mazeline RCR, 220nhp (574ihp)	7.5	1845	Prototype French auxiliary screw frigate
AJAX [Blockship]	British	3013	176–0 deck × 48–6 × 22–11 53.6 × 14.8 × 7.0	28–32pdr, 26–8in, 2–68pdr, 4–10in	2–cyl Maudslay HDA, 450nhp (931ihp)	6.8	1846	Prototype screw battleship converted from Third Rate of 1809
AMPHION [Frigate]	British	2025	177–0 deck × 43–2 × 19–0 53.9 × 13.2 × 5.8	6–8in, 14–32pdr; 2–68pdr, 14–32pdr	2–cyl Miller HDA, 300nhp (592ihp)	6.75	1846	Prototype British auxiliary screw frigate, converted from sail while building
NAPOLEON [Battleship]	French	5120	234–5 deck × 55–1 × 27–1 71.5 × 16.8 × 8.3	32–30pdr, 4–22cm; 26–30pdr, 4–22cm; 14–16cm	2–cyl Indret geared, 960nhp (574ihp)	12.1	1850	First true steam battleship; class of nine
AGAMEMNON [Battleship]	British	5080	230–0 deck × 55–4 × 24–2 70.0 × 16.9 × 7.6	34–8in; 34–32pdr; 1–68pdr, 22–32pdr	2–cyl Penn trunk, 600nhp (2500ihp)	11.4	1852	First British purpose designed steam battleship
PYLADES [Corvette]	British	1991	192–9 deck × 38–5 × 19–7 58.8 × 11.7 × 5.9	1–10in pivot, 20–8in	2–cyl Penn trunk, 350nhp (1100ihp)	12.6	1854	Medium sized cruiser
MERRIMACK [Frigate]	American	5298	256–11 × 50–2 × 20–8 78.3 × 15.3 × 6.3	2–10in, 14–8in, 24–9in	2–cyl HRCR, 972ihp	8.8	1855	Large US frigate; rebuilt as CSS *Virginia* in Civil War
DAPPER class [Gunboat]	British	233bm	106–0 deck × 22–0 × 6–9 32.3 × 6.7 × 2.1	2–68pdr RML pivot	2–cyl Penn trunk 60nhp (270ihp)	7.5	1855	Mass-production Crimean War gunboat; 118 ordered
NIAGARA [Spar deck corvette]	American	5440	328–10 × 53–8 × 24–8 100.2 × 16.8 × 7.5	12–11in shell	3–cyl Fulton HDA, 1955ihp	10.9	1856	Influential frigate-sized 'sloop'
SINOP [Battleship]	Russian	5585	248–0 × 59–6 × ? 75.6 × 18.1	135 guns	Maudslay, 800nhp	11	1858	Largest Russian battleship of the day; Black Sea
ORLANDO [Frigate]	British	5678	336–0 × 52–0 × 23–10 102.0 × 15.8 × 7.3	28–10in; 12–68pdr	2–cyl Penn trunk, 1000nhp (3617ihp)	13	1858	British response to US and French commerce raiders
DUNCAN [Battleship]	British	5950	252–0 deck × 58–0 × 26–10 77.8 × 17.7 × 8.2	36–8in; 36–32pdr; 28–32pdr and 1–68pdr	2–cyl Penn trunk, 800nhp (3428ihp)	13	1859	Ultimate steam two-decker
VICTORIA [Battleship]	British	6959	260–0 deck × 60–0 × 27–10 79.2 × 18.3 × 8.5	32–8in; 30–8in; 12–32pdr; 26–32pdr and 1–68pdr	2–cyl Maudslay HDA, 1000nhp (4403ihp)	12.3	1859	Ultimate steam three-decker

3

Iron Hulls and Armour Plate

THE final element in the creation of the modern warship was the adoption of iron as the preferred material for hull structures. Iron allowed naval architects to escape from the limits imposed upon their work by timber, however well fastened. Yet, as with steam, the iron hull was not particularly well suited to naval service. Iron ships had to be protected by armour before they could take their place in the line of battle.

The pioneers

Iron hulled canal boats had been built before the French Revolution, but the requirements of this service were far removed from those of sea voyages. The first scientifically constructed iron vessel, the passenger barge *Vulcan*, built in 1819 for use on the Forth and Clyde Canal introduced the concept of accurately following the sheer draught. In view of the real difficulties of using iron ships at sea, compass deviation and fouling caused by marine growths, the world's navies had little or nothing to do with the subject until the late 1830s. Similarly the pioneer iron shipbuilders in Britain were based outside the traditional centre of shipbuilding, the Thames, notably on the Clyde and the Mersey.

The first iron hulled vessel to make a sea crossing was *Aaron Manby*, built at Tipton in Staffordshire, knocked down and re-erected at Rotherhithe on the Thames in 1822. She was then steamed across the Channel and up the Seine, arriving in Paris on 10 June 1822, to operate a service between Paris and le Havre.

Napier commanded this voyage, having used a large part of his wartime prize money to promote the venture. Further vessels were built in England with engines from Manby's French foundry at Charenton, but the service was a commercial failure, almost ruining Napier in the process. By contrast *Aaron Manby* continued to serve in various capacities until 1855.[1]

Although he would ultimately lose a large amount of money in this speculation Napier gained a considerable experience of iron ships and steam propulsion. In 1828 he advised the Lord High Admiral to build in iron, to get rid of dry rot, noting that an iron ship 'will float lighter'. The waterline area of this proposed brig would be lined with timber, because 'a shot passing through iron would leave a hole considerably larger and more difficult to stop, than one passing through timber'. The hull should be built of ¾in plate, in consultation with Manby. The subject was not pursued. However, as late as 1842 he was seen by Laird as the most suitable officer to forward a proposal for iron warships to the Admiralty. It has been suggested that he became a bitter critic of the iron warship in the 1840s. In fact he did not object to the trial of iron in 1845, only to the number of ships ordered before any serious testing had been carried out.[2]

A more striking proposal was submitted in 1828 by the artillery designer and rocket pioneer General Sir William Congreve. Believ-

1. F M Walker, 'Precision Construction: Iron's Contribution to Modern Shipbuilding', in *Metals in Shipbuilding: Conference of the Historical Metallurgy Society* (London 1990), pp25–29.
H P Spratt, *The Birth of the Steamboat* (London 1958), pp113–116.
W H Chaloner & W O Henderson, 'Aaron Manby, Builder of the First Iron Steamship', *Transactions of the Newcomen Society* 29 (1953–55), pp77–91.
J S Allen, 'History of the Horseley Company to 1865', *ibid* 58 (1986–87), pp113–138.
2. Napier to the Duke of Clarence, 25 June 1828, in C Napier, *The Navy*, pp53–55.
Napier to Laird, 15 May 1842, Laird MSS.
D K Brown, *Before the Ironclad*, p90.

The first operational iron warship was built for a navy that is almost unknown today, namely the Bengal Marine, a naval arm of the Honourable East India Company. The Nemesis *was ordered in 1835 from Laird's Birkenhead shipyard, a company that had already built twenty-seven iron steamers. Laird was a vociferous advocate of iron construction and undoubtedly the most experienced shipbuilder in the new material. As shown in this modern painting,* Nemesis *was a conventional paddle steamer in every respect except her hull construction. (Cammell Laird)*

ing the Royal Navy might be required to pass the Dardanelles Forts he advised that a wooden hulled steam battery, driven by underwater wheels, should be coated in cast iron armour 8in thick from 12ft above the waterline to 1ft below. The Controller of the Navy rejected the plan as impracticable.[3] Aside from the inefficiency of the underwater wheels, and the sheer weight of the cast iron blocks, the plan reflected a lifetime's experience with artillery. There was no requirement for such a vessel at the time, but it was strikingly similar in concept and layout to the first ironclads.

Iron ships at sea

While the Royal Navy left the development of the iron ship to the commercial sector in the 1830s, it did make a vital intervention in the practical science of using iron vessels at sea. The Birkenhead shipbuilder John Laird, sharing the innovative and enquiring approach that characterised his fellow Scots on the Clyde, made an early commitment to the iron ship. His third iron steam ship, *Garry Owen*, built for service on the river Shannon, included iron water-tight bulkheads, a feature of all his later vessels. In 1835 this vessel was used for Admiralty-sponsored experiments on the problem of compass deviation in iron reinforced and iron built vessels. The Admiralty ordered further trials in 1837 by the Astronomer Royal, Sir George Airy, aboard the General Steam Navigation Company's *Rainbow*, another Laird ship. These produced a system of correction that worked well enough to permit transatlantic voyages in the following year.

Having apparently surmounted this fundamental problem the Admiralty was quick to test an iron ship, ordering the Channel packet *Dover* from Laird in 1839. In fact the Airy system was unreliable, as more recent work makes clear. However, the railway boom had reduced the cost of iron, and increased the number of men skilled in metal construction. This reduced the price of iron ships. However, Laird went one stage further, building an iron warship on speculation in the same year. *Nemesis* became a celebrity through her ubiquity and success in the First China War (1841–43), where she served with the East India Company's Bengal Marine, although they actually

Laird was so convinced of the value of iron construction that he began a paddle sloop on speculation which he planned to sell to the Royal Navy. However, the ship was rejected by a naval inspector and she was eventually sold to the Mexican navy as the Guadeloupe, *seeing action in the war against Texas in 1843. (NMM)*

purchased her only in 1841. The flat and shallow hull was fitted with two drop keels to permit her to carry sail at sea. The hull was divided by six bulkheads, which were given a linked pumping system before she reached the Far East. The naval architect Augustin Creuze wrote a favourable report on her for the Admiralty before she left Britain.

Laird had already built several iron ships for the East India Company, including a pair that were used to explore the Tigris and Euphrates, but *Nemesis* was the first iron warship. After a harrowing passage to India, during which her hull developed a serious compression fracture, the compass proved unreliable and the growth of marine organisms on her bottom reduced speed to a marked extent, *Nemesis* acted as the lead ship in the Opium War. The Laird-built *Phlegethon*, also of the Bengal Marine, played a similar, if less publicised role. The report of *Nemesis*'s commander, William Hall, a half pay Royal Navy lieutenant, had a considerable influence on the decision of the Admiralty to move into iron ships in 1844–45. However, her success was rather overstated. In the Chinese rivers she suffered no fouling, had no need of her compass and the inferior Chinese artillery did not inflict any serious damage. The latter effect was aided by the high temperature – modern research has indicated that wrought iron is far less brittle when warm. Furthermore, the pace of development in Britain continued unabated, with no-one waiting on the results of *Nemesis*.

The Navy accepted the value of light iron hulls for riverine work, ordering three gunboats for the Niger from Laird in 1840, following the success of his *Elburkah* on the Niger. These were the first iron warships to serve in a major navy. *Mohawk*, ordered from William

Fairbairn for service on the Great Lakes, proved a tolerable success. Laird built a larger speculative warship, the 878-ton No 42, hoping to sell her to the Royal Navy. He even offered to convert her for a screw propeller, but she was finally sold to the Mexican Government as *Guadeloupe*. Dupuy de Lôme, who visited Laird and other iron shipbuilders, notably Brunel's *The Great Britain*, formed a high opinion of Laird's work. De Lôme's report and sustained advocacy of iron had a profound influence on French policy. The success of the early iron ships rested on their lighter hulls, superior strength, resistance to the strains of their machinery, water-tight bulkheads and increased capacity. By the early 1840s a number of commercial yards had developed the facilities needed to build in iron, but the Royal Dockyards did not attempt to match this new skill.

The iron frigate programme: a premature effort

The success of the pioneer iron auxiliaries persuaded the Admiralty to order a regular iron warship. Demonstrating their usual caution they elected to build the 850-ton *Trident* on the Thames, where she could be closely supervised, despite Laird's primacy in the field. She was launched in 1845, to be followed within two weeks by *Birkenhead*, the first iron frigate, which had been ordered from Laird. It is singularly unfortunate that this strong and well thought-out vessel should be best known to history for the manner of her loss. After the rejection of iron warships she was converted

3. Congreve to Admiralty, 27 March 1828, PRO Adm 1/4478 & endorsements.

The Royal Navy showed a keen interest in iron warships, a small iron steamer, Trident, being ordered in April 1843, followed immediately by an ambitious iron frigate launched in December 1845 as the Birkenhead. Best known to history for her tragic loss in 1852 – and the immaculate behaviour of the troops she was carrying – the ship has an equal claim to fame as an important step in the development of the iron fighting ship. She was originally brig rigged but this modern painting shows the ship without square canvas on the main. (By courtesy of D K Brown)

into a troopship, and in the process her wing and transverse bulkheads were opened. On 26 February 1852 she struck a reef off the coast of South Africa and, as the forward section of the ship filled with water, broke up with heavy loss of life.

In February and March 1845 four very large iron screw frigates were ordered, from Scott and Robert Napier on the Clyde, Fairbairn and Ditchburn & Mare on the Thames. Napier's *Simoom* was the largest (2920 tons, 246ft × 41ft × 17ft 6in). All four were to have been armed as war steamers, rather than sailing frigates, with heavy guns on the upper deck and between four and twelve 32pdrs on the main deck. However, before completion one was sold and the other three were downgraded to transport service, their machinery being replaced by engines intended for blockship frigates. During the Crimean War *Vulcan*, *Simoom* and *Megaera* served with distinction in the transport role.

At the time the Admiralty was widely criticised for making too large a commitment to iron before gaining adequate experience, im-

plying that the decision was purely technical. In fact the dominant factor was the shortage of slipway space in the Royal Dockyards to build large steam frigates. Unwilling to build wooden ships in private yards, after the unfortunate experience of the Napoleonic War, the Board elected to buy iron ships to supplement the efforts of the Royal yards.[4]

Altogether less creditable was the blind rush into iron by the United States and France. Neither country had a tradition of iron shipbuilding, nor a dynamic mercantile sector, so their efforts should be seen as little more than

imitation, the most sincere form of flattery. The French built an iron colonial steamer in 1837, based on British experience. Sending Dupuy de Lôme to study in Britain increased their awareness of the advantages of the new material, and in 1842 the engine works at Indret began a small iron ship, along with the dockyards at Toulon, Cherbourg and Rochefort. These vessels were joined by two iron royal yachts and a pair of iron screw ships. In early 1845 de Lôme submitted plans for a 28-gun iron hulled frigate with 90mm (2½in) armour over the waterline and battery. The navy responded by ordering armour trials. However, the French were quick to follow Britain in abandoning the iron warship.[5]

The American move, to build the Great Lakes steamer *Michigan*, was if anything, even more of a leap in the dark. Secretary of the Navy Upshur, inspired by the British iron ships sent out to the Lakes, elected to use the order to promote iron shipbuilding and test the new material. *Michigan* was ordered in early 1842.

4. A E Fanning, *Steady as She Goes: A History of the Compass Department* (London 1986), ppxxxii–xlii. Herbert to Peel, 4 September 1844, BL Add 40,450, f122.

5. S S Roberts, 'The Introduction of Steam Technology . . .' pp321–7, 376–8, 422.

Britain was quick to combine the new technologies of iron construction and screw propulsion in the 1845 programme of four large iron frigates, each built by a specialist merchant shipbuilder. The largest was the Simoom of 2920 tons, seen here in later life after conversion to a troopship – shown by the large number of boats. (CMP)

The French iron paddle corvette Euménide *(1848) was one of eight iron-hulled ships ordered in 1845. Dupuy de Lôme, the leading French naval architect had made a study of British iron shipbuilding and was impressed by the potential of the new material when he inspected the* Guadeloupe. *The 1845 programme was designed to develop French iron industries, but France also had second thoughts about iron in the late 1840s. (Marius Bar)*

At this time American shipbuilders had yet to produce their first iron seagoing vessel, although some were hoping to import wrought iron plates from Britain. Therefore the constructor based the structure of *Michigan* on *Nemesis* and a British merchant steamer. She served for eighty years, but was the only American iron hulled warship built for the navy before the Civil War.[6]

The rejection of iron warships followed British experimental work. Doubts about the safety of iron under fire were raised in various quarters, from reactionary artillerists to progressive shipbuilders. The First Sea Lord, Admiral Cockburn, ordered a series of trials, held in great secrecy at Woolwich between August 1845 and September 1846. The results were inconclusive, for iron ships with the strong wooden lining proposed by Captain Napier (*Simoom* used 10in) were safe enough. How-

The iron frigates had not entered service when a general reaction against the vulnerability of unarmoured iron hulls led the Admiralty to order the conversion of the frigates to troopships with engines of reduced power. Megaera, *built by Fairburn, was completed as a frigate but not commissioned as such; she first went to sea as a trooper as seen here. (NMM)*

ever, there was no evidence to support these craft against the attacks of Napier, who objected to the number that were built, or Symonds, who condemned them for a variety of reasons connected with his own prejudices and Whig attacks on the Admiralty. When the Whigs took over they staged a trial that was guaranteed to prove their point, selecting the lightly built and badly corroded harbour tender *Ruby* to be shot to pieces by *Excellent* at a range of only 450yds. Having proved the point the Admiralty secured further 'evidence' and six months later condemned the entire Conservative programme of iron ships. Three of the frigates were converted into troopships, their large engines being removed, to be re-used in the wooden screw battleships *Duke of Wellington*, *Algiers* and *Hannibal*.

Further trials were carried out between 1849 and 1852, but they did not reverse the opinions already strongly held. Wooden targets offered better protection, and were more easily repaired. These conclusions were logical and accurate. The iron hull could not be used where it might have to face heavy gunfire. As a result the additional problem of rapid fouling was merely another reason for ignoring iron. Modern research largely supports this decision: wrought iron is not a suitable material for shipbuilding, becoming brittle at temperatures below 20 degrees celsius, and lacking resistance at right angles to the plane of the plate, the direction from which most damage would be expected, either under fire, or running on shore.

Armour and the shell gun

The concept of the armoured warship requires some thought. It is important that the purpose of the armour is understood. The alternatives

are a protection for the crew, or for the ship. Early armour projects were intended to protect the crew, since there were no ship-killing weapons. The most famous examples were the 'turtle ships' employed by the Korean Admiral Yi Sun-sin to defeat the Japanese invasion of Korea in the 1590s. These craft were fitted with an iron carapace making it impossible for their enemies to enter and attack the crew. It is also suggested that their protection extended down to the waterline, to prevent the hull being holed by rams. Using their loopholes for man-killing firepower, and a limited amount of ramming, these craft destroyed the cohesion of the Japanese fleets, allowing other Korean vessels to complete the victory. These vessels posed problems that the numerically superior Japanese could not solve, despite a five-year hiatus. Yi Sun-sin was killed in his final victory, and his ships were never called upon again.[7]

The growth of heavy artillery and of heavily built wooden sailing warships rendered such ideas obsolete within decades. The ship of the line was rarely sunk by gunfire, even when closely engaged, although a few exceptions, such as the French *Vengeur* at the Glorious First of June (1794) are known. The massive scantling of a wooden battleship was proof against heavy shot, on the lower decks at least (at Trafalgar *Victory* suffered no fatal casualties on the gun deck). The perfection of the explosive shell for use at sea, along with heavier guns, gave an impetus to the idea of armouring the ship. Paixhans's trials with the old 84-gun *Pacificateur* demonstrated that ships could now be destroyed. At Navarino in 1827 the British 84 *Asia* literally smashed in the hull of her Turkish opponent with concentrated close range broadsides of 32pdr shot. The new artillery and improved powder of the post-1815 era posed a far more serious threat to the ship, even without shellfire, than hitherto. These developments were paralleled by improvements

6. B A Rodgers, 'The Iron Sentinel: USS *Michigan*, 1844–1949', MA Thesis (University of East Carolina 1985).
D L Canney, *The Old Steam Navy*, pp18–21.

7. G Parker, *The Military Revolution* (Cambridge 1988), pp108–110.

in iron founding and in particular the rolling of wrought iron plates. Both Fulton's and Congreve's batteries were premature, but the idea of a ship safe against gunfire was gradually taking hold.

Henri-Joseph Paixhans's *nouvelle force maritime* comprised shell guns mounted aboard small armoured steam ships, building on the work of Andreossy in the 1790s, and the numerous trials of horizontal shell firing that followed. Paixhans was not alone in promoting shells – the Stevens family of Hoboken New Jersey offered an elongated shell in 1814, between building the first successful screw steam ship, in 1804, and attempting the first ironclad warship in 1842. Both the French and American innovators were quick to realise that the new missiles would force navies to adopt protection for the crew, and the ship. Paixhans rejected the big ship, unaware of the potential of wrought iron; the Stevenses waited. While Paixhans's guns were adopted everywhere, his armoured warships were not taken up. The French experimented with armour, and several more officers came forward with plans. All were looking to overturn British supremacy with a novel weapon. Cast iron was soon abandoned as armour, but it required international tension to secure the funds for a novel armoured warship.

Steam had opened new opportunities. A sailing ship could not protect her motive power in action, but a steam engine offered a smaller target. The first naval officers to contemplate steam warships were interested in protecting the boilers, engine and paddle shafts from damage. Napier urged the Lord High Admiral to protect the steam plant of *Dee*.

> It has been proved, that a combination of oak timber, iron plates, bales of linen, cotton, or reams of paper, four feet thick, will protect the boilers and engines against an eighteen pound shot, and without that protection, a steam boat is entirely useless in war.

Ten years later Captain Matthew Perry, USN called for inclined iron bulwarks to be fitted to *Fulton II*, 'to cause all shot striking them from any direction to ricochet'.[8]

Both men were concerned to protect the motive power of the ship, without which the early steamers were useless. At this stage such ideas gained little support from those in authority. The objections were obvious enough: iron would reduce seaworthiness, endanger the ship if she were to lose stability, corrode, and ruin compass performance. It would require pressure from a higher source, and the threat of war, to bring armour to sea.

Perhaps the most remarkable effort of the era came from the United States, in the form of the 'Stevens Battery' of 1842. The success of wrought iron boiler plates rivetted up into 4½in plate in defeating 64pdr shot at close range persuaded the Stevens brothers that an ironclad warship could be built. With Anglo-American relations in a state of near crisis they anticipated following Fulton, building a battery to drive off blockading warships. Unfortunately they tried to run before they had learned to walk. In one 1500-ton ship they proposed to adopt rifled breech-loading shell guns, inclined armour and high pressure machinery for high speed. On 14 April 1842 Congress authorised the Navy to contract for this vessel and appropriated $250,000 to begin work. Even then little was done to build the vessel; a dry-dock was dug to build her in, and experiments carried out on propellers. In 1845, after $31,000 had been paid, further funds were stopped, pending the delivery of plans. Unfortunately the perfectionist aspect of Robert Stevens's character led him to radically redesign the ship before beginning work. Once aware of Ericsson's 12in wrought iron gun, fitted aboard *Princeton*, Stevens changed from a ship of 250ft with one propeller and 4½in plate to one of 415ft, two propellers, eight times greater horsepower and 6¾in plate. Despite his arguments with the Bureau of the Navy, the hull of the ship was completed by 1856, when Robert Stevens died. All work then ceased, and despite the sudden need for armoured ships she was not completed during the Civil War.

In 1868 Edwin Stevens left $1 million for her completion, to a new design with a turret, but even so she remained incomplete. Her remains were broken up in 1881. There was too much novelty in the ship for her to have been a success, had she been completed. Unlike the majority of inventors the Stevenses were wealthy, and so were prepared to stand on their dignity, rather than bow to the Navy Bureau. The 'Stevens Battery' had very little influence abroad; in Britain Scott-Russell, a friend of Robert Stevens, became an advocate of armour, but his voice carried no weight in the 1840s.[9]

The Crimean War, coastal assault and wrought iron plate

The strategy of the Anglo-French war against Russia posed new problems for warship design-

8. Napier to the Duke of Clarence 10 November 1827, in C Napier, *op cit*, pp50–1.
S E Morison, *Old Bruin: Commodore Matthew C Perry* (Boston 1967), p129.

9. J P Baxter, *The Introduction of the Ironclad Warship* (Cambridge, Mass 1933), ch II & IV. Still a major source on the period.
S C Tucker, 'The Stevens Ironclad Battery', *American Neptune* 51 (1991), pp12–22.

*Just as steam came to naval use in a floating battery (*Demologus*) so armour was first applied to a similar type. During the Russian War France devised a vessel that could take on the fortifications of the Crimea at close quarters and this inevitably meant armour (boxes of round shot were proposed but following a British suggestion 4in wrought iron on a wooden backing was used instead). The five vessels were powered but were barely fast enough to preserve steerage. Nevertheless they proved successful in action and inspired thoughts of more seaworthy ships. This is* Dévastation *after the war. (Marius Bar)*

ers. From the beginning of the war in March 1854 it was evident that the allies would have a massive superiority at sea, the Russian fleet having no steam battleships, or large screw steam ships. Therefore, as the allies would be taking the war to Russia, any naval action would involve attacking shore positions rather than engaging other ships. This vitiated much of the work carried out by Britain and France over the preceding decade in creating screw steam fleets to oppose one another. The British implemented their 'Cherbourg Strategy' by building gunboats and mortar vessels, but the French pioneered another line.

The Battle of Sinope, on 30 November 1853, had a profound effect on both the diplomacy of the crisis and the opinions of the French Emperor on warship design. The action was, in itself, hardly worthy of note. Six Russian battleships mounting over 600 guns took six hours to destroy a squadron of frigates. The use of shells, while they produced a considerable effect, clearly did little to speed up this particular battle; the one Turkish steamer managed to escape with news of the disaster.

Louis Napoleon III, who considered himself an expert artillerist, was concerned that French ships might have to face shells. Therefore he proposed a shell-proof battery for coastal assault. His first thoughts, using iron boxes filled with 6pdr shot as armour was soon proved to be impracticable, but 4in thick wrought iron plate, suggested by Thomas Lloyd, Chief Engineer of the Royal Navy, was adopted. Hitherto, this had not been available at such thicknesses, and the armour projects of the 1840s had all been forced to rely on far less effective laminated armour built up from boiler plates. The French tests were successful, but the First Lord of the Admiralty, once again Sir James Graham, insisted on British trials. These were conducted in September 1854 at Portsmouth, and demonstrated that well supported 4in plate could resist 32pdr shot at 300yds, although they were less satisfactory when faced with the 68pdr shot. The British trials were ordered to meet Graham's concern at the cost of the ships, and in the face of his marked preference for a strategic concentration on the Crimean campaign. Five batteries were ordered to a British design on 4 October. They were wooden hulled with bluff extremities and flat-bottomed. The armour was bolted to the hull and connected by tongue and groove joints, a time consuming and counter-productive arrangement. These ships were never easy to steer, made only slow progress under steam, and even with a temporary rig installed they had to be towed for much of

their passage overseas. One of the British vessels, *Aetna*, was destroyed by Fire at Scott-Russell's yard on the Thames. Scott-Russell proposed reworking the armour and other materials into a seagoing vessel, but the Admiralty employed the armour on a modified battery built in the dockyard at Chatham. In the following December three iron hulled variants were added, specifically for the 1856 assault on Cronstadt.

In the event not one of the British ships went into action, largely because they were intended for the Baltic, where they were not required in 1855. The pressures of the war led the French to send their batteries to the Black Sea. Three went into action at Kinburn on 17 October 1855. The fort, with two outlying batteries was built at sea level, largely of sand, and was armed with 24pdr guns. It was a weak position, and easily enfiladed. The batteries joined a battle already won by mortar and gunboat fire, and concluded soon after by nine battleships. From a French perspective the success of *Dévastation*, *Lave* and *Tonnant* was proof positive of technological superiority. However, the facts make rather less impressive reading. The batteries were at least 900yds from the forts, and they were hit between 29 and 55 times each, but the guns were only 24pdrs and at that range they could not penetrate the hull of a wooden battleship. The British two-decker *Princess Royal* engaged the fort from 650yds, and came away with two wounded, by splinters after a shot that struck the edge of the main deck gangway. By contrast *Dévastation* lost two killed when a shot entered one of the over-large gunports. Admiral Lyons, the British Commander-in-Chief, summed up the reason for the prominent place given to the new ships in contemporary accounts, but concluded by admitting their value:

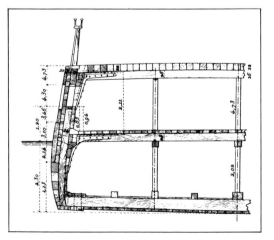

A structural section of the French Russian War batteries. (From Admiral Paris' Souvenirs de Marine)

It is amusing to see how delighted Bruat [the French Admiral] is to send a favourable account of the Emperor's pet batteries. He attributes the fall of the place to them, whereas they had but little to do with it. The mortars ploughed the whole fort up and rendered it impossible for anyone to live in it, and then the tremendous fire of the ships [of the line] gave them the coup de grace . . . still you may take it for granted that floating batteries have become elements in amphibious warfare, so the sooner you set about having as many good ones as the French the better it will be. I am told that the shells broke into pieces on striking the vessels before they had time to explode. The French no doubt go to great lengths in their praises of this favourite weapon of their Emperor's; but make all the allowance you please for that, and there will still remain too much in favour of it to admit of its being discarded without a fair trial.[10]

The degree to which the French accounts were puffed up for Napoleon III has never been given due weight in historical accounts of the Kinburn action, the first use of armoured steam warships in battle. It is significant that as with every other important advance of the period, armour was first used on warships that were eccentric to the main roles of sea power.

The armoured battery was not an individual weapon that, single handedly, turned a battle. It served as an important component in the new coast attack fleet; it could only operate where the defences had already been beaten down by mortars and gunboat fire, and where it could be protected from hostile warships. To this end the British planning for the assault on Cronstadt in 1856 was complicated by the presence of one or two steam battleships, and twenty or thirty screw gunboats, while the forts were armed with large and powerful guns. However, the ambitious plan devised by the Baltic Fleet Surveying Officer, Captain Sulivan, must be taken seriously. Sulivan, an outstanding officer, had directed every major operation in the Baltic, with complete success, and knew more about the approaches to Cronstadt than anyone. He believed that an integrated force of batteries, gunboats, mortar vessels and blockships could secure firing positions to the north of the island from which the dockyard and arsenal could be destroyed, improving on the success of the bombardment of Sveaborg in August 1855. The Russians were so concerned by these plans, which were obvious enough, that they brought General Todleben, the hero of Sevastopol, to organise

10. Lyons to Sir Charles Wood (First Sea Lord), 20 October 1855, BL Add 49,537, f27 quoted in A D Lambert, *Crimean War*, p256; see also pp197–8 & 256–60.

France was unable to build enough armoured batteries for requirements so the British undertook five similar floating batteries, but in 1855 ordered three more with iron hulls. These were the first iron, armoured warships to go to sea. One of them, HMS Terror, is depicted in this photo at Bermuda during the American Civil War. (NMM)

the defences. They also opened negotiations for peace. Sea power was never more influential. For the first time in modern warfare one side had a real technological advantage, from the availability of steam, improved heavy artillery and a major industrial base to build any new weapons quickly. Russia could not compete at sea, and was therefore at a severe disadvantage.[11]

Postwar planning for an ironclad battleship: *Gloire*

Although the value of the batteries at Kinburn was uncertain, few could be in any doubt that armour had arrived. The only questions remaining were how to employ it on a seagoing battleship, and when. In answering these issues France and Britain ended one building race, and launched another. The French accepted that an ironclad battleship was inevitable. They ordered no new screw battleships after 1855, merely converting their remaining stock of old sailing ships to steam and conducting further armour trials. That they had no spare slipways made the decision somewhat easier to reach. This policy was confirmed by the appointment

of the 40-year-old Dupuy de Lôme as *Directeur du Matériel* (Chief Constructor) on 1 January 1857. The implication of this was that an ironclad would be built in the following year. Dupuy completed the plans of his new ship in November 1857, and secured orders for six ironclads in March 1858, creating another round of alarm in Britain.

Although an entirely new design the pioneer seagoing ironclad, Dupuy's famous *Gloire*, was in essence a wooden steam battleship cut down to a single deck, plated overall with 4½in armour with the benefit of extensive iron structural reinforcement and an iron deck. She was, as her designer admitted, a dead end. The French iron industry was unable to provide enough iron for more than one iron hulled ship per year, forcing de Lôme, a long term advocate of iron, to build only one ship, *Couronne*, which was little more than an iron *Gloire*. She made no real use of the opportunities of iron construction, had similar dimensions to the wooden ships, no effective internal subdivision and the same armament. However, she did prove greatly superior to her half-sisters in one respect. *Invincible* and *Normandie* had been built of unseasoned timber, and only lasted ten years before being stricken as unfit for further service. *Gloire* served slightly longer, but wooden hulled ironclads were not a healthy type, few lasting very long. *Couronne* was still afloat in 1930. It would be hard not to conclude that at the technical level the French had allowed the success of 1855 to cloud their

---

11. H N Sulivan, *Life and Letters of Admiral Sir B J Sulivan* (London 1896).
A D Lambert, *Crimean War*, ch 20–22.

Warrior *(top) and* Gloire *to the same scale. The fame of* Gloire *as the first seagoing ironclad has rather obscured her shortcomings as a fighting ship. Industrial weakness meant that the ship had to be constructed in wood, which precluded effective water-tight compartmentation; the original battery of 16cm rifled muzzle-loaders had a poor performance against armour and was carried at little more than 6ft from the waterline; she was also a poor sea-boat and rolled heavily, although her sister,* Normandie *was the first ironclad to cross the Atlantic.*

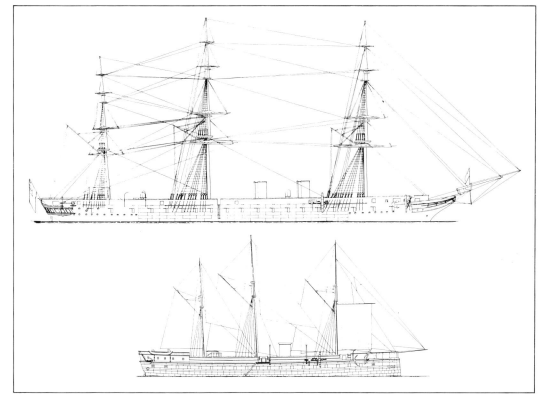

judgement. They would have been better advised to wait for Britain to start the ironclad race, using the time to improve their industrial capacity. However, this ignores the political situation. Napoleon III wanted to reinforce his success at the Peace of Paris in 1856 by coercing Britain into supporting his nationalist reorganisation of Europe. A powerful battle fleet was a vital element of this policy, and France had already lost the wooden steam battleship race.[12]

The combination of political requirement and de Lôme's conviction that the ironclad was the battleship of the next decade ensured that the French had a clear idea of the role of their ironclads. *Gloire* was a battleline unit, intended to operate in a fleet with similar ships. In consequence the French employed only two basic designs for their first sixteen ironclads. The two-deckers *Magenta* and *Solferino* were an attempt to mount 50 guns behind armour in a wooden hull, to serve as strong points in the line of battle – the role of the three-decker in the wooden ship era. The remaining fourteen ships were single-deckers, only two of which had iron hulls.

Gloire was designed for a light barque rig, but this was soon exchanged for a full ship rig of almost three times the size. This had to be reduced, since she was a poor sea-boat and rolled badly.

The British did not ignore the ironclad warship between 1855 and 1858. They elected to continue trials, but ultimately to wait on the French before acting. The First Lord, Sir Charles Wood, was well aware that Kinburn had not been an adequate test for armour, sanctioning further trials which were specifically intended to prepare the way for a sea-going ironclad. By February 1858 Walker believed that the trials had made sufficient progress to justify building an experimental armoured corvette. This vessel was similar in most respects to *Gloire*, a wooden hulled design based on existing battleships. Only the armour would be in any way novel. However, there was no reason to start building ironclads, even as an experiment, particularly as naval spending had been severely pruned following the Crimean War.

The situation was altered by news of the order for *Gloire*, which reached London in May 1858. Persuaded that the French were equal in the number of wooden battleships, the British government regarded these new units as an added source of concern. Under pressure from the Queen, the Prime Minister, Lord Derby, held a Parliamentary Committee of Enquiry on the subject. The members of the Committee were advised to pay especial attention to the opinions of Walker. Walker did not yet believe that the ironclad would replace wooden ships. However, he did believe it to be essential that Britain should match the six French ships, and do so quickly. His famous statement of British construction policy, oft quoted, bears repeating.

> Although I have frequently stated it is not in the interests of Great Britain, possessing as she does so large a navy, to adopt any important changes in the construction of ships of war which might have the effect of rendering necessary the introduction of a new class of very costly vessels until such a course is forced upon her by the adoption by Foreign Powers of formidable ships of a novel character requiring similar ships to cope with them, yet it then becomes a matter not only of expediency, but of absolute necessity. This time has arrived. France has now commenced to build frigates of great speed with their sides protected by thick metal plates, and this renders it imperative for this country to do the same without a moment's delay.

This was an accurate reflection of Walker's approach, but it did not cover developments between 1815 and 1848, when Britain had pioneered the paddle steamer, the paddle warship, the screw propeller and the iron warship. Walker supported his statement of 22 June 1858 with a call for the construction of six ironclads, to match the French. Two would be built with wooden hulls in the Royal Dockyards, the remaining four of iron in private yards. The design would be a stretched version of the February proposal, with more powerful machinery to match the design speed of *Gloire*. The Admiralty, while alarmed by the French ships, elected to continue work on wooden battleships, while preparing to build two ironclads in the following year. In part this reflected Walker's view that the new Armstrong breech-loading rifled guns would make armour obsolete. Furthermore, Walker was far from certain of the function of the ironclad.

> They must be regarded as an addition to our force, as a balance to those of France, and not as calculated to supersede any existing class of ships; indeed no prudent man would, at present, consider it safe to risk upon the performance of ships of this novel character, the Naval Supremacy of Great Britain.

Such opinions were deeply troubling to a minority Tory government desperate to save money. They were reflected in the design of the first British ironclad, the slow rate at which Britain ordered the new units, and the numerous designs which were tried.

Warrior, the first modern warship

Between the decision to order an ironclad and the sealing of the design a further series of armour trials was conducted. In October 1858 *Excellent* mounted armour on the old razee frigate *Alfred*. The plates resisted 68pdr shot, but were penetrated by a single wrought iron shot from a Whitworth rifled gun. This proved little, for the gun burst in firing the shot. It would be another six years before any gun in service could penetrate 4½in armour, and much longer before shells could follow the same path. These trials also established a basic rule on the relative value of projectiles. One 68pdr shot had approximately the same effect as five 32pdr projectiles striking close together. Later in the month two Crimean batteries were subjected to sustained fire. The wooden hulled *Meteor* proved far more durable than the iron hulled *Erebus*, emphasising the importance of heavy wooden backing for armour. The French had drawn the same conclusions from a close inspection of the Kinburn batteries. Modern studies indicate that the wooden backing did not support the armour against the impact of shot, but merely damped out the severe shock wave generated when a shot struck one of the exposed bolt heads. It was the failure of the bolts, rather than the armour, that destroyed many of the early trial targets. The bolts holding *Warrior*'s armour were fitted with rubber washers in an attempt to meet the problem. The French used an effective, if unusual system of screws to fix the armour of *Gloire* and her derivatives.

Finally, on 27 November 1858, the First Secretary to the Admiralty Henry Corry, who had been heavily involved in the iron frigate programme, persuaded his colleagues to order an ironclad. While they specified a wooden hull Walker was already moving towards iron as his preferred material. He had been prepared to order iron ships in July, and now found a vital reason to adopt iron. Wood made a better backing for armour, but it could not be stretched beyond the limits set by *Gloire*. Walker wanted to outmatch the French ship, which was always referred to as a frigate, in every respect, and that required a longer, finer hull for high speed. His conception of the new naval warfare involved the ironclads fighting at the distance where their armour made them invulnerable, and to do this they had to have

12. J Chantriot, 'La Frégate-cuirassée *La Gloire*', in *Marine & Technique Au XIX Siècle* (Paris 1988), pp347–371.
W E Echard, *Napoleon III and the Concert of Europe* (Baton Rouge 1983).

While the Gloire *was a battlefleet unit, originally completed with a light rig and in practice limited to home deployment, the British response,* HMS *Warrior, was effectively an iron-built version of a big frigate like the* Mersey *and likewise capable of world-wide operations.*

superior speed. These views were heavily influenced by Captain Hewlett of HMS *Excellent*, who urged him to give the new ship the speed to choose her range. Walker had always seen the ironclad as a large frigate, following *Mersey*, rather than a battleship. The *Mersey* type were armed for long range action with heavy guns. *Warrior*, which shared their general layout and hull form, would also adopt their armament.

The design specification for the 'Frigate of 36 guns cased with Wrought Iron Plates' was issued on 27 January 1859. The armour was to be of 4½in, covering the ship from the upper deck to 5ft below the load waterline with a wooden backing equal to the topsides of a battleship. Iron was the 'most suitable material' although he was prepared to consider wooden designs, but they must be armoured from stem to stern, while the iron ship was to rely on a central armoured section around 200ft long to carry the guns, the remainder being heavily

subdivided. The bow was to be strong enough for 'running down'. A speed of 13½kts was required, while the ship was to be rigged as an 80-gun battleship. The midship port should be 9ft out of the water.

This specification was sent to the seven Royal Yards, which could only hope to build in wood, along with eight of the most prominent iron shipbuilders in the country. The latter would supplement the limited experience of working in iron available in the Surveyor's Office. With so many guns on the main deck, 34 in all, each separated from its neighbour by 15ft for ease of operation, the ship would be long. This made it inevitable that the ironclad would be even longer than *Mersey*, the longest ever wooden warship. This made an iron hull inevitable, both for adequate strength, and to allow the bow and stern to be unarmoured. Walker was not alone in thinking that armoured extremities would make the ship plunge badly in a head sea, a fallacy that was only disproved by experience.

When the tenders arrived they were examined by the Chief Constructor, Isaac Watts, and rejected in favour of the 'in-house' design. All were deficient in different areas, but the

best commercial tenders, those from the Thames Ironworks and Robert Napier, secured priority when orders were given. The final design was submitted to the Board in January 1859, and approved on 29 April, after ser-

The iron structure of the Warrior *shows an outline similarity with its wooden forebears in this model of the midships areas. The transverse frames and the knee-like brackets of the beams imitate wooden practice, but note the deep longitudinals parallel to the keel.* (ScM)

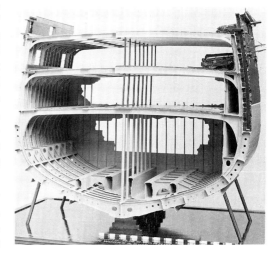

ious misgivings about the size and cost of the ship. Corry and the First Lord, Sir John Pakington, displayed considerable courage in the face of opposition from the Prime Minister and the Treasury.

The detailed design of the ship was carried out by Watts, liaising with Walker and the Chief Engineer, Thomas Lloyd. The claims of John Scott-Russell to a half-share of the credit should be dismissed; neither Watts nor Walker gave him any role in the design. He, and the other iron builders, provided information that influenced the detailed draught, but he had no role in the concept or form of the ship.

As might be expected with a novel ship of great size and cost, Watts took no risks with *Warrior*. The design was conservative in every aspect from the great strength of the frames to the diagonal tie plates on the upper deck, which were unnecessary on an iron ship. In addition the ironclad was left with the profile of *Mersey*, a knee bow, figurehead and frigate stern. The total effect was to make the hull unnecessarily heavy, sacrificing much of iron's additional load carrying capacity. If Watts did not fully understand iron, which appears to have been the case, he made a very good effort with his first design. The conservatism of the details was essential, for *Warrior* was among the most remarkable steps ever taken in the

evolution of warship design. There was nothing in the ship that might spoil the overall effect. *Warrior* was so far in advance of her contemporaries that she would have been in no danger from any combination of wooden ships, and would have had little trouble with *Gloire*. The French ship had a badly cramped gun deck battery, over-large gunports and less effective guns. However, where the French looked to an ironclad battleline, *Warrior* was still a great frigate, a fact reinforced by her poor station-keeping and general unsuitability for operating in concert with other ships.

The new ship was powered by the largest set of marine engines yet built. Between 1850 and 1860 the Royal Navy relied on two firms for the engines of new large warships. Maudslay's had remained at the head of the list of pre-ferred contractors since the 1820s, but they had been joined by John Penn and Sons of Greenwich. Penn pioneered the oscillating paddle wheel engine, and the trunk engine for screw ships. This last was the preferred engine for all high power installations, and it was adopted for *Warrior*. The previous two sets of large trunk engines were of 1000nhp, installed in the 120-gun *Howe* and the great frigate *Orlando*. This basic design was expanded to 1250nhp, using ten rather than eight boilers. Using steam at 20–22lbs per square inch,

working at 50–56rpm, these drove *Warrior* to the unprecedented speed of 14.3kts, a figure that remained unsurpassed for a further fifteen years. With sail and steam she comfortably ex-ceeded 17kts. Her heavy rig was that of an 80-gun ship, exactly the same rig as the *Mersey* class, because she had the crew to use such a large wind trap. Walker had hoped to fit four masts, but lacked the time to do so; instead *Achilles* was given four masts, while the three *Minotaur*s received five. This heavy rig was used to save coal while cruising, and was of less use once it became clear that the new ships were battlefleet units. The large iron ships rarely left the Channel, where they could be docked, and so had little opportunity to make long passages under sail. This was appropriate, for *Warrior* was the first British capital ship to be designed as a steam ship with sail as an auxiliary.

As a gun platform *Warrior* was a great ad-vance over her predecessors, largely on account of her bilge keels and careful calculation of weights. Her half-sister *Achilles* was even stead-ier. The armament adopted for *Warrior* was changed during her construction. Walker had a marked preference for a single-calibre battery, to simplify fire control and ammunition supply. He had carried this into the wooden battle-ships, where each deck was armed with only one type of gun. For *Warrior* he proposed forty 68pdr 95cwt guns, the only available type that could damage armour. The 10in shell guns fit-ted to *Orlando* were rejected as unsuitable for combat with other ironclads. While she was completing the War Office adopted the Armstrong rifled breech-loading (RBL) sys-tem. Initially *Warrior* received ten 100pdrs and four 40pdrs. In the event these guns proved inferior to the old smooth bore as armour-piercing weapons, and moreover, were not par-ticularly safe. Walker would have either re-armed the ship entirely, or once aware of the defect, removed all the Armstrong guns. However, after he retired as Controller *War-rior* was left with a badly arranged mixed bat-tery. However, the French guns of the period were all inferior to the 68pdr, particularly once wrought iron shot had been developed. In ad-

The first generation of iron-hulled ironclads was supplemented by the conversion of numbers of the now outmoded wooden steam battleships still on the stocks. Like the early French ironclads, their wooden hulls lacked longitudinal strength so they were never entirely satisfactory but they provided numbers quickly. This photograph shows the prototype, the Royal Oak, *originally a 91-gun two-decker but cut down and lengthened, fitting out at Chatham in 1863. (NMM)*

Achilles, an improved version of Warrior, *under construction in a drydock at Chatham in 1862. The framing of the central section of the hull has reached as far forward as a water-tight bulkhead – there were 106 water-tight compartments in all – before which the workmen pose. This was the first iron-hulled ironclad built in a Royal yard but the Dockyards were quick to familiarise themselves with the new technology. (NMM)*

dition French plates were inferior to those rolled in Britain, so in consequence even 6in plate could be penetrated by the old gun.

Warrior's armament as completed was twenty-six 68pdr 95cwt, ten 100pdr 82cwt RBL, four 40pdr 32cwt RBL. Two 100pdrs and the 40pdrs were mounted on the upper deck, leaving twenty-six heavy guns behind armour and eight unprotected on the main deck. The ship was also fitted to fire Martin's molten iron shells. These spectacular missiles were hair-lined hollow shells that were filled with liquid iron before firing. The object was to spread a source of inextinguishable heat across the deck of a wooden warship. Trial results were promising, and they were ordered to be fitted to the first ironclads. The rapid demise of the wooden warship ensured that this refinement of the red-hot shot was never used in action, but the threat alone was enough to condemn the old order to the pages of history.

To emphasise the frigate antecedents of the design, *Warrior*'s gunports were narrow, but deep. She could use her guns at long range, but during construction the ports were reduced in width by 20in, to provide better protection for the gun crews.

Although an improved Warrior, *as completed* Achilles *revealed a very different profile. She had a blunt ram bow, a rounded stern, which protected the steering gear (a criticised feature of the earlier ship), better protection, and a unique four-masted full rig that spread the largest sail area of any British warship. She steamed and sailed well although her great length made her unhandy and the rig was so unbalanced that the first mast was removed in 1865 and the foremast moved forward. (IWM)*

Warrior was built by Thames Ironworks at Blackwall between 25 May 1859 and 29 December 1860. She received her engines nearby in the Victoria Dock, and was fitted out at Chatham, by one of Lord Cochrane's sons, and was later joined by a certain Lieutenant Fisher as Gunnery Officer. During her two commissions with the Channel Fleet *Warrior* and her sister, the Clyde-built *Black Prince*, demonstrated the utter futility of Napoleon III's challenge. France did not build a battleship of similar dimensions until after 1870, by which time Britain had moved on to even more formidable ships. The six long ironclads for which Walker and Watts were responsible proved a valuable investment. They were still serviceable, and in most cases in service thirty

years later. However, the problem of marine fouling was not solved; *Warrior* was docked on average every ten months during her first commission, merely to preserve her speed. As there were no docks outside the British Isles long enough to take her this ensured that she and her type were not sent abroad.

Iron hulls were finally adopted because they were the only way in which the new design parameters of armour, speed and firepower could be squared. Fouling was now merely an annoying, if inevitable, problem. After *Warrior* the warship would never be the same again; something that can be said with justice for very few ships in the history of naval architecture.

The first ironclads

The British and French followed up their early ironclads with a further series of derived designs. The French ships were no improvement on the original, and when the prestige system of Napoleon III came under pressure from Prussia, the naval programmes began to slip. The French accepted that they had, once again, lost the naval race: after the block order of ten *Gloire* derivatives in 1861 no more ironclads were ordered for four years, and the first of those completed as late as 1870. Britain completed six long ironclad frigates – *Achilles*

offered a fully armoured hull, and the three *Minotaur* class were an attempt to enclose 50 guns behind armour on a single gundeck. In addition there were four reduced derivatives, the *Defence* and *Valiant* classes, and six ironclad frigates converted from incomplete 91-gun wooden two-deckers, all of which were equal to *Gloire*. This miscellaneous collection might have lacked the homogeneity of the French fleet, but it was incomparably more powerful. In 1863 the Royal Navy adopted a new approach to naval architecture.

Leaving aside developments in the United States, which will be covered in Chapter 4, the rest of the world took up the ironclad with alacrity. By now accustomed to change, and well aware of the lessons being extracted from Kinburn, there was no reason not to exploit the new opportunities. Russia built ironclad batteries without engines in 1855–56. They moved into armoured warships in 1862, converting two large frigates and ordering three iron hulled coast defence ships of an expanded floating battery type. The latter were part of the defensive aspect of Russia's new naval strategy; they were the seaward arm of the defence of Cronstadt. After 1855–56 the Russians were well aware of the threat from the Royal Navy, and their policy for the next thirty years was aimed at local defence, with an element of oceanic raiding to draw off British forces. The ironclad provided an opportunity to shift to a strategy more in tune with Russia's true interests than the obsolete battlefleet of Nicholas I.[13] The Italian and Austrian navies staged a small scale version of the Anglo-French naval race in the Adriatic, which came to a head at the Battle of Lissa on 20 July 1866, the only fleet action of the ironclad era. The tactics of Admiral Tegetthoff, relying on the ram, reflected the weakness of his own artillery – the powerful Krupp pieces for which the ship had been designed were not delivered because Prussia and Austria were at war, which only emphasised the general inability of guns to sink ironclad ships. When his flagship *Ferdinand Max* rammed *Re d'Italia* the ram suddenly became the preferred ship-killing weapon of many naval officers. This was an entirely misleading development, for the Italian ship had been lying dead in the water, her rudder shot

away, before being struck. Any ship with steering way on could avoid a direct hit.[14]

The two ships involved in this famous incident were typical of those used by the medium powers in the 1860s, namely wooden hulled vessels based on *Gloire*. The fact that the Italians were still buying abroad, while the Austrians could build at home reflected great credit on the Habsburg navy's infrastructure. However, such ships were not in the same league in terms of fighting power as *Warrior* and her type. In this respect the rest of the world lagged far behind. The iron hulled warship had opened up an almost limitless horizon for larger, more powerful and better designed ships. With her wealth, industrial power and commitment Britain exploited these opportunities to a far greater extent than her rivals. The British capital ships were the best in the world. The prominence of coast defence types in the third rank naval powers testified to their recognition of the power of Britain, and to a lesser extent France, to assault their coastal forts.

Conclusion

The naval revolution that took place in the first half of the nineteenth century had a profound effect on the strategic power and tactical roles of naval forces. The Royal Navy in particular pioneered several of the most important developments, from steam warships and the screw propeller, to iron hulls and at the end of

the fifth decade produced the first modern warship. *Warrior* summarised everything that had taken place since 1815 in one rounded package. Powered by steam, built with scientific precision (in comparison to wooden shipbuilding at least) of iron, armed (partly) with rifled breech-loading guns, protected by solid wrought iron plate 4½in thick and powered by the largest set of marine engines yet built, with sail reduced to an auxiliary role. For the next century her type would develop and prosper. By taking the lead in such a decisive manner the Royal Navy forestalled any French challenge, and for the next forty years was able to get by with a curious fleet of specimen ships, including long obsolete units like *Minotaur* and *Agincourt*.

These developments should not be taken out of context. Without the rapid advance of iron and steam industries, and of the economic strength to pay for such costly ships, design could not have progressed. Furthermore, the international situation, both in times of war and of tension, gave a major stimulus to innovation, and to adoption. These developments have hardly been hinted at in the preceding three chapters, more from lack of space than from any lack of intrinsic importance. They

13. J W Kipp, 'Russian Naval Reformers and Imperial Expansion: 1856–1863', *Soviet Armed Forces Review* (1977), pp118–137.

14. D K Brown & P Pugh, 'Ramming' in *Warship 1990* (London 1990), pp18–34.

The only two-decked broadside ironclads were the two French Magenta *class ships launched in 1861 (this is* Solferino*); they were also the first with a spur ram. The two-decked arrangement was an attempt at a more powerful ship since the wooden hull could not be built longer – and even then only the midships portion of the battery decks could be armoured. (IWM)*

should be borne in mind when considering the pace and nature of change. The Royal Navy had to be one of the world leaders in any new naval technology that promised to affect the nature of war at sea, while France sought a solution to the strategic impasse of being second in novelty and innovation. Because Britain had more to lose than France had to gain, the results of this process were inevitable, and it is only surprising that this was not more widely recognised in France. The other powers moved at the speed they could afford, or deemed necessary. Russia showed little interest until it was too late; the Americans fluctuated between major intellectual leaps, such as *Demologos* and the Stevens Battery, and the pathetic attempts to circumvent Ericsson's rights with the Hunter Wheel. Among the smaller powers Spain, Sardinia and Naples showed real interest in new technology; others were simply too poor to join the process, and all found it impossible to keep up with the engineering power of Britain. Only when a nation possessed similar wealth and industrial power could it hope to

challenge British seapower, and only if their interests were as vitally tied up with the sea would they be prepared to make the supreme effort. Between 1815 and 1860 these requirements could not be met by any other nation.

Andrew Lambert

The British answer to the French Magentas *was the huge* Minotaur *design which was intended to carry the same number of guns but on a single deck and all behind armour.* Northumberland, *shown here, was completed with fewer guns but of larger calibres and was also fitted with an armoured conning tower visible between the fourth and fifth masts.* (CMP)

The ram bow of the Minotaur *and the embrasure for a forward-firing gun (obscured by the row of seamen) reflect the new importance of end-on tactics after centuries of broadside gun duels. The efficacy of the ram was greatly exaggerated by a few untypical incidents and, paradoxically, the introduction of revolving gun mountings eventually re-established the line ahead as the basic fighting formation because the broadside was still the bearing on which maximum firepower could be developed.* (CMP)

Iron and Armoured Warships: Typical Vessels 1820–1865

Ship or class [type]	Nationality	Dis-place-ment (tons)	Dimensions (loa × breadth × draught) (feet–inches) (metres)	Armament	Machinery	Speed (max, kts)	Launch dates	Remarks
AARON MANBY [Merchant ship]	British	116bm	120–0 × 17–2 × 2–3 / 36.6 × 5.2 × 0.68	None	2–cyl oscillating, 50nhp; paddle	5	1821	First seagoing iron ship
CONGREVE BATTERY [Floating battery]	British	3000	150–0 × 45–0 × 14–0 / 45.7 × 13.7 × 4.3	4–10in mortars, 20–68pdr carr	1–cyl horizontal; 4 sub-surface paddle wheels	?	Never	Project of 1822; 500 tons of 8in cast iron plate
NEMESIS [Iron paddle steamer]	British (Bengal Marine)	660bm	184–0 × 29–0 × 6–0 / 56.1 × 8.8 × 1.8	2–32pdr, 4–6pdr, 1 Congreve rocket launcher	2–cyl Forrester, 120nhp, paddle	8	1839	The first iron warship; built for the navy of the East India Co
GUADELOUPE [Iron paddle steamer]	Mexican (British-built)	878	187–0 deck × 30–0 × 9–0 / 57.0 × 9.1 × 2.7	2–68pdr pivot, 2–24pdr	2–cyl Forrester, 180nhp; paddle	9	1842	Private venture iron warship, sold to Mexico
BIRKENHEAD [Iron paddle frigate]	British	1918	210–0 × 37–8 × 15–9 / 64.0 × 11.5 × 3.6	4–10in, 4–68pdr	2–cyl Forrester SL, 536nhp; paddle	12	1845	Pioneer iron frigate; converted to troopship 1851
OBERON [3rd Class paddle sloop]	British	1055	172–4 × 28–0 × 10–10 / 52.5 × 8.6 × 3.3	1–68pdr pivot, 3–32pdr carr	2–cyl Rennie oscillating, 260nhp, paddle	10.5	1847	Smaller iron steamer; used as Mediterranean mail packet
EUMÉNIDE [Iron paddle corvette]	French	936	196–0 deck × 30–7 × 11–0 / 59.7 × 9.3 × 3.4	2–30pdr, 4–16cm	2–cyl Hallette oscillating, 300nhp; paddle	8	1848	Largest of French iron programme of 1845; for W African station
SIMOOM [Iron screw frigate]	British	2920	246–0 deck × 41–0 × 19–7 / 75.0 × 12.5 × 6.0	12–32pdr; 2–68pdr and 4–32pdr	4–cyl Boulton and Watt horizontal, 350nhp (616ihp); 1 shaft	7.9	1849	Largest of 1844 iron frigate programme
DÉVASTATION [Floating battery]	French	1640	173–11 × 43–10 × 8–10 / 53.0 × 13.4 × 2.7	16–50pdr; 2–18pdr carr	2–cyl Schneider HP, 150nhp (317ihp); 1 shaft	3.5	1855	Crimean War battery; 4.3in side armour on wooden hull
GLATTON [Floating battery]	British	1535	172–6 deck × 45–3 × 8–8 / 52.6 × 13.8 × 2.6	14–68pdr	2–cyl Miller horizontal, 150nhp (693ihp); 1 shaft	4.5	1855	Crimean War battery; 4in iron armour on 6in teak backing
GLOIRE [Broadside ironclad]	French	5630	255–6 deck × 55–9 × 27–10 / 77.9 × 17.0 × 8.5	36–16cm RML	2–cyl HRCR, 2500ihp; 1 shaft	12.5	1859	World's first seagoing ironclad; 4.7in armour over wooden hull
WARRIOR [Broadside ironclad]	British	9137	420–0 × 58–4 × 26–0 / 128.0 × 17.8 × 7.9	2–100pdr RBL, 4–40pdr RBL; 8–100pdr RBL, 26–68pdr	2–cyl Penn trunk, 5267ihp; 1 shaft	14	1860	First iron-hulled seagoing ironclad; still afloat at Portsmouth
MAGENTA [Broadside ironclad]	French	6715	282–1 deck × 56–8 × 27–8 / 86.0 × 17.3 × 8.4	16–55pdr SB, 34–16cm BL, 2–22cm RML bow	2–cyl HRCR, 3450ihp; 1 shaft	13.0	1861	Class of two; only two-decked broadside ironclad
PRINCE CONSORT [Broadside ironclad]	British	6832	273–0 deck × 58–6 × 24–0 / 82.2 × 17.8 × 7.3	7–7in BL, 8–100pdr SB	2–cyl Maudslay HRCR, 1000nhp; 1 shaft	12.5	1862	Converted from wooden Second Rates during construction
HACHE class [Gunboats]	French	93	86–4 × 16–2 × 4–7 / 26.3 × 4.9 × 1.4	1–16cm	60ihp; 1 shaft	5–6	1862–64	Small unarmoured iron gunboats; nine vessels
PERVENETZ [Coast defence ironclad]	Russian	3277	221–9 deck × 53–9 × 19–6 / 67.6 × 16.2 × 5.9	34 guns SB	HDA, 1067ihp; 1 shaft	9	1863	Small coastal ironclad; first (of three) built in Britain
MINOTAUR [Broadside ironclad]	British	10,690	407–0 × 59–6 × 27–9 / 124.0 × 18.1 × 8.5	4–9in MLR, 24–7in MLR, 8–24pdr SB	2–cyl Penn trunk, 6700ihp; 1 shaft	14.8	1863	Largest broadside ironclads; class of three
RE D'ITALIA [Broadside ironclad]	Italian	5869	275–0 deck × 55–0 × 20–3 / 83.8 × 16.8 × 6.2	6–72pdr, 32–16cm	2–cyl SE, 1845ihp; 1 shaft	10.8	1863	Wooden hulled; rammed and sunk at Lissa (1866) by *Ferdinand Max*
FERDINAND MAX [Broadside ironclad]	Austrian	5130	274–9 × 52–4 × 23–5 / 83.8 × 16.0 × 7.1	16–48pdr, 4–8pdr, 2–3pdr	2–cyl horizontal, 2925ihp; 1 shaft	12.5	1865	Flagship at Lissa; wooden hulled

Notes:
Armament abbreviations: carr = carronade; RML = rifled muzzle-loader; BL = breech-loader; SB = smooth bore pressure; HRCR = horizontal return connecting rod;
Machinery abbreviations: SL = side lever; HP = high SE = simple expansion

4

The American Civil War

THE American Civil War was a major conflict in terms of numbers that fought, historical importance, and technological developments. The latter is particularly true in naval technology. Yet, as has been previously pointed out, the most important innovations in naval technology such as the armoured warship, iron construction, steam power, rifled and breech-loading ordnance, had their origin before the American war.[1] Even the USS *Monitor*, considered the most revolutionary as well as the most famous warship used during the war, incorporated little that was entirely new.[2]

The war began in April 1861 when Fort Sumter in Charleston (South Carolina) harbour was fired upon by military units of the newly declared Confederate States of America. Between December 1860 and February 1861 seven Southern states proclaimed their independence from the United States. In February they formed their new government. After the firing on Fort Sumter and US President Abraham Lincoln's call for troops to suppress what he called an insurrection by individuals against their legitimate government, four additional states, Virginia, North Carolina, Tennessee and Arkansas, seceded and joined the newly established nation.

The Union Navy

Shortly after the bombardment of Fort Sumter occurred, President Lincoln not only called out troops, but proclaimed an economic blockade of the Southern coastline; this blockade would eventually encompass some 3400 miles running from the Chesapeake Bay to the Mexican border. The establishment and implementation of this blockade would become the principal objective of the Federal navy during the war. All other naval activities, including combined operations and the hunt for commerce raiders, would be subordinated to this overriding strategy.

The blockade necessitated a large navy, of far more warships than were available at the beginning of the war. On 4 March 1861 the number of vessels in the navy, including receiving ships, vessels in ordinary, and ships both in and out of commission, numbered 90. By December 1864, when the navy was at or near its maximum strength, it contained 649 vessels, with a total tonnage of 510,396. These vessels were armed with more than 4600 guns. Between 1861 and 1866, 179 vessels were built and launched, and 497 were purchased or obtained by transfer from another government agency. The 179

ships that were constructed and completed during the war were all steam vessels. The 649 vessels that comprised the Federal fleet in 1864 consisted of 113 screw steamers, 52 paddlewheelers, 49 ironclads, 323 miscellaneous steamers purchased or captured and fitted for naval purposes, and 112 sailing vessels of all kinds.[3]

The Federal navy department purchased every available merchant steamer in Northern ports that could be converted into a naval vessel. There was no dearth of merchantmen as at the outbreak of the war the American merchant marine was second only to Great Britain in tonnage and numbers of vessels. Unfortunately, many of them proved unseaworthy, particularly for blockade duty. However, for riverine warfare, flat-bottomed river steamers, New York fireboats, and even double-ended ferryboats were serviceable – any sizeable vessel that could carry one or more guns could be employed.

Although the converted vessels were valuable, purpose designed warships were required for protecting oceanic trade and offshore blockade duty. Of the ninety warships in the naval service in early 1861 only forty-two were actually in commission. Nearly half of those out of commission were considered 'unserviceable', while those in commission included sailing

1. William N Still, Jr, 'Technology Afloat', *Civil War Times Illustrated* (November 1975), pp5–10.

2. James P Delgado, *A Symbol of American Ingenuity: Assessing the Significance of USS Monitor* (National Park Service, Washington, DC 1988).

3. Charles O Paullin, *History of Naval Administration* (Annapolis 1968), p280.

The big frigate Franklin *was laid down in 1856 but construction was slow and the ship spent most of the Civil War on the stocks, not being launched until 1864. The requirement for such large (5300-ton) and deep draughted vessels was minimal during the war and resources were concentrated on ironclads and smaller cruisers. Seen here in the Thames off Tilbury Fort after the war, the ship was the flagship of the European squadron at the time. (CMP)*

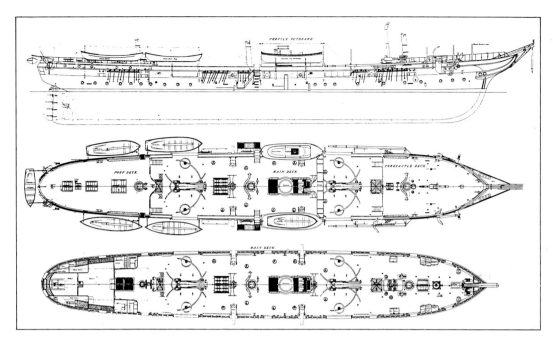

ships. Over half of the serviceable warships were on distant station, scattered all over the world. It would be months before all returned and were outfitted for wartime duty.

Many of the prewar ships were not suitable for blockade or coastal operations. Paddle-wheelers such as the sloops *Susquehanna* and *Powhatan* expended too much fuel and generally were too deep-draughted for inshore blockade. The five screw propelled frigates of the *Merrimack* class and the sloop *Niagara*, although heavily gunned, also displaced far too much water for the shoal waters off the Southern coast. They were too slow to chase speedy blockade runners and their heavy guns were at times difficult to fire in a seaway. In 1857 Congress authorised the construction of five screw propelled sloops. Four of this class, *Hartford*, *Richmond*, *Pensacola*, and *Brooklyn*, saw extended service in the war. With relatively shallow draught and large battery, they proved to be efficient in river and coastal operations. The final class of prewar vessels used during the war were designed for coastal work. Seven of this class, *Tuscarora*, *Kearsarge*, *Oneida*, *Wachusett*, *Iroquois*, *Seminole* and *Narragansett*, participated in the war. As one authority wrote, 'In the sloops of war of 1858, the navy obtained the most versatile and reliable ships of the entire wooden steamer era . . . The key to their success was . . . in a reasonable combination of capacity, firepower, speed, and mechanical reliability'.[4]

Two of the 'ninety-day gunboats' as fitted for riverine warfare with topmasts struck. The nearer ship is the Unadilla, *which gave her name to the whole class.* (US Army Military History Institute, by courtesy of Donald L Canney)

Union wooden warships

While the warships were being fitted out and deployed for blockade service the Union government initiated a naval shipbuilding programme. Excellent facilities were available. Eight of the ten Navy Yards were in the North, and the huge naval facility at Norfolk, Virginia, was retaken in 1862. Extensive shipyards, ordnance works, and machine fabricating facilities existed in the Northern states.

To implement this programme, Union Secretary of the Navy Gideon Welles depended upon

two members of his department, John Lenthall, chief of the Bureau of Construction, Equipment, and Repairs, and Benjamin F Isherwood, Engineer-in-Chief. Lenthall had been the navy's ship architect for a number of years. He designed many of the vessels that were completed in the 1850s, including the large steam frigates. He was reputed to be a fine naval architect but conservative when it came to new designs, building techniques, and materials. Isherwood was a young naval engineer whose published works illustrated his innovative outlook. The two complemented each other and contributed to the design of most of the new warships added to the navy during the war.[5]

The navy's most pressing need was small

4. Donald L Canney, *The Old Steam Navy: Frigates, Sloops, and Gunboats, 1815–1885* (Annapolis 1990), p83. See also Andrew Lambert, *Battleships in Transition: The Creation of the Steam Battlefleet, 1815–1860* (London 1984), p114.

5. John Niven, *Gideon Wells* (New York 1973), p349; Edward W Sloan, III, *Benjamin Franklin Isherwood* (Annapolis 1965), p28.

The 150pdr Parrott rifled muzzle-loader on Nipsic's *midships pivotting mount; there were also two 9in Dahlgrens on broadside mountings aft, plus a few smaller guns. The armament of Union gunboats varied but this fit is not atypical.* (US Army Military History Institute, by courtesy of Donald L Canney)

swift gunboats that could operate in shallow waters. In May 1861 Lenthall met with a number of private shipbuilders to discuss the navy's needs for new warships. Isherwood, as Lenthall's assistant and the one directly in charge of steam construction, was present. The Engineer-in-Chief mentioned two gunboats built in New York for the Russian government. They were small (691 tons) and shallow draught, built to operate on the Amur river. Isherwood suggested that their design was ideally suited for small gunboats to operate in Southern waters. The builders present agreed that vessels of this design could be built economically and quickly. Within two months the keels of twenty-three of these vessels had been laid, and the first of this class, *Unadilla*, was completed in 93 days, earning for that class the name 'ninety-day gunboats'.[6]

As with all classes of wooden warships there were variations. The first four of this class completed had some 60 per cent less boiler power than the other nineteen. Batteries were changed depending upon the availability of particular types of ordnance. As an example, *Unadilla* carried one 11in Dahlgren smooth bore, two 24pdrs and one 20pdr Parrott rifle. All of them were rigged as fore topsail schooners with gaff topsails. Their nominal crew was one hundred officers and men.

In March 1862 the last of the twenty-three *Unadilla* class was commissioned. By that date most of the others in that class had been assigned to the various blockading squadrons. They participated in many of the combined operations along the Southern coastline and rivers including the naval battle in April 1862 below New Orleans, Louisiana. Ten of this class were involved in this engagement. As blockade vessels they made 146 captures.[7]

Their accomplishments were impressive despite serious defects. They were poor sailers; their machinery frequently broke down; the steering mechanism was inefficient; and they were slow, maximum speed being 8–9kts. This often put them at a disadvantage in carrying out blockade responsibilities.

In August 1862 a second class of shallow-draught gunboats were authorised. Eight of this *Kansas* class were completed. Two distinct hull designs characterised this class: two of the vessels, *Pequot* and *Maumee*, were smaller than

the other six and incorporated sterns that were radically different from the rest of the class. Furthermore, they did not have bowsprits.

Three of this class, *Nipsic*, *Shawmut*, and *Nyack*, were powered by machinery designed by chief engineer Isherwood. This machinery consisted of two back-acting cylinders, of 30in diameter and 20in stroke. The remaining five had a variety of engine designs: two, *Kansas* and *Yantic*, had directing-acting engines; *Saco* and *Maumee* had vibrating-lever engines; and *Pequot* was fitted with a Wright 'segmental' engine.[8] All eight vessels were originally rigged as two-masted topsail schooners. These vessels performed very well during the Civil War, although they saw less service than the 'ninety-day' gunboats because of their late entry into the conflict.

In June 1861 Union naval secretary Welles created a board of strategy to plan and recommend future operations. The board drew up a series of reports designed to make the blockade more effective. These reports emphasised the need to occupy designated points along the Southern coastline. These points would become bases for the blockade squadrons as well as potential staging areas for raids and invasion. The acceptance of these reports made extensive combined operations an operational necessity.[9] These reports recognised that naval units would have to operate on the narrow shallow rivers that characterised the Southern waterway system. The need for warships capable of river service led to the development of a type known as double-ender gunboats.

'Double-enders' were side-wheel, light draught vessels theoretically designed with both bow and stern lines identical to preclude the necessity to reverse direction. According to

Donald L Canney in his book *The Old Steam Navy: Frigates, Sloops, and Gunboats*, forty-eight double-enders were built during the war. He points out that several of them, particularly those of the initial group, were really not double-enders. A number were designed with sterns different from their stems or their wheels were not located at mid-point along the hull. He concludes that they were called double-enders because of a second rudder at the bow.[10] The disparity in design is at least partly explained by the experimental nature of these initial double-enders. Seven different yards built them, with the Navy Department intending to adopt the most acceptable one as a prototype. *Port Royal* was considered the best of this class and potential contractors for double-enders were instructed to follow her design. The ships' batteries varied, as did the ships themselves, but *Port Royal* carried one 100pdr, six 24pdrs and one 10in shell gun. They were all fore and aft schooner rigged. All of these vessels were flat-bottomed and poor sailers in open waters; fortunately, however,

6. E W Sloan, *op cit*, p30; D L Canney, *op cit*, pp91–92; William N Still, Jr, *Monitor Builders: A Historical Study of the Principal Firms and Individuals Involved in the Construction of the USS Monitor* (Washington, DC 1988).

7. D L Canney, *op cit*, p95. Paddle wheel vessels were generally faster than screw types. In wooden hulls it was easy for the screw/engine/shaft to get out of line. This is significant, in light of the fact that most fast runners were paddle powered and being chased by screw Navy steamers – the Navy wanted the machinery below decks out of the line of fire.

8. D L Canney, *op cit*, pp104–105.

9. Rowena Reed, *Combined Operations in the Civil War* (Annapolis 1976).

10. D L Canney, *op cit*, p109.

Conemaugh, *one of the first group of so-called 'double-enders', was launched from the Portsmouth Navy Yard in May 1862. This 1105-ton vessel was capable of 11kts and was armed with one 100pdr Parrott RML (seen here just forward of the funnel), one 11in Dahlgren aft, and six 24pdrs.* (US Navy Historical Center, by courtesy of Donald L Canney)

their primary service was on the rivers and in confined waters where they performed well.

The second design, *Sassacus* class, was not only the most widely constructed type of double-ender, but the largest single class of Union warship built during the war, some twenty-eight being built. The gunboats in this class were schooner rigged, and were armed with two 100pdrs, four 9in guns and two 24pdr howitzers. They performed satisfactorily during the war. They were fast for their size, averaging over 8kts; several could make 14kts. Vessels in this class participated in a number of actions including the Battle of Mobile Bay and the engagement with the ironclad *Albemarle* in the North Carolina Sounds.

The *Mohongo* class was the third and final class of double-enders laid down during the Civil War. Seven were begun in 1863 but only one, *Suwanee*, actually saw service during the conflict. Of all the unarmoured vessels built by the Union during the war the *Mohongo* class was the only one to use iron in the construction of the frames and other parts of the hull structure. Although more seaworthy than the other double-enders, they were still poor sailers. They were, however, reasonably fast, averaging over 10kts. Armament was not standard on the different vessels in this class. Some carried four 9in Dahlgren smooth bores and two 100pdrs as pivots; others carried 60pdr Parrott rifles and 8in Dahlgrens. All of them carried howitzers on the hurricane deck.[11]

The double-enders of all classes were reasonably serviceable vessels for operations on rivers and other sheltered waters. As blockaders, particularly, on the open sea, they were unsatisfactory.

Federal strategy called for an invasion of the Confederacy by way of the Mississippi river and its tributaries. Initially, military operations, including riverine on the Western rivers, were to be carried out by the army. In May 1861 a naval officer, Commander John Rogers, was ordered to the West (in the American Civil War the area generally between the Appalachian mountains and the Mississippi was considered the West; the area beyond the Mississippi was called the Trans-Mississippi West) to help the army in creating a naval force. No new wooden vessels were constructed. Instead the army and later the navy purchased river steamers and converted them into gunboats. Shallow-draught, lightly built and with high pressure boilers exposed on deck, they were unsuitable for combat, although few alterations were made. Thick oak bulwarks were installed and pierced for broadside guns; decks were strengthened to carry the heavy guns; and the boilers and steam fittings were lowered as much as possible into the hold.[12] Later cotton bales would be used as protective 'armour' on open decks.

In addition to riverboats, several snagboats were converted into gunboats. In September 1861 the army turned over to the navy most of its 'western navy'. By the end of the war more than a hundred naval vessels were stationed on the Mississippi river and its tributaries.[13]

In April 1862, Flag Officer David G Farragut ascended the Mississippi river and after defeating a small Confederate naval force, forced the surrender of New Orleans, Louisiana, the most important port in the South. For several months his deep sea vessels ranged up and down the Mississippi, linking up with the river gunboats, and co-operating with land forces in combined operations.

Before Farragut's force entered the Mississippi to begin its assault on the New Orleans defences, a Confederate warship, *Sumter*, slipped out of the river, avoided the Union blockaders, and disappeared into the Gulf of Mexico. *Sumter* was the first Confederate commerce raider to be deployed against Union

11. *Ibid*, pp119–120.

12. John D Milligan, *Gunboats Down the Mississippi* (Annapolis 1965), pp6–7.

13. C O Paullin, *op cit*, pp282–283.

The Mohongo *class, the final double-ender design, adopted iron for large parts of the hull. This may have contributed to the fact that two of the class enjoyed long postwar careers,* Monocacy *surviving until 1903. This ship spent large parts of her later commissions in Far East waters, where she is seen in this photograph.* (CMP)

The river ironclad St Louis *(later* Baron de Kalb*) was one of the 'Pook turtles', designed to US Army requirements by Samuel M Pook, although eventually operated by the Navy. The slanting armoured casemate is obvious but there is also a conning tower – multi-faceted like a cut diamond – just forward of the funnels. The class was involved in some of the fiercest fighting of the riverine war, and* de Kalb *was sunk by a mine in the Yazoo river in July 1863.* (Naval Photographic Center, by courtesy of Donald L Cannery)

shipping. *Sumter*'s escape was a factor in the Union Navy Department's decision to build 'fast screw steamers' for ocean operations. Secretary Welles created a board of officers to determine specifications. They recommended what became known as the *Sacramento* class.

Six *Sacramento* class vessels were built. Donald L Canney claims that they were 'dimensionally extended versions of the *Ossipee*-class ships,' as far as structural lines were concerned.[14] With a length of 229ft, they displaced 2100 tons. Armament varied: five of the ships were originally fitted with three pivot guns, two 11in Dahlgren smooth bores and one 150pdr Parrott rifle, but the batteries differed from ship to ship and were modified during the war and afterwards.

*Sacramento*s, like most Civil War classes of multi-numbered vessels, differed in construction detail and dimensions. They were barquentine rigged, but with limited sailing capabilities. Two of this class, *Canandaigua* and *Lackawanna*, had bowsprits. They were relatively fast vessels averaging from 8kts to 10kts under sail and steam, and quite seaworthy. They performed creditably during the Civil War, engaging in extensive blockade duty as well as distant service pursuing Confederate commerce raiders. *Canandaigua* participated in a number of attacks on Charleston, South Carolina; *Ticonderoga* joined units of the North Atlantic Blockading Squadron in bombarding Fort Fisher near Wilmington, North Carolina; and *Monongahela* and *Lackawanna* engaged the Confederate armourclad *Tennessee* in the Battle of Mobile Bay. This class of vessels continued in service after the Civil War ended.

Union armoured warships

Although the wooden ships contributed significantly to the Union war effort, it was the armoured vessels that captured the attention of the public during the war and of historians thereafter. It is not surprising that the Civil War witnessed the first full-scale employment of armoured vessels. The emphasis that European powers were placing on the construction

of ironclads was generally known in American naval circles. Ironically the Union navy, which as mentioned earlier had to assume an offensive strategy in order to win the war, adopted as its principal ironclad a type of vessel that was basically defensive in nature. Early in August 1861 Congress appropriated $1,500,000 for the 'construction or completion of iron or steelclad steamers or steam batteries,' and authorised the creation of a board of naval officers to examine proposals and make recommendations. In September the board recommended that contracts be awarded for three vessels: a seagoing broadside vessel, *New Ironsides*; a lightly armoured wooden vessel, *Galena*; and a revolving-turret vessel, *Monitor*.

While the board of naval officers had been deliberating, the army had already contracted for seven ironclads for service on the Mississippi river and its tributaries. These vessels were known as 'Pook turtles' after their designer, Samuel M Pook, or the 'City' class because they were named after western river ports. They were commissioned as *Cairo*, *Carondelet*, *Cincinnati*, *Louisville*, *Mound City*, *Pittsburgh*, and *St Louis* (later *Baron de Kalb*). They were wooden, flat-bottomed light draught and low freeboard centre-wheelers measuring 175ft in length. With slanted casemates partially covered with 2½in armour they resembled in appearance the Confederate armourclads. They came under naval control after becoming operational.

Each of the Pook vessels carried thirteen guns: four 42pdr rifles, three 8in Dahlgren smooth bores, six 32pdr smooth bores; the only variation was that *St Louis* was armed with a 32pdr in lieu of one 8in Dahlgren. The seven river gunboats had defects found on nearly all of the armoured vessels built during the Civil War – they were underpowered, too heavy, and vulnerable to plunging fire. Nevertheless, they

saw more service than any other class of river ironclad, fighting in various engagements from Fort Henry in early 1862 to the Siege of Vicksburg in 1863 and beyond. Three of them, *Cairo*, *Cincinnati*, and *Baron de Kalb* (ex-*St Louis*), would be sunk.[15]

The army was also responsible for the conversion of four large river vessels into ironclads. A snagboat was converted into the casemated armourclad *Benton* while *Essex*, also casemated, was a rebuilt centre-wheel ferryboat. *Benton* carried fourteen heavy guns while *Essex* carried six. Two side-wheelers named *Lafayette* and *Choctaw* were purchased in St Louis and converted into armourclads. Although *Lafayette* would have a sloping casemate, *Choctaw* would have a fixed 'turret' with inclined sides and a curved top or 'dome' and pierced to hold four guns. Just forward and aft of the wheel were two small casemates. On top of the forward casemate, which housed two howitzers to sweep the decks and repel boarders, was located a conical shaped pilothouse, covered with two inches of iron. *Choctaw* had 2in layers of iron while *Lafayette*'s sloping casemate was covered with 1in iron over 1in india rubber. The navy took over these armourclads and operated them throughout the war.

In 1862 the navy contracted for three ironclads on the western rivers. *Chillicothe*, *Tuscumbia*, and *Indianola* were casemated vessels, but differed somewhat in particulars. *Tuscumbia* was the largest of the three, displacing 915 tons, measuring 178ft in length and 75ft in breadth, and drawing 7ft of water. She had four engines

14. D L Canney, *op cit*, p87.

15. Edwin C Bearss, *Hardluck Ironclad: the Sinking and Salvage of the Cairo* (Baton Rouge 1966); J D Milligan, *op cit*; D Canney, unpublished MS on Union armoured vessels. Specifications for these vessels can be found in the appropriate volumes of the *Dictionary of American Fighting Ships* (Washington, DC 1965–72).

There is no good contemporary depiction of the New Ironsides, *the Federal Navy's only broadside ironclad. This heavily retouched photograph was probably taken at the end of the war since the ship fought without top hamper in her early campaigns. The scissor-action divided gunport lids can just be made out. (US Navy Historical Center, by courtesy of Donald L Canney)*

which drove two side wheels and twin screw propellers. She mounted three 11in Dahlgren smooth bores firing forward and two 9in guns firing aft between her wheels. *Indianola*'s tonnage was 511, her length 175ft, and her beam 52ft. Because of her smaller dimensions her draught was only 5ft. She had similar motive power to *Tuscumbia*, and carried two 11in Dahlgren smooth bores to fire forward and two 9in to fire astern. *Chillicothe* was the smallest of the three, displacing only 395 tons. She was 162ft long and 56ft in beam, with a draught of 4ft. She had two engines to propel her two side wheels. Her armament consisted of two 11in Dahlgren smooth bores housed to fire forward. None of the three had broadside guns nor did *Chillicothe* have stern chasers.

These three river armourclads were regarded as inefficient. *Chillicothe*'s first commanding officer pronounced her a 'cumbersome scow', and after the battle of Grand Gulf in April 1863 *Tuscumbia*'s captain referred to his vessel as a 'disgrace'.[16]

The light draught river armourclads were one of three basic types of ironclad introduced by the Union in its construction programme of 1861–62. The navy contracted for a second type, a more conventional seagoing vessel named *New Ironsides*; and *Monitor*, primarily a harbour defence vessel. The navy also agreed to build a lightly armoured wooden vessel, *Galena*.

Of these types, *New Ironsides* and *Monitor* represented a fundamental divergence of opinion over the type of warship the navy should employ. The chief engineer, the chief naval constructor, and an undetermined number of naval officers, including such influential ones as Samuel Du Pont and David G Farragut, were critical of the light armament *Monitor* type and favoured more offensive seagoing cruisers with their guns mounted in broadsides. Nevertheless, *New Ironsides* was the only seagoing armoured cruiser to be completed during the war. An improved model, *Dunderberg*, was laid down but not completed until after the conflict had ended.

New Ironsides was a traditional broadside type, but 170ft out of 230ft of her hull was covered with iron armour 4½in in thickness. The armour belt covered the sides and deck, generally

amidship, with bow and stern armoured. This citadel protected her main battery. Classified as a frigate, this powerful ironclad spent her entire Civil War career with either the South Atlantic or the North Atlantic blockading squadrons. *New Ironsides* was the most effective Union armoured vessel in the combined operations along the Southern coastline. She participated in numerous bombardments along the southeastern coast, and although hit frequently by enemy fire, was only put out of action briefly when damaged by a Confederate torpedo boat. The ship was armed with fourteen 11in Dahlgren smooth bores and two 8in (150pdr) rifled guns on the broadside, and two 5.3in (50pdr) Parrott rifled guns on the upper deck. *New Ironsides* was barque rigged, and although effective inshore, her shallow draught and flat bottom made her a poor sailer in deep water.

The board of naval officers who had recommended the three original armoured vessels wrote that 'ocean going [armoured] cruisers are for the time being impracticable.' In 1864 the US Congress published a *Report of the Secretary of the Navy in Relation To Armored Vessels*. In general the Report was Secretary of the Navy Gideon Welles's defence of the monitor type, but it also included a number of letters from various naval officers critical of the idea of seagoing ironclads. Captain John R Goldsborough, for example, wrote, 'If any solid benefit is to be derived from iron plating applied to a sea going vessel . . . it is quite apparent that it is only to be done by limiting its use to her most vitally exposed parts. . . ' The Federal Board of Ordnances observed that 'upon a balance of advantages and disadvantages, a cruiser intended for sea service had better carry no armor at all.' As mentioned earlier, to a great degree the blockade of the Southern coastline determined Union naval strategy, in-

cluding the ship construction programme during the conflict. For example, one of the three ironclad vessels initially approved for construction was *Galena*. She was according to Commodore Joseph Smith, senior officer of the Ironclad Board, 'a lighter boat . . . intended to have more speed [than other ironclads] to work in part under canvas'. *Galena* resembled the wooden steam warships of that day except that the upper part of her sides were rounded inward or tumbled-home at an angle of about 45 degrees to deflect projectiles. She had 3¼in of plating in an interlocking rail and plate pattern. Armament was two 100pdr Parrott rifled guns and four 9in Dahlgren smooth bores. Although schooner rigged, all her masts, except the fore lower mast for a lookout position, were removed. In May 1862 *Galena* ascended the James river in Virginia and engaged Confederate batteries at Drewry's Bluff. She was badly damaged, her thin armour being penetrated eighteen times. Later the armour was removed, and she completed the war as a wooden hulled warship.

Of the three initial armoured vessels approved by the Union Navy Department, *Monitor* was the most revolutionary and by far the most important during the Civil War. Major reasons for this include the influence of Assistant Secretary of the Navy Gustavus Fox and *Monitor*'s designer, John Ericsson, and the impact of the battle between *Monitor* and the Confederate ironclad *Virginia* in March 1862.

Monitor was a unique vessel. Instead of a standard ship hull she had a large overhanging armoured 'raft' measuring 172ft by 41ft 6in supported by a lower section 122ft long and

16. William N Still, Jr, 'The New Ironclads', in *The Guns of 62* (Garden City, NY 1982), p53; J D Milligan, *op cit*, pp99–101; *Dictionary of American Fighting Ships*.

This painting by the well known British authority on warships Dr Oscar Parkes shows Galena *in her fighting trim (the ship was schooner rigged for passage-making). The tumblehome and individual plate-and-rail pattern of the armour are clear.* (US Naval Photographic Center, by courtesy of Donald L Canney)

34ft wide. The entire hull was iron. The 'raft' was designed to increase stability in a seaway and protect the hull from ramming. The vessel's powerplant consisted of two boilers and two engines of Ericsson's own design, which he believed would propel her at 9kts. The armourclad incorporated numerous technical advances including forced ventilation of living spaces, a protected anchor which could be raised and lowered without it (and also crew members) being exposed to enemy fire, and a protected pilothouse. The revolving turret carrying the ship's battery of two 11in Dahlgren smooth bore guns was considered the most novel feature, although the concept of such a gun tower was not a new one.

In service *Monitor*'s best speed was 6–7kts. Designed as a harbour defence vessel, she was not seaworthy and had to be towed from port to port. Because of her low freeboard, which res-

ulted in waves washing over the deck, her ventilation system was inefficient. Even with the blowers working and hatches open, temperatures of 178 degrees (fahrenheit) in the engine room and 120 degrees in living spaces were recorded in the summer of 1862. The turret, 20ft in diameter and 9ft high, was steam operated on a central spindle. The ship was armoured with 4in laminated iron plate on her sides, 1in on deck, and eight layers of 1in plate on the turret.[17] *Monitor* was lost in a gale off Cape Hatteras, North Carolina, on 31 December 1862.

Even while *Monitor* was under construction the Union Navy Department had asked Congress for $12 million to construct twenty additional turreted vessels. These were designed by the Chief of the Bureau of Construction and Repair and were to mount two turrets to the design of Captain Cowper Coles of the Royal Navy. Although the Coles turret was superior to that designed by Ericsson, the Swedish inventor prevented its adoption by the American navy. In fact, one might say that the broadside-versus-turreted ironclad dispute was not nearly

so controversial in 1862 as the type of turret to be used. In addition to the Ericsson and Coles turrets, a third design by James B Eads was considered. Eads's turrets were installed on the *Milwaukee* class of river monitors and were probably the most sophisticated of the three. The guns in the turret were mounted on a steam-operated elevator which dropped them to a lower deck where they were loaded, then hoisted and run out through ports opened by automatic steam-operated shutters. Even the *Milwaukee* class, however, carried only one Eads turret; the other was of Ericsson's design.[18]

Monitor's engagement with the CSS *Virginia* in Hampton Roads produced such an intense enthusiasm in the North that a 'monitor craze' swept the Union. Until the end of the war the navy would concentrate on monitor construction. Of the eighty-four ironclads laid down by the Union during the war, sixty-four were of the *Monitor* or turreted types. Three weeks after the battle in Hampton Roads, ten improved Ericsson monitors were contracted – the *Passaic* class, which would see more service than any other class of monitors.

17. W N Still, *Monitor Builders*, p24; Edward M Miller, *The USS Monitor, the Ship that Launched the Modern Navy* (Annapolis 1979).

18. W N Still, 'Technology Afloat', p42.

Comparative profiles of the CSS Virginia, *ex-*Merrimack *(top) and* USS Monitor, *the shaded areas representing the armour. The difference in design philosophies is as apparent as the disparity in size.* (From H W Wilson's *Battleships in Action*)

Comparative sections of the CSS Virginia, *ex-*Merrimack *(top) and* USS Monitor, *showing the different methods of mounting the armament and the basic dispositions of the armour.* (From H W Wilson's *Battleships in Action*)

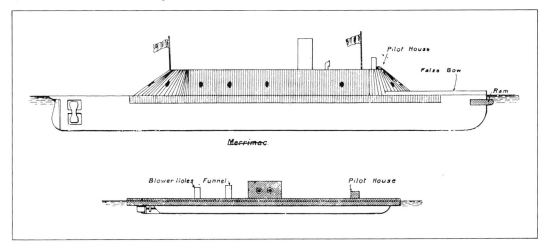

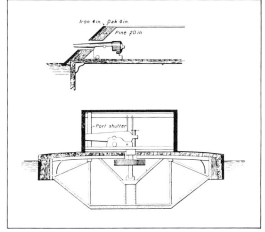

The ten *Passaic*s included *Montauk, Catskill, Patapsco, Lehigh, Sangamon* (later renamed *Jason*), *Camanche, Nahant, Nantucket, Weehawken,* and *Passaic.* They had a single turret, but included improvements such as a pilothouse on top of the turret, increased thickness of armour plate, a permanent smoke stack, and a more powerful battery. The *Passaic*s were to carry two 15in Dahlgren smooth bores and deck howitzers, but several carried one 11in or an 8in Parrott rifle instead of one 15in. These vessels as a class were to see more service than any others of the monitor fleet. They were the major ironclad units of both the South Atlantic and North Atlantic blockading squadrons, and participated in the combined operations against Charleston, Savannah, and the James river and participated in the Mobile Bay Battle.

In 1862 the Union Navy Department also initiated the construction of double-turreted monitors. *Onondaga* and four of the *Miantonomoh* class, *Monadnock, Agamenticus* (later renamed *Terror*), *Tonawanda* (later renamed *Amphitrite*), and *Miantonomoh* were laid down during the Civil War but only two, *Onondaga* and *Monadnock,* were completed. These vessels were twin-screw ironclads, but without the overhang or raft characteristic of the Ericsson monitors; *Onondaga* was iron hulled, but the rest were built of wood. *Onondaga* was armed with two 15in Dahlgren smooth bores and two 8in Parrott rifles (one of each type per turret). The other four were slightly larger than *Onondaga* and carried four 15in smooth bores in the two turrets. This

class was considered to be the most efficient of the monitor type built during the war, and remained in service for many years afterwards although their wooden hulls had to be replaced with iron.

In September 1862 orders were given to various builders for nine more Ericsson monitors. *Canonicus, Catawba, Oneota, Mahopac, Manhattan, Tecumseh, Saugus, Manayunk* (later *Ajax*), and *Tippecanoe* (later *Wyandotte*) were similar to the *Passaic* class but with certain significant improvements. These included a defensive slope around the base of the turret to prevent jamming, a heavier battery of two 15in guns, and a better ship-like hull design. Five of this class were commissioned in time to see Civil War service. *Tecumseh* was sunk by a Confederate torpedo (mine) during the Battle of Mobile Bay.

The last of the coastal monitors contracted for in 1862 were the two giant single-turret monitors, *Puritan* and *Dictator.* Displacing more than 3000 tons and with a large fuel capacity these vessels were intended as oceangoing vessels. The hull sides were armoured with 6in of plate and the 24ft diameter turret (for two 15in Dahlgrens) with 10in of armour. The funnel and ventilation shaft bases were also armoured. *Dictator,* after being commissioned in December 1864, joined the North Atlantic blockading squadron but saw no action. *Puritan* was never completed.

The most numerous single class of monitor type vessel built was the *Casco* class. In the spring of 1863, contracts were signed for the

construction of twenty of this type. However, during the war only eight were completed and they were considered unseaworthy. Five of them were converted to torpedo boats, but none saw action.

Monitors were also constructed for operations on the western rivers. Shortly after the Hampton Roads engagement between *Monitor* and *Virginia,* a contract was signed with shipbuilder James Eads to build three single-turreted monitors of his own design. Two of these river monitors, *Osage* and *Neosho,* were unlike other monitors in that they were propelled by stern-wheels. Unfortunately, these wheels (protected by armoured casings) made it impossible for the turrets for two 11in Dahlgrens to turn a full 360 degrees. They were unusual looking vessels with virtually nothing showing above the waterline but the turret, the iron plated house for the stern paddle wheel and the tall thin stacks.

The third river monitor, *Ozark,* was larger, screw propelled, and carried additional armament of questionable value – four pivot guns located upon the open deck. Eads received a second contract for monitors. The four vessels built under this contract – *Chickasaw, Kickapoo, Milwaukee,* and *Winnebago* – were double-turreted ironclads with one turret by Ericsson's design and one by Eads's design. These vessels carried four 11in Dahlgren guns each – two per turret – and were the only monitors ever built with four screws and rudders. The sides were armoured with 3in of laminated plate, and the turrets with 8in. These were relatively effective ironclad vessels for river and coastal waters and the only class of monitors that made their designated speed. They were principally employed with the West Gulf blockading squadron operating in Mobile Bay and its vicinity.

The monitor type had the great advantage of achieving a maximum of impenetrability through two radical factors – low·freeboard

Agamenticus, one of the double-turreted second generation monitors; a hurricane deck was added in an attempt to make these ships more seaworthy and two were able to make noteworthy voyages – one across the Atlantic and the other to San Francisco around South America, although both ships were escorted. (US Navy Historical Center, by courtesy of Donald L Canney)

Kickapoo, a double-turreted shallow draught monitor of James Eads's design. Although each turret mounted two 11in Dahlgren smooth bores, the forward turret was of Eads's pattern, a sophisticated design which revolved on a ball bearing race and made extensive use of steam power for run-out, elevation, recoil-damping and lowered the guns below deck for loading. Note the turtleback hull form. (US Navy Historical Center, by courtesy of Donald L Canney)

and the concentration of guns in an armoured turret. The guns could be aimed without moving the ship. In confined and sheltered waters the monitors were excellent defensive ships, but they had serious defects that affected Union naval operations. A majority of them were essentially floating batteries that had to be towed from station to station. They were unseaworthy and had so little buoyancy that a leak could be fatal. For these reasons they were unsuitable for blockade service, the primary mission of the Union navy. In anything but a flat calm a monitor's deck was awash. The crew had to remain below with hatches battened down. As Admiral Du Pont wrote: 'How can such vessels lay off [ports] . . . and protect the wooden vessels.'

Even more important was their unsuitability for offensive operations. Loading their guns usually required from six to eight minutes. 'This delay,' as John D Hayes wrote in his introduction to the Du Pont papers, 'violated the cardinal principle of naval gunnery, volume of fire.' In the attack by *New Ironsides, Keokuk,* and seven monitors on Fort Sumter in April 1863, only 139 rounds were fired by the combined batteries of the ironclads' twenty-three guns. At the same time seventy-six guns in the Confederate forts rained some 2206 shots on the Union vessels. As Du Pont wrote to naval secretary Welles,

> I . . . remind the Department that ability to endure is not a sufficient element wherewith to gain victories, that endurance must be accompanied with a corresponding power to inflict injury upon the enemy . . . that the weakness of the monitor class of vessels . . . is fatal to their attempts against fortifications.[19]

The Confederate States made strenuous efforts to build or acquire powerful warships in Europe. Among the most potentially dangerous were two seagoing turret ships ordered in Britain from Lairds of Birkenhead, with two Coles type turrets each mounting two 9in MLRs. Although they were nominally building for Egypt, their eventual destination was clear to the British government and political pressure forced their seizure in 1863. They later served in the Royal Navy as the Scorpion *and* Wyvern, *this photo depicting the latter as fitted with tripods to reduce the standing rigging that masked the turrets' firing arcs.* (CMP)

The most unusual turreted vessel commissioned during the Civil War was the converted wooden sloop of war *Roanoke.* Like her sister ship, *Merrimack,* converted by the Confederates into *Virginia,* she was cut down, and three centreline turrets were installed. With a high freeboard, she was not a monitor type vessel. Because of instability and a deep draught, *Roanoke* was considered unsuitable for active service and spent the war defending New York harbour from possible attack by Confederate cruisers.

Outside the mainstream of Union armourclad development was *Keokuk,* ex-*Moodna,* designed by C W Whitney, one of Ericsson's partners. After considerable lobbying, the 150ft turtlebacked design was accepted by the Navy Department in the excitement following the Hampton Roads battle. The ship was built at Underhill's New York yard between April 1862 and March 1863. Unlike the monitors, *Keokuk* carried one 11in Dahlgren smooth bore in each of two circular fixed armoured gunhouses, but her real weakness was the armour scheme of horizontal iron bars alternating with wood and covered with thin plate. This was to be her undoing, being unable to resist heavy close range fire during the attack on Charleston; *Keokuk* was withdrawn from action but sank the following day from damage received.

The Confederate States Navy

The general military policy of the Confederacy was defensive. This was in part an inevitable response to Northern strategy and in part due to the nature of the war. Southerners were not trying to conquer the North, but wanted only to preserve their recently proclaimed independence. For that reason Confederate strategy generally developed around the same objectives toward which the Union forces were aiming. In practice this meant an attempt to post adequate forces at all threatened points along the extensive frontier of the Confederacy, including the western rivers and sea coast. This strategy of defence determined Confederate naval policy. The blockade followed by the implementation of General Winfield Scott's plan to recover the South (a plan which envisioned the seizure of Southern ports to seal off all commerce and the control of the main transportation arteries from Ohio to the Gulf of Mexico) made inescapable the navy's concentrated efforts to defend the key ports, inlets, bays, and rivers in the beleaguered nation. As

19. John D Hayes (ed), *Samuel Francis DuPont: A Selection From His Civil War Letters,* 3 vols (Ithica, New York 1969), vol III, p153.

part of this strategy, cruisers such as *Alabama*, *Nashville*, and *Shenandoah* were to attack and destroy Union shipping in order to divert naval vessels from the blockade. The Confederate navy made no serious effort to challenge Union naval superiority at sea. Its primary objectives were simply to prevent the capture of key points within the Confederacy and to hold or re-open the major ports to foreign commerce. In order to accomplish these objectives, the Confederate government had to create a navy.

The Confederate navy, established in February 1861, inherited five small vessels from the seceded states. In addition, four revenue cutters, three slavers, two privately owned coastal steamers, and *Fulton*, an old side-wheeler laid up in the Pensacola Navy Yard, Florida, were purchased or seized. As a stop-gap measure the Navy Department continued purchasing merchant steamers for conversion into warships, but Confederate Secretary of the Navy Stephen R Mallory determined to initiate a warship construction programme at home and abroad.

In May 1861 naval agents were sent to Great Britain and France to obtain vessels that could be used for commerce raiding. Later the department contracted for the construction of armoured warships in both countries. *Stonewall*, however, was the only one of these ironclads to reach Confederate hands. Built in France for the Confederacy, the French government's decision that she could not be turned over to the North American belligerent resulted in her sale to Denmark, which was at war with Prussia. Denmark, however, no longer had use for the ironclad (the conflict being then over) so her builders successfully turned her over to the Confederates. She reached Cuba in May 1865 only to discover that the Civil War was over.

Stonewall had a composite hull with a long ram bow. She was rigged as a brig with a bowsprit that could be run in. Armed with one 10in and four 6.4in Armstrong muzzle-loading rifles, *Stonewall* was considered a powerful warship, and could have done considerable damage to the Union if the war had not ended. She was sold to Japan after the war and served as *Kosetsu* and later *Adzuma*.

The most successful Confederate commerce raider was the Laird-built Alabama, *a conventional screw sloop with a stump barque rig (no topgallants). She was armed with one Blakely 100pdr (6.4in) MLR and one 68pdr smooth bore on pivots, and six broadside 32pdrs. In the famous battle off Cherbourg, shown here in a contemporary engraving, USS* Kearsarge's *two 11in Dahlgrens gave her the advantage, although the ships were reasonably well matched in most respects.*

Commerce cruisers

The Confederates were more successful with their wooden commerce cruisers. During the war agents of the Southern government purchased or contracted abroad for eighteen vessels that were designated or intended to be cruisers. Seven became operational as raiders (*Alabama*, *Chickamauga*, *Georgia*, *Florida*, *Rappahannock*, *Shenandoah*, and *Tallahassee*). The remainder became blockade runners, were seized by the British and French governments, or were not completed during the war. *Alabama* was the most successful of the Confederate cruisers obtained in Europe.

Constructed by Laird's shipyard in Birkenhead as hull number 290, and armed with one 6.4in Blakely rifled muzzle-loader, one 68pdr and six 32pdr smooth bores, *Alabama* destroyed more than sixty merchant ships during her spectacular career. She was barque rigged with a single screw propeller. In June 1864 the Confederate warship was sunk after an engagement with the USS *Kearsarge* off Cherbourg, France.

Commerce cruisers were also converted from merchant ships or built within the Confederate states. In addition to a large number of privateers that operated during the early months of the war, four vessels were fitted out as raiders – *Clarence*, captured by *Florida*, *Tuscaloosa*, fitted out by *Alabama*, *Nashville*, and *Sumter*. *Sumter* was actually the first Confederate cruiser. Originally the barque rigged steamer *Habana* she was converted into a commerce raider and sailed from New Orleans, Louisiana, in June 1861. During her brief career, she captured eighteen prizes.[20]

---

20. Georges W Dazell, *The Flight From the Flag* (Chapel Hill, NC 1940), pp30–63.

21. William N Still, Jr, *Confederate Shipbuilding* (Columbia, South Carolina 1987), pp13–14.

Wooden gunboats

Although no cruisers were constructed within the Confederacy, a large number of wooden gunboats were contracted for. These gunboats can be placed into three broad categories: (1) a group of at least four side-wheel steamers; (2) three classes of steam screw vessels designed by Confederate Chief Naval Constructor John L Porter; and (3) the so-called Maury gunboats, a class of small vessels conceived by Matthew Fontaine Maury, former oceanographer in the United States Navy.[21]

The first group to be laid down were the four side-wheel gunboats, *Bienville*, *Carondelet*, *Gaines*, and *Morgan*. The first two were built near New Orleans and destroyed to prevent their capture by Farragut's fleet in the spring of 1862. *Gaines* and *Morgan* were constructed at Mobile, Alabama, and were units of the Mobile Squadron. Armament varied but in August 1864 *Morgan* carried one 7in and one 6in rifle and four 32pdr smooth bores. Records of their performance are scarce, although they seem to have been capable of 10kts. The evidence, however, indicates that the two engines on each vessel were too weak. Nevertheless both vessels fought well in the Battle of Mobile Bay against a much superior Union force. *Gaines* was run aground and *Morgan* continued to participate in the defences of Mobile until that port was surrendered in May 1865.

The most extensive of all the Confederate navy's shipbuilding programmes was the one conceived by Commander Maury. Since the early 1840s Maury had been advocating a navy based on the premise that large numbers of small, light draught gunboats, quickly and cheaply produced, were equal or superior to large warships carrying the same number and type of armament. He was also convinced that the South lacked the facilities needed to build large warships, including armourclads. The famed

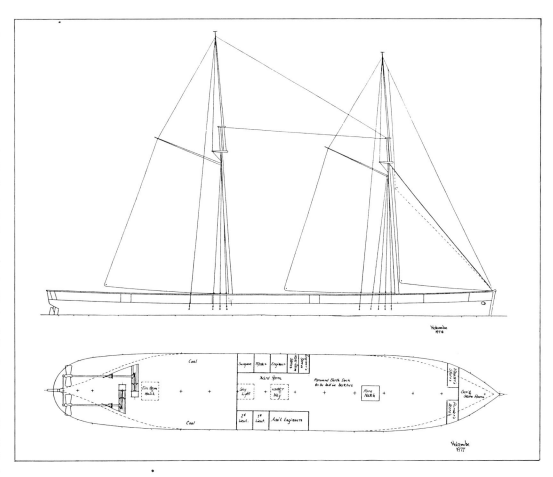

oceanographer estimated that one of his proposed wooden gunboats could be built in a few weeks for approximately $10,000. Largely because of Maury's popularity and political influence the Confederate Congress passed a bill in December 1861 authorising the construction of 100 such gunboats.

The design as adopted called for a screw propelled gunboat measuring 106ft long overall, 21ft in beam, 8ft in depth, and drawing 6½ ft of water. Reminiscent of Thomas Jefferson's gunboat policy in the early 1800s, Maury's vessels would have 'neither cabin, nor steerage, nor any accommodation on board'. They were to carry two guns, a rifled 32pdr forward and a 9in Dahlgren smooth bore aft. Fifteen were laid down and five completed; the remainder were burned on the stocks.[22] The five completed were *Hampton*, *Nansemond*, *Drewry*, *Isondiga*, and *Torch*. The first three were built in Norfolk, Virginia, and the remaining two in Savannah, Georgia.

There were variations in the design: length and breadth varied from 106ft to 116ft, and 18ft to 21ft respectively. Two of the fifteen laid down were also sail rigged. The Maury gunboats were too small to act effectively as gunboats, but they performed creditably as auxiliary vessels, serving as tenders for the ironclads.

Ten of the Porter design gunboats were built; one of 110ft, two of 130ft, and seven of 150ft length. They were all built on a 10ft depth of hold and were both sail and steam powered. The two largest classes were to be equipped with twin screws; the number of screws intended for the smaller class is not known.[23] The 150ft *Macon* class was apparently intended for mass building by the Confederate government. As with nearly all of the classes of vessels built by the Confederacy, the machinery for this class varied from vessel to vessel depending upon what was available. *Macon's* two engines, for example, were horizontal, direct acting, and condensing. The horsepower for *Macon* is not known. The same is true of armament. *Macon's* battery consisted of four smooth bore 32pdrs and two rifled 32pdrs, while *Peedee*, a second vessel in this class, mounted one 7in rifle, one 6.4in rifle, and one 9in smooth bore.

The Porter designed wooden gunboats provided useful service during the Civil War. Although information is scarce, they appear to have performed well in an auxiliary capacity as picket boats, patrol craft, and in support of the armoured vessels. However, far more information is known about the Confederate ironclads.

Armoured vessels

On 9 May 1861 the Confederate Secretary of the Navy Stephen Mallory wrote in an oft quoted report: 'I regard the possession of an iron armoured ship as a matter of the first necessity . . . inequality of numbers may be compensated by invulnerability; and thus not only does economy but naval success dictate the wisdom and expediency of fighting with iron against wood.' That same day the Confederate Congress appropriated $2 million for the purchase or construction of ironclads in Europe. Although the Confederacy would contract for several powerful armoured vessels in Britain and France, initial efforts were unsuccessful, so Secretary Mallory determined to construct ironclads within the Confederacy. In the middle of July 1861 the decision was made to convert *Merrimack* into *Virginia*, and six weeks later contracts were awarded for the construction of two ironclads later named *Arkansas*

and *Tennessee* to be built at Memphis; a fourth, *Mississippi*, was to be built at New Orleans. In September *Louisiana* was also laid down in New Orleans. These five initial ironclads were all unusually large and were designed to operate on the open sea as well as on inland waters. These vessels were designed not only to break the blockade, but as Secretary Mallory wrote, to 'traverse the entire coast of the United States . . . and encounter, with a fair prospect of success, their entire Navy'. In other words, Mallory's initial ironclad strategy was offensive in nature.[24]

The strategy was a failure. Only three of the vessels, *Arkansas*, *Louisiana*, and *Virginia* became operational; the other two were destroyed while still under construction. Of the three that were commissioned only *Arkansas* was used for offensive purposes. During her brief career, she achieved some dramatic suc-

22. Robert Holcombe, 'Big guns and Little Ships: The Confederate Navy's Maury Gunboat Program', unpublished MS, Confederate Naval Museum, Columbus, Georgia.

23. Robert Holcombe, 'The Macon Class', unpublished MS, Confederate Naval Museum, Columbus, Georgia, p4.

24. William N Still, Jr, *Iron Afloat: The Story of the Confederate Armorclads* (Columbia, South Carolina 1985), pp10–11.

cess, despite her poor design and construction. She was 165ft in length and carried a battery of ten guns. Her armour was made up of railroad T-section rails, and she was powered by inadequate river boat machinery. The casemate, unlike those found on the other Confederate ironclads, was perpendicular rather than slanted. On 25 July 1862 this awkward looking warship ran through a large fleet of Union vessels anchored above Vicksburg and successfully resisted several planned attacks to destroy her. In August she was to participate in a combined operation on Baton Rouge, Louisiana, but because of a breakdown in her machinery the ironclad was blown up by her crew.

Louisiana's career was brief, and less successful. As envisioned by her builder, E C Murray, the armourclad was to be 264ft in length, 64ft in beam, with a battery of twenty-two guns and propelled by two paddle wheels and two 4ft propellers. The most unorthodox feature in his design were twin wheels on the centreline, one abaft the other in a well. She was still being fitted out when Admiral Farragut's squadron began its ascent of the Mississippi river. The large Confederate ironclad was towed down the river and moored near Fort Jackson. Here as a floating battery she engaged the Union vessels and was destroyed by her crew when the fort surrendered.

Virginia achieved the most notable success of the initial ironclads. She was converted from the captured and partially destroyed screw frigate *Merrimack* at the Gosport Navy Yard in Norfolk. She is frequently considered to be the prototype of all the Confederate ironclads, but in fact was an experimental vessel and constructed only because the Confederacy needed to get a powerful ironclad operational as quickly as possible in that part of the South.

Armed with two 7in Brooke rifles, two 6.4in Brooke rifles, six 9in Dahlgren smooth bores and two 12pdr smooth bore howitzers, the transformed *Merrimack* had a casemate or armoured superstructure 170ft long at its base,

with the ends horizontally rounded. The upper deck of the casemate was an iron grating 2in thick. Conical pilothouses of cast iron were superimposed on each end of the upper deck. The armour, rolled from railroad iron into plates, was attached in two layers, the first course running horizontally, and the second vertically. The rounded ends along with the bow and stern of the hull being submerged were unique; no other Confederate ironclad incorporated these features. She had weaknesses as do most experimental ships, the most serious in the case of *Virginia* being her powerplant. Her engines were the same ones that had been on *Merrimack* and were too weak for a wooden frigate much less a heavily armoured ship. Her speed was generally 6kts and 8kts at maximum. The steerage was so poor that it took from thirty to forty minutes to turn 180 degrees. On 8 March 1862 she attacked units of the Union North Atlantic blockading squadron in Hampton Road, Virginia, and destroyed the frigate *Congress* and the sloop of war *Cumberland*. The following day she fought *Monitor* and for over a month successfully defended the entrance to the James river. Early in May, Norfolk, Virginia, was captured; with no base and a draught too deep to ascend the James, the ironclad was destroyed by her crew.

By 1862 the Confederate Secretary of the Navy had given up his determination to build large seagoing ironclads within the Confederacy and instead decided to concentrate on small, shallow draught, harbour defence, armoured vessels. There are various factors to explain this change in policy: the apparent unseaworthiness of *Virginia* and the ironclads build in New Orleans and Memphis, the pressing need for defensive vessels, and the belief that the South would be able to obtain powerful seagoing armoured vessels in Europe. Approximately forty of these small, harbour defence ironclads were laid down within the

Confederacy and half of them were completed.[25]

These small defence ironclads were designed by naval constructor John Porter. He developed a standard design which was sent to builders and contractors throughout the Confederacy. The original plan was for a 150ft flat-bottomed vessel with hull to be partially armoured and casemate to be completely covered with iron armour. The ironclad would carry a battery of six guns and be screw propelled. Although this design was utilised by the shipbuilders, it is, nevertheless, almost impossible to generalise about the Confederate armourclads. There were noticeable differences, because of modifications in size, machinery, armour, and battery. In size they ranged from *Albemarle* and *Neuse* (139ft) up to several under construction during the latter months of the war that were over 250ft in length. The 310ft *Nashville* was the largest of this type.

The thickness of armour measured from 2in to 8in, but all of it was 2in laminated iron plate. On several vessels such as *Arkansas* and *Louisiana* railroad iron (T-bars) was substituted because rolled plates were not available. The marine engines and boilers varied from ship to ship. Some of them were manufactured in the South; more of them were salvaged from other vessels. The method of propulsion consisted of either wheel or screw or a combination of both, as in *Louisiana* (two wheels and two screws). A majority of them were screw steamers with either one or two propellers, but several such as *Nashville* and *Missouri* were paddle-wheelers because of the availability of that kind of machinery. The machinery and propulsion units were notoriously inadequate and inefficient.

The Confederacy had more success in arming its ironclads than in providing motive power for them. There was really never a shor-

25. *Ibid*, pp79–85.

Most Confederate ironclads bore a strong family resemblance – a hull of very little freeboard surmounted by a slanting armoured casemate – but the industrial shortcomings of the Southern States meant that they varied in size, machinery, armament and armour. This drawing shows the Fredericksburg, *one of the shallow draught Porter design, armed with four guns – an 8in MLR forward and a 11in smooth bore aft (both could be traversed for axial or broadside fire through appropriate ports), plus two 6.4in rifles on the broadside. The ship was completed in early 1864 and, after an active career on the James river, was burned to avoid capture in April 1865.*

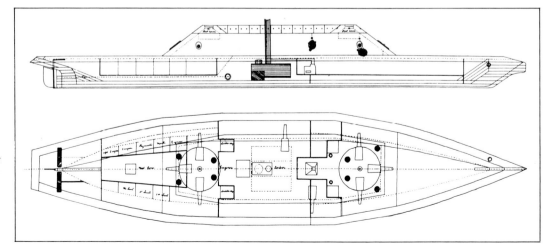

At 1273 tons the Tennessee *was the largest completed Confederate ironclad and was armed with two traversing 7in and four broadside 6in Brooke RMLs. The ships's short career climaxed at the Battle of Mobile Bay, where she fought against overwhelming odds for three hours until surrendering after the funnel and steering chains were shot away. The latter were exposed on deck, protected only by shallow troughs – a decided design weakness. This engraving shows the variety of Union vessels involved, which included the sloops* Hartford *(Farragut's flagship),* Monongahela *and* Lackawanna, *the double-turret monitors* Chickasaw *and* Winnebago, *and the* Canonicus *class* Manhattan. *Although the ships are bunched for artistic effect, the closeness of the action is not exaggerated.*

tage of heavy guns although some of the ships' initial batteries consisted of a variety of guns. Smooth bores were carried at one time or another by nearly all of the armourclads, but in contrast to the Union navy, which advocated them during and after the war, the Confederate navy concentrated on rifled guns.

The 150ft *Richmond*, laid down at the Navy Yard in Norfolk and completed in Richmond, was the first of Porter's harbour defence vessels to be commissioned. She was armed with four 7in Brooke rifles and two 9in smooth bores. Other 150ft ironclads included *Chicora*, *Raleigh*, *Palmetto State*, *North Carolina*, *Huntsville*, *Tuscaloosa*, and *Savannah*. Larger vessels included *Jackson* (*Muscogee*), *Fredericksburg*, and *Milledgeville* (175ft); *Virginia II*, and *Charleston* (180ft): *Missouri* (183ft); *Columbia*, *Texas*, and *Tennessee* (216ft); and *Nashville* (310ft). Porter also designed a smaller vessel of this type to be used in the North Carolina sounds. Only two of these 139ft ironclads, *Albemarle* and *Neuse*, were completed.

Although the casemated ironclad remained the standard 'home water' vessel constructed within the Confederacy, two double-ended ironclads with a pair of octagonal casemates were laid down in Richmond and Wilmington. They were similar in appearance to the Union 'double-turreted' monitors, but since the case-

mates were not moveable turrets, pivot guns were to be utilised. Neither vessel was completed because of the lack of iron armour. No monitor types were constructed in the Confederacy, although one to be built at Columbus, Georgia, was approved. The proposed vessel was apparently never laid down, since Secretary of the Navy Mallory preferred the standard casemated ironclad. Less than two months before General Lee surrendered at Appomattox Court House, the Secretary was writing:

> for river, harbor, and coast defense, the sloping shield and general plan of armored vessels adopted by us . . . are the best that could be adopted in our situation. In ventilation, light, fighting space, and quarters is believed that the sloping shield presents greater advantages than the *Monitor* turret.

The ironclads did contribute significantly to the Confederate war effort. They did not break or seriously challenge the Union blockade, but after the spring of 1862, this was not their primary objective. From then until the end of the war their primary objective was to defend the rivers, inlets, and ports. In this they had some success. Of the five seaports – Savannah, Charleston, Wilmington, Mobile, and Gal-

veston – taken in the last six months of the war, two were taken by land forces from the rear and two indirectly as a result of pressure from the rear. In all of the cities but one, Galveston, the Confederate navy had ironclads as part of the harbour defence. Nevertheless, they had serious defects in design and construction. The fundamental problems of weight, speed, seaworthiness, and mechanical inadequacies were never solved.

Armourclads used during the American Civil War were inferior to their European counterparts. For example, the armour plate on Confederate and Union vessels was laminated, usually 2in in thickness, while by 1865 British mills were rolling plate as much as 12in thick.

In ship design the US Navy continued its opposition to seagoing armoured ships and until the 1880s the *Monitor* type remained the standard armoured vessel primarily because of the emphasis on a strategy of coastal defence. It was not the raft-like monitor nor the casemated ironclad, but the large, high freeboard, centreline, multiple turret, armoured ship that was the forerunner of the modern capital ship. Modern warship design was primarily a result of developments in Europe.

William N Still

American Civil War: Typical Ships 1861–1865

Ship or class	Type	Displacement (normal) (tons)	Dimensions (loa × breadth × depth in hold) (feet–inches) (metres)	Armament	Machinery	Speed (max design kts)	Launch dates	Numbers built
Union Navy **UNADILLA**	'90-day gunboat'	691	156–4 × 28–0 × 12–0 *47.6 × 8.5 × 3.7*	1–11in Dahlgren SB 2–24pdr, 1–20pdr RML	2–cyl RCR, 380–400nhp, 1 shaft	10	1861–62	23
PEQUOT	Gunboat	836	171–6 × 29–0 × 12–0 *52.3 × 8.8 × 3.7*	1–150pdr RML, 2–32pdr SB, 1–30pdr RML	Wright segmental, 1 shaft	12	1868–64	8

Ship or class	Type	Displace-ment (normal) (tons)	Dimensions (loa × breadth × depth in hold) (feet–inches) (metres)	Armament	Machinery	Speed (max design kts)	Launch dates	Numbers built
PORT ROYAL	Side-wheel 'double-ender'	1163	207–0 pp × 34–4 × 11–6 63.1 × 10.5 × 3.5	1–100pdr RML, 6–24pdr SB, 1–10in shell	1–cyl IDA, 630ihp, side-wheels	11	1861–62	12
SASSACUS	Side-wheel 'double-ender'	1173	236–0 × 35–0 × 12–0 71.9 × 10.7 × 3.7	2–100pdr RML, 4–9in SB, 2–24pdr SB howitzers	1–cyl IDA, 1468ihp, side-wheels	14	1862–63	28
MOHONGO	Side-wheel 'double-ender'	1370	255–0 × 25–0 × c12–0 77.7 × 7.6 × c3.7	2–100pdr RML, 4–9in SB	1–cyl IDA, 850ihp side-wheels	12	1864–65	7
SACRAMENTO	Screw sloop	2100	229–0 × 38–0 × 17–0 69.8 × 11.6 × 5.2	1–150pdr RML, 2–11in SB, 1–30pdr RML	2–cyl RCR, 1304ihp, 1 shaft	12	1862	4
CAIRO	River ironclad ('Pook turtle')	512	175–0 × 51–2 × 6–0 53.3 × 15.6 × 1.8	4–42pdr RML, 3–8in SB, 6–32pdr SB	2 high pressure NC, centre-wheel	8	1861	7
NEW IRONSIDES	Broadside ironclad	3486	230–0 × 57–6 × 23–0 70.1 × 17.5 × 7.0	14–11in SB, 2–150pdr RML, 2–50pdr RML	2 HDA, 700ihp, 1 shaft	7	1862	1
GALENA	Ironclad	950 as built 738 (1863)	210–0 × 36–11 × 12–8 64.0 × 12.2 × 3.8	2–100pdr RML, 4–9in SB	2–cyl Ericsson VL, 320ihp, 1 shaft	8	1862	1
MONITOR	Monitor	987	170–0 × 41–0 × 10–6 52.4 × 12.5 × 3.2	2–11in Dahlgren SB	2–cyl Ericsson VL, 320ihp, 1 shaft	6	1862	1
PASSAIC	Monitor	1875	200–0 × 46–0 × 10–6 70.0 × 14.0 × 3.2	1–15in, 1–11in Dahlgren SB	2–cyl Ericsson VL, 320ihp, 1 shaft	7	1862–63	10
ONONDAGA	Twin turret monitor	2551	228–0 × 52–9 × 12–10 69.5 × 16.1 × 3.9	1–15in SB, 1–150pdr RML in each of 2 turrets	4–cyl HRCR, 640ihp, 2 shafts	7	1863	1
TECUMSEH	Monitor	1034 2100	223–0 × 43–8 × 13–6 68.0 × 13.3 × 4.1	2–15in Dahlgren SB	2–cyl Ericsson VL, 320ihp, 1 shaft	8	1863–64	9
DICTATOR	Monitor	4438	312–0 × 50–0 × 20–6 95.1 × 15.2 × 6.2	2–15in Dahlgren SB	2–cyl Ericsson VL, 3500ihp, 1 shaft	9	1863	1
OSAGE	River monitor	523	180–0 × 45–0 × 4–6 54.9 × 13.7 × 1.4	2–11in Dahlgren SB	2 horizontal NC, stern-wheel	7.5	1863	2
MILWAUKEE	River monitor	1300	229–0 × 56–0 × 6–0 dr 69.8 × 17.1 × 1.8	4–11in Dahlgren SB in two turrets	4 horizontal NC, 4 shafts	9	1863–64	4
Confederate Navy STONEWALL	Armoured ram	900	187–0 × 32–8 × 14–4dr 57.0 × 10.0 × 4.4	1–10in (300pdr) RML, 2–6.4in (70pdr) RML	2 HDA, 1200ihp, 2 shafts	10	1864	1
ALABAMA	Screw sloop	1050	220–0 × 31–8 × 14–0 dr 67.1 × 9.7 × 4.3	1–6.4in (110pdr) RML, 1–68pdr SB, 6–32pdr SB	HDA condensing, 300ihp, 1 shaft	13	1862	1
MORGAN	Side-wheel gunboat	863	202–0 × 38–0 × 13–0 61.6 × 11.6 × 4.0	1–7in RML, 1–6in RML, 4–32pdr SB	2 high pressure, side-wheels	10	1862	2
HAMPTON	Screw gunboat	166	106–0 × 21–8 × 5–0 dr 32.3 × 6.6 × 1.5	2 guns	2 HDA, 1 shaft	?	1862	5
VIRGINIA	Ironclad		262–9 × 38–6 × 22–0 dr 80.1 × 11.7 × 6.7	2–7in RML, 2–6.4in RML, 6–9in SB, 2–12pdr howitzers	2–cyl HRCR, 1 shaft	7	1862	1
RICHMOND	Harbour defence ironclad		150–0 × 34–0 × 14–0 dr 45.7 × 10.4 × 4.3	4–7in Brooke RML, 2–9in SB	2 engines, type unknown	6	1862	1

Notes:

Length is overall, except pp = between perpendiculars. Depth is in hold, except dr = mean draught. Armament: most Union RMLs were Parrott guns and most SBs Dahlgrens; the Confederate guns were usually of the Brooke pattern, both RML and SB. Machinery abbreviations: (H)RCR = (horizontal) return connecting rod, also called back-acting; NC = non-condensing; IDA = inclined direct acting; HDA = horizontal direct acting; VL = vibrating lever.

5

The Era of Uncertainty 1863–1878

DURING this period in Britain warship design became a matter of public concern. There were innumerable articles and pamphlets supporting one side or the other in the many controversies of the day and debate both in Parliament and in learned Institutions was keen, even heated. For the first time, public opinion could influence the Board through the press and Parliament. Much of this debate was ill-informed as, over a short period, subjects including stability, rolling, powering and structural strength became scientific disciplines rather than matters of opinion. There were strong personalities involved whose views and conflicts were important.

The latter part of the period was dominated by the aftermath of the loss of HMS *Captain* and unjustified fears for the safety of very different ships. Parliamentary Committees examined every aspect of warship design thoroughly and, as regards detail, competently, but their broader view of the role of the warship was naive. Throughout the era there was little serious thinking or discussion on the purpose of the navy and the way ships would be handled in battle and, in consequence, the requirements for individual ships were not soundly based. In many cases a British warship would be designed simply to be 'better' than some new foreign ship. British technical leadership was such that it is appropriate for this chapter to focus on developments in the Royal Navy, discussing overseas work where they were ahead or influenced British design.

It is interesting to note that during this era there were many occasions in which the head of the design department was credited with the work of a brilliant assistant; often, the assistant's reward would be to become the next head.

As outlined in Chapter 3, *Gloire* and *Warrior* initiated a race between guns of rapidly increasing size and power with armour to match that power. Since iron plates weigh 40 pounds for every square foot per inch of thickness and there are many square feet in the side of a battleship, it is clear that thick armour had to be severely limited in extent. This led to a rapid rise in the individual cost of ships which, with successive governments dedicated to economy, led inevitably to a decrease in numbers of ships. The pace of change led to rapid obsolescence adding further to the cost of owning a modern navy.

Development was not a steady progression; great leaps forward were accompanied by industrious exploration of blind alleys, even the best of designs had concealed flaws while lesser ships might still have features worth developing. The division into categories of the following sections is arbitrary and there is sometimes a considerable overlap in time between them.

Reed and the experimental period, 1863–70

Isaac Watts retired as Chief Constructor in 1863 and the First Lord, the Duke of Somerset, chose Edward J Reed as his successor. Reed had had a very unusual career and the appointment was far from universally welcomed. As an apprentice, he won a scholarship to the Central School of Mathematics and Naval Architecture in 1848 where many of those who were to become his assistants in later years were his classmates. After graduating, he found his work and prospects were frustrating and he resigned to become editor of *Mechanics' Magazine* and later Secretary of the Institution of Naval Architects (INA). While so employed, he offered some

The inexorable drive towards heavier and more powerful guns meant that fewer would be mounted, and since armour needed to be thicker to counter the new weapons, weight restricted the area that could be protected. One logical answer was an armoured box battery, a concept first tried in the Royal Navy with the small ironclad sloops Research *and* Enterprise. *Reed, the originator of this layout, designed an ironclad corvette which the Admiralty accepted in 1863 and ordered as the* Pallas. *As shown here, the ship carried four 7in muzzle-loaders in a central battery, with the hull cut away fore and aft of it to allow some axial fire, but there were also single 7in breech-loaders in the bow and stern as chase guns.* (CMP)

designs to the Admiralty and in 1862 was brought into the Admiralty to develop his ideas for armoured sloops.

These three conversions showed several features which were typical of Reed designs. They all had a narrow 4½in belt to protect the waterline throughout its length and a small number of heavy (100pdr smooth bore) guns concentrated in a short, armoured battery with ingenious arrangements to give the end guns a wider arc of fire towards the axis of the ship. Technically, Reed deserves great credit for these ships as he proved it possible to build armoured ships much smaller than previously believed possible, though they lacked a clear role.

Two more studies were developed after he became Chief Constructor. The first of these became *Pallas*, similar to his conversions, with a wooden hull but a reduced length:beam ratio and confirming that very small armoured vessels had no operational value. They were the first real designs with which Reed had been associated and he no doubt learnt much both about design and the workings of the Admiralty.

As Chief Constructor, Reed was responsible for the last three ironclads converted from the wooden steam battleships of the *Duncan* class. These too had a waterline belt and a box battery with a small number of heavy guns. Though these and Watts' four earlier wooden hulled broadside ironclads were always, rightly, seen as second rate compared with the iron hulled ships, they were fully the equal of *Gloire* and the fifteen other French wooden ships. A wooden hull is not suitable to carry the concentrated weight of heavy guns and armour, particularly when exposed to the vibration of early propulsion plants.

Reed also designed *Lord Warden* and *Lord Clyde*, often described as the heaviest wooden ships ever built. The main purpose was to use some of the stock of seasoned timber held in the Royal Dockyards and their design style was akin to Watts' ships with twenty-four 7in MLR (muzzle-loading rifles) and overall armour. Their hull construction was unusual, comprising an iron skin over their oak frames, then a 6in backing to their 5½in armour with, overall, a Muntz metal sheath, insulated by a layer of wood.

Since most of the loads in a seaway would be taken by the iron skin it does not seem correct to refer to them as wooden ships though they did reduce timber stocks. The iron skin must have given their builders, Pembroke and Chatham Dockyards, valuable experience in iron shipbuilding.

Centre battery ships

Bellerophon was more representative of Reed's ideas, derived from the sketch which he produced before he joined the Admiralty and he was rightly proud of her. The central battery mounted ten 9in MLR and, being short, could be protected with 6in plates.

The loads on the structure are less on a shorter ship leading to a lighter structure and, though this could still not be quantified, it was understood in general terms. As a result, due to her different proportions and a somewhat more efficient structure, *Bellerophon*'s structure was about 1000 tons lighter than that of *Warrior*. The shorter ship also handled better, aided by her balanced rudder, which needed only eight men to operate (in bad weather, *Minotaur* needed up to seventy-eight men).

Table 5/1: Turning Circles

	Diameter (yds)	Time taken (minutes–seconds)
Warrior	760	7–46
Bellerophon	378	4–54

It was believed at the time that length was needed to obtain high speed but Froude was to show a few years later that it only applied to faster ships than *Bellerophon*. Reed had been prepared to accept a penalty in power for his shorter ship and it would seem that he was pleasantly surprised that the penalty was so small. On the measured mile *Warrior* made 14.1kts with 5267ihp while *Bellerophon* needed 6521ihp for 14.2kts. At lower speeds the difference was much less, as shown by their fuel consumption with similar Penn trunk engines.

Table 5/2: Fuel Consumption

	Coal (tons)	Distance travelled (nm)
Warrior	800	2100
Bellerophon	560	1970

Bellerophon's structure was on what Reed called the 'Bracket Frame' system, probably devised by Barnaby. Reed was fully entitled to take credit for this work as he would have been blamed for any failure. Compared with *Warrior*, the double bottom was extended round the turn of the bilge with five deep longitudinal girders either side joining the inner and outer bottoms. The transverse frames were further apart and built as separate, intercostal 'brackets' between the longitudinals.

A feature of Reed's centre battery ships was their relative shortness which made them manoeuvrable when steaming, but few were good under sail. This is Sultan *using both steam and sail. This ship had a second armoured battery at upper deck level, which can be seen projecting beneath the main shrouds. (CMP)*

Table 5/3: Hull Weight

	Weight (tons)	% Dspt	Hull wt × 1000 / (L × B × Depth)
Warrior	4970	53	6.4
Bellerophon	3652	49	5.3

The last column is quite a useful parameter for comparing structural weight and shows that Reed and Barnaby had made a considerable advance in the design of an efficient structure.

The timber backing to the armour was reduced to 10in with longitudinal iron girders, 2ft apart, running through it. The shell plating behind the armour was 1½in thick, and was intended to stop splinters (from shell or shot that had been broken in piercing the armour) from entering the hull, though it reduced her potential weight advantage over *Warrior*.

The next ship, *Hercules*, designed in 1865, carried eight of the new 10in MLR (18-ton), which fired a 400lb projectile. It was claimed that a round could be fired every 70 seconds. Recessed ports for the end guns of the battery enabled them to fire on the quarters but axial fire at bow and stern was from a single, lightly protected 9in and two unprotected 7in. Great efforts were made in many centre battery ships to enable some guns to fire fore and aft along the axis using recessed sides. It is most unlikely that such schemes were effective as the blast from the short guns of the day would cause serious damage to the structure. She had 9in armour on the battery and for the belt amidships, reduced to 6in at the ends. Tests on a replica at Shoeburyness showed it could resist a 600lb shot.

The French contemporaries, Dupuy de Lôme's *Océan* class, still had wooden hulls but introduced the barbette mounting. In this mount, the gun was on a turntable, inside a fixed ring of armour over which it fired. This enabled the guns to be carried high up with a good command and theoretical axial fire, though at some risk of damage to the structure. *Océan* carried four 9.4in guns in barbettes above the corners of a battery carrying four 10.8in guns. The crew of early barbettes were

In 1867 four smaller ironclads of the Audacious *class were authorised. Designed for service on Britain's foreign stations, they had a shallow draught and emphasised seakeeping and the steadiness of a good gun platform. This is* Invincible, *probably in the early 1870s after the full ship rig had been reduced to a barque. The double height battery is visible amidships; the topside is recessed fore and aft of the upper deck casemate.* (CMP)

exposed to small arms fire but methods were devised for loading under cover and shields fitted to protect the exposed crew, though they remained unprotected from shells bursting below the barbette.

Hercules was the model for *Sultan*, laid down in 1865, in which an upper deck battery provided a degree of end-on fire. Much later, under Barnaby, this style was further developed in *Alexandra*, laid down in 1873. She carried two 11in MLR and ten 10in in a double-tiered battery. The upper layer had 8in armour, the lower 10in with a 12in belt, reduced to 6in at the ends. The sides were cut away fore and aft of the battery to give a geometrical possibility of axial fire but these embrasures threw up vast clouds of spray in a seaway making her very wet. These centre battery ships were all handsome vessels and well liked.

In 1867 the Admiralty, concerned over the growing number of big French armoured cruisers in distant waters, decided to build a number of smaller armoured ships. Reed's design for *Audacious* carried ten 9in in a double-tier battery with 6in armour and an 8in belt. The class was intended to have a shallow draught and it was not thought possible to put the power of 4800ihp through a single screw which would not project below the keel. They had two four-bladed screws which did not hoist and, in consequence, they were slow under sail, even though they had the highest ratio of sail area to displacement of any battleship.

Rolling in a seaway had been a matter of concern for some years since it would always make accurate gunnery difficult and, in extreme cases, could cause the ship to capsize. The interaction between irregular waves and a moving ship is extremely complex and, until

William Froude presented his theory to the INA in 1861, ideas on the subject were entirely wrong. In particular, he showed that the ship with least stability rolled least. 'Stability' is a word used to convey several very different meanings but, applied to ships, it should always be a measure of the forces tending to bring the ship upright when heeled. In the 1860s this was equated with the power to carry sail without excessive heel due to the wind which, for small angles of heel, is measured by the metacentric height (GM).

A rolling ship may be compared with a pendulum. If the pendulum is tapped regularly as it reaches the end of its swing, the angle through which it moves will increase rapidly and Froude showed that the same applied to ships; the action of waves occurring at its natural frequency of roll would cause the heaviest rolling.

Ships with a low metacentric height have long roll periods and long period waves are less common. More important, a stiff ship with a high GM and a correspondingly short period will build up roll more quickly. The roll angle may not be much more than that of a ship with a small GM but the roll will be more rapid, causing much greater sideways forces.

Reed was quick to realise the importance of Froude's work and intended the *Audacious* class to have a low GM with the centre of gravity raised by an upper deck battery, but the ships completed with a GM less than safe. This was shown by an inclining experiment which had only become a routine test in the previous few years, even though it had been known and used by the Royal Navy in the 1790s. In this experiment a weight is moved a known distance across the deck, giving a heeling moment which, when the ship is steady, is equal to the

Besides his work for the Royal Navy, Reed also designed warships for export, customers including Turkey, Japan and the rising power of Prussia – soon to be a unified Germany. The most powerful unit in the new German Navy was the König Wilhelm, *a central battery ironclad like the first generation of Reed ships, that was originally laid down as the Turkish* Fatikh *and purchased while still building at Thames Iron Works.* (CMP)

righting moment. The righting moment is the product of the displacement times the GM times the angle of heel giving the value of the GM. The GM of the *Audacious* class was corrected by adding ballast and they proved steady and safe in a seaway. One of them, *Vanguard*, was sunk by collision in 1875, but this was no reflection on her stability.

Two similar ships of the *Swiftsure* class, with deeper draught and a single screw were also built. They were copper sheathed to reduce the effect of fouling, with a double layer of wood to insulate the copper from the iron hull preventing electrolytic corrosion.

Finally among centre battery ships there was *Temeraire*, designed by Barnaby in 1873 as a result of a minority report of the Committee on Designs (see below). She mounted two 11in and four 10in MLR in a battery up to 11in thick. In addition, she had two more 11in (25-ton) guns on the upper deck, in barbettes, on hydraulic mountings, so that the guns were normally behind the armour ring and only briefly raised for firing. Though apparently successful, this arrangement was very heavy and was not repeated.

Structural strength

Up to the 1860s structural design had been on the basis of intelligent comparison with previous ships and there was usually a big factor of safety leading to a hull heavier than strictly necessary. Reed realised the need for a more scientific approach and initiated work by his staff, much of it being due to the young William White.

Even in calm water, the loading of weight and buoyancy will strain a ship. Some sections will have more weight than buoyancy and will try to move down relative to neighbouring sections with more buoyancy while still satisfying the overall law that weight equals buoyancy. The force due to this attempt at relative movement is known as shearing force and is resisted by the rigidity of the sides, so much greater in an iron, rivetted vessel than in a wooden, planked ship. When these forces are summed over the whole length of the ship they tend to bend her, known as the bending moment. The ends may droop, known as hogging, which puts the deck in tension and compresses the bot-

tom; or the ends may rise, sagging, which has the opposite effect on the structure.

In waves these forces and moments are much increased and alternate in direction, first stretching, then compressing deck and bottom. In general terms this behaviour was recognised at the turn of the century by designers such as Snodgrass and Seppings but the scientific basis was only stated by Rankine in 1866. Reed's work, presented to the Royal Society in 1871, extended and clarified the subject, setting the way in which it could be used in practice against the scientific background.

Turret ships

During the Crimean War Captain Cowper Coles had mounted a 68pdr on a raft for shore bombardment and had been impressed with the ease of training, using the raft as a turntable. After the war he persevered in the design of turntable mountings for heavy guns, leading to a design of turret or 'shield' as he called it. Initially, he also believed himself capable of designing the ships to carry his turrets and his heated advocacy of nonsensical designs, such as his eight-turret ship of 1859, led to a bitter feud with the constructors.

The value of the turret itself was in little doubt and a prototype carrying a single gun was built and fitted to the armoured battery *Trusty* in 1861. During trials it was shown that the turret mounting could fire 12 rounds in 6 minutes 5 seconds, nearly twice as fast as a similar gun on the broadside. The turret was

For really heavy guns the best compromise between protection and effectiveness was the revolving turret, which had been tried on HMS Trusty *even before the American Civil War tested the concept in action. The problem for a seagoing ship was how to combine the sailing rig that was still necessary for cruising range with clear arcs of fire. Early attempts to take the turret to sea were confined to coast defence ships which needed no rig. Britain's first turret ship was the* Royal Sovereign, *a radical conversion from a 121-gun three-decker that was completed with one twin and three single turrets on what had been the lower gundeck. The only rig was some fore and aft steadying canvas.* (CMP)

then fired on and hit by 29 rounds from 68pdrs and 110pdrs but was still able to train freely.

The Admiralty saw the next step as a coastal defence vessel and *Prince Albert* was designed by Watts and ordered in February 1862 to carry four 9in MLR in single turrets with a 4½in belt on a draught of 20ft. The turret was trained by hand, eighteen men being able to complete a revolution in a minute but these men were out of sight of the turret officer and control was difficult.

In April of the same year (1862), the Admiralty approved the conversion of the steam three-decker *Royal Sovereign* into an unrigged turret ship for coastal defence. She carried one twin and three single turrets with 10.5in SB (smooth bores) initially, later replaced by 9in MLR. The turret had 5½in armour over 14in of teak and a ½in skin with a further 4½in of iron on the face. Her draught of 25ft limited her value for her stated role of coastal defence. In 1866 *Bellerophon* fired three rounds from a 9in with 43lb charge at a range of 200yds against *Royal Sovereign*'s after turret. None of them interrupted the working of the turret but the one that hit the back disturbed a plate.

The Admiralty's appreciation of the value of turrets was reinforced in March 1862 when news of the action between USS *Monitor* and CSS *Virginia* reached England (described in Chapter 4). There were important differences between the Coles and Ericsson turrets; the former passed through the upper deck and was supported on rollers on the deck below while Ericsson's turret was supported on a central spindle and when not turning rested on the upper deck; it was turned by a steam engine.

There were still problems with an ocean-going turret ship as fuel consumption was still too high to do without sail for long passages while Reed, rightly, pointed out that the upper deck of a fully rigged ship with its innumerable ropes was not an ideal site for a turret. Coles believed that a solution was possible using tripod masts which would eliminate most of the standing rigging and the Admiralty lent him constructors to help him to develop his ideas. Coles then demanded that these design studies

be judged by a committee of seamen and shipbuilders with half nominated by him.

Understandably, the Board ignored this demand and appointed a committee of naval officers who came out in support of a rigged turret ship subject to certain conditions. This ship, *Monarch*, was designed by Reed in accordance with the committee's views, though he remained doubtful of the combination of turrets and full rig. He pointed out that *Hercules* carried the same number of guns on each broadside, though they were smaller (*Monarch* carried four 12in) and had thicker armour as well as being a better sailing ship.

Coles was also unhappy with the *Monarch*. He objected to her freeboard of 14ft and to the forecastle and poop which prevented axial fire but which Reed and naval officers thought essential to seakeeping. After further lobbying by Coles, the First Lord, the Duke of Somerset, against the advice of the Controller and Reed, decided that a rigged turret ship should be built in accordance with Coles' concept, to be designed and built by a shipbuilder which Coles could select from a short list of approved contractors. He chose Lairds who submitted proposals in July 1866 for both single- and twin-screw ships, the latter being preferred.

Reed's initial scrutiny, six days later, noted that the freeboard was only 8ft, which he accepted as the Board's direction. He thought at first that the weight and stability estimates were reasonable but after further checks wrote again on 24 July saying that the estimate of weights was too low and that the centre of gravity was likely to be much higher than Laird had assumed for they had not calculated this vital parameter. The Controller, Spencer Robinson, objected even more strongly, particularly to the low freeboard, but the First Lord approved the design on 23 July. His letter was to prove ambiguous saying that the design

was the 'entire responsibility' of Coles and Laird, though the Admiralty would oversee the workmanship and materials. It failed to make clear the conditions for acceptance after which the Admiralty would be responsible for her safety.

Captain was built in dry-dock and when she was floated out in March 1869 it was already clear that she was grossly overweight. While some overweight material was certainly worked into her, it is clear that the basic problem was the poor estimates made in the design stage by Lairds. It is quite wrong to suggest that the designers were let down by the builders. The designer is responsible both for accurate estimates and for seeing that the yard work was within those limits. *Captain* was not even built to the drawings; she completed 5in deeper than intended. Since, by then, she was 735 tons over weight, corresponding to a 22in loss of freeboard, that 5in extra freeboard was welcome, leaving her with a mere 6ft 7in. Admiralty weight estimates of the day were generally accurate.

Lairds had only completed their calculation for the position of the centre of gravity as the ship went to sea and, because she was of novel style, they recommended an inclining experiment. Their calculations belatedly confirmed Reed's view that the centre of gravity was higher than they had expected on the basis of their early, crude comparison. She won high praise as a steady gun platform during her first two voyages and was inclined at the end of the second.

Up to the late 1860s, it had been assumed that metacentric height, by itself, was a reliable measure of stability and of the risk of capsize. This was a reasonable generalisation for the traditional high-freeboard ships but could be very misleading for low freeboards. When a ship heels to large angles, particularly when the

Although Laird's had built two small masted turret ships for the Confederate States in 1865 (but sequestered by the British Government), the first truly seagoing turret ship was HMS Monarch. *In contrast to her ill-fated contemporary* Captain, *she was a high freeboard ship with good seakeeping qualities. The main features of the ship's main armament can be seen in this photograph of the upper deck – the four 12in MLRs in the two Coles turrets. Note the hurricane deck over turrets. (CMP)*

deck edge is immersed, the calculation of righting moment becomes much more difficult than assumed in the metacentric approach. Though the basic theory existed, the equations were very difficult to solve, but one of Reed's many bright young men, Barnes, derived a numerical method of solution which, though tedious in the extreme, could be applied to ships.

After *Captain* was inclined, while she was at sea, Barnes calculated her stability at large angles. He showed that the maximum value of the righting moment, which was small, occurred at only 21 degrees. Any steady heeling force, such as wind on the sails, which blew her past that angle would probably capsize her. Since these were virtually the first such calculations, no comparison was possible and the danger to *Captain* was not immediately apparent. While the significance of Barnes's results was under discussion, *Captain* was at sea with the fleet and the wind was rising. During 6 September 1870, she was sailing with the sea washing over the deck edge. Round about midnight the wind increased and shortly after she capsized with the loss of 473 men out of the 490 on board. Captain Coles was amongst those lost.

Reed had already resigned (9 July 1870) tired of the continual argument over the danger of low freeboard and other matters. Spencer Robinson, whose views were even more forthright, was forced to resign; Coles, whose intolerance started the tragedy though he was not responsible for the design of *Captain* or for the capsize, was dead; while Childers, the new First

Lord had lost his son in the disaster. The aftermath of the disaster involved many years of difficulty for the constructors' department as politicians and seamen failed to understand the root causes of the loss of *Captain* and were suspicious of all low freeboard ships. *Captain* was lost because of the combination of low freeboard and sailing rig, made worse by a lack of clear responsibility for the design which was carried out very superficially by Lairds. The subsequent court martial report and, even more, later accounts need to be read with extreme caution as virtually all gave evidence which was 'improved' over what they had said before the disaster.

Breastwork coastal defence ships

Reed's concern was over the rigged turret ship and he was greatly attracted by the style of Ericsson's *Monitor*, while recognising that that ship, too, had hazardous features. Her low freeboard led to a serious risk of flooding round the base of the turret or through hatches and ventilation openings. Reed, again, was right as the loss of *Monitor* off Cape Hatteras showed.

When, in 1867, the Australian colony of Victoria wanted a ship for the defence of Melbourne, Reed proposed a variant on the low freeboard ship which overcame the risk of flooding through openings. Above the low hull, which had 8in armour, he placed an armoured deckhouse, also 8in thick, which car-

ried the two twin 10in turrets and also all hatches and vent openings were run up through this 'breastwork'. *Cerberus* at 3340 tons was heavily armed and armoured and well suited to a role in which her most formidable opponent was likely to be an armoured cruiser. In *Cerberus* Reed had made a major step towards the modern battleship; her remains may still be seen at Melbourne.

Then, in 1868, the Board asked for the smallest possible low freeboard monitor to carry two 25-ton guns with 12in armour. *Glatton* was a small breastwork ship of 4910 tons with a draught of 19.5ft, making her unsuitable for coastal work. Her speed was 12kts in calm water with a freeboard of 3ft; this could be reduced to 2ft in action by flooding empty bunkers which carried 240 tons of coal when full. She rarely left the Solent, although once venturing as far as the Thames. The four ships of the *Cyclops* class resembled *Cerberus* with two twin 10in guns and 8in armour.

Rams

The mobility of the steam ship together with the claimed invulnerability of armoured vessels encouraged the use of ramming tactics. Most big armoured ships and many smaller vessels had strengthened bows, often projecting, to make them effective in ramming. It is strange that when most ships had their guns arranged for broadside fire, tacticians assumed they would fight end-on.

There were many attempts at ramming during the American Civil War (1861–65) and the few successes were widely publicised. The ram gained additional support from the sinking of two ships at the Battle of Lissa (1866). In addition, a number of important warships were accidentally sunk in collision which was read as supporting the case for ramming. In fact, the true conclusion was the opposite – ships whose manoeuvrability was too poor to avoid collision were unlikely to succeed in ramming an enemy trying to evade. Ramming was effective only against ships incapable of manoeuvre, usually stopped, and even then damage to the ramming vessel was often severe. As a means of

In any future naval war with Britain, French strategists expected the Royal Navy to try to enforce the kind of close blockade that was so successful in the Napoleonic period. Therefore the French navy showed an understandable interest in coast defence ships, including armoured rams and breastwork monitors. Tonnant, laid down in 1875, was a further variation on the theme – a low freeboard ship armed with two single 34cm in barbettes with thin shields over. (CMP)

Mastless turret ships

Reed's *Devastation* was a radical departure from previous designs of battleship, the first without sails. She was a much enlarged *Cerberus* with a very low freeboard hull cased in armour except for a shallow forecastle. Above the hull there was an armoured breastwork carrying the two twin 12in turrets. Between the turrets there was a tall and narrow superstructure, blossoming out into a hurricane deck with two funnels, ventilation openings and a conning tower.

The abolition of sails affected every aspect of the design; her complement was 358 instead of the 633 needed for *Sultan* of about the same size. The air resistance of masts, yards and rigging would reduce *Sultan*'s speed under steam by 1–2kts against a moderate head wind. Reed was quite right in claiming that the central battery system gave as good or better arcs of fire than those of a fully rigged turret ship, but with masts gone *Devastation*'s arcs were superb. Since the breastwork raised the turrets well above the forecastle and quarterdeck, the risk of blast damage was minimised and axial fire was a reality rather than the geometrical fiction of many earlier ships.

Devastation's turrets were 30.5ft in diameter

sinking ships by letting water in, the ram was superseded by the torpedo.

Though the case against ramming now seems overwhelming, it was strongly supported at the time by many naval officers and naval architects. The first attempt at a seagoing warship designed primarily as a ram was the French *Taureau*, designed by Dupuy de Lôme in 1863. On a displacement of 2433 tons she carried a 6in belt and a 2in deck over her wooden hull. There was a light turtle deck overall. She had a turning circle of 230yds and a speed of 12½kts but was a very bad sea-boat and rarely left harbour.

She was followed in 1865 by the four slightly larger ships of the *Cerbère* class (3523 tons), also wooden hulled and with a belt up to 8.7in but only a 0.6in deck. Their turning circle was about 310–370yds and they, too, were dreadful sea-boats.

Reed was an enthusiastic supporter of ramming and designed the Royal Navy's first ram in 1868. *Hotspur* was an iron hulled ship of 4000 tons with an 11in belt and a single 12in gun rotating inside a fixed, armoured pillbox. This gun could not be used on the all important forward bearings because of blast damage to the deck. She had a speed of 12.6kts and a turning circle of 400yds. The belt armour, 11in amidships and tapered to 8in at the ends, was swept down at the stem to support the ram. Her short hull and low freeboard led, inevitably, to poor seakeeping and, together with a small coal supply, meant that she was mainly used for harbour defence.

Rupert was intended to be a sister ship but

was redesigned to be much larger (5440 tons) with an 11in belt and a conventional turret mounting two 10in MLR. Again, the guns could not fire forward as a mast was positioned in front of the turret. Her speed was 12kts and she was wet in consequence of her low freeboard. Both *Hotspur* and *Rupert* were modernised, with improved gun armament, but their fighting value remained negligible.

The first captain of *Rupert* had much praise for his ship but suggested many ways in which a new design could be better and these suggestions were borne in mind when Barnaby designed *Conqueror* in 1878. She and her sister *Hero* were bigger ships at 6200–6400 tons with two 12in BL (breech-loaders) and a belt of up to 12in. They were also faster at 14kts, but the low freeboard limited their speed in all but a calm and they also rolled heavily. They went to sea very occasionally, but spent much of their long service alongside the dockyard wall.

The 1870s saw the British build a series of small, coast defence type vessels, some of which were equipped as rams. One of these was Rupert, *seen here in the late 1880s. (CMP)*

with the bottom of the gunports 13ft above the waterline and with 14in armour on the face. A steam engine trained the turret but loading and elevation was by hand, requiring a crew of twenty-two in each turret. Her sister ship, *Thunderer*, had the forward turret replaced soon after completion by one carrying the more powerful 38-ton gun. This was worked hydraulically; the muzzle-loading guns were depressed below the deck for loading using hydraulic rams. The turret crew was reduced to ten men.

The low freeboard was thought to increase the chance of being hit on deck and she was given 2–3in protection on the deck over the belt. The total weight of armour amounted to some 27 per cent of the displacement instead of 15–16 per cent as in earlier ships, possibly because of the weight saved by omitting sails. *Devastation* was also notable as the last battleship designed to be driven by the Penn trunk engine.

Devastation was still building when Reed resigned and Barnaby took over. In the near panic after *Captain* capsized, grave fears were expressed over her safety. Barnes's new stability curves showed that her maximum righting moment was much greater than that of *Captain* and even though it was reached at only a slightly greater angle, the new ship was safe since it was without the overturning force of wind on the masts and sails. However, the First Lord, without consulting the Chief Constructor, decided to extend the breastwork to the side and further aft with light structure

which, though not necessary for stability, did provide much needed accommodation space.

Devastation was designed to carry 1800 tons of coal, which would have enabled her to cross the Atlantic under steam, but she was overweight, partly in consequence of the extensions, and only 1400 were carried. Even so, trials showed she could steam for over 5000 miles at 10kts. Her freeboard at the bow was under 10ft, which made her incapable of steaming hard into head seas, but she took part in a number of comparative trials with more traditional ships and was thought to have done well.

Froude's paper of 1861 had set out the basic theory of rolling but there were a number of difficulties in applying this work, solved in a further series of papers. In 1871 he tested a number of different sizes and arrangements of bilge keels on a 9ft model of *Devastation*, first in still water and then in waves off Portsmouth. These tests gave overwhelming evidence of the value of deep bilge keels and, in later tests with an 18ft model in waves, an average roll of 20 degrees, with occasional capsizes, was reduced to 1–2 degrees by keels of equivalent to 6ft depth.

Later, *Devastation* herself was used for rolling trials which confirmed the model results. She was first rolled in still water when a roll of 7 degrees was built up by the action of 400 men running across her deck eighteen times. Later Froude obtained further measurements at sea in the Bay of Biscay using a most ingenious automatic recorder of his own design

(now displayed in the Science Museum, London). It should be noted that measurements with a simple pendulum will considerably exaggerate the rolling of a ship to an extent which depends on its position in the ship. The actual roll angle depends on the ship's course and speed relative to the waves and the roll angles quoted in contemporary reports mean very little.

Reed had designed a successor to be called *Fury* which was to be a little longer and, with more powerful machinery, a knot faster. The hull had been completed up to the bottom of the belt when *Captain* capsized and work was suspended. Various proposals were put to the Committee on Designs by Barnaby and others, most of which were accepted. *Fury* was not only redesigned but also given a new name, *Dreadnought*. Barnaby was given much less freedom in design than Reed at a time when the Board was even less clear on strategy, tactics and the type of warship needed. In consequence, Barnaby's designs are often criticised though they were just what he had been asked for. Arguments were bitter and with Barnaby married to Reed's sister, with Reed a near neighbour, it would seem that the disagreements continued, even at home.

The re-design of *Dreadnought* was carried out by White. The belt was increased to 14in and the breastwork armour was brought out to the side and also extended to bow and stern with the unarmoured structure giving considerably greater freeboard. Her engines were the first compounds fitted to a British battleship; they were three-cylinder, double expansion (split low-pressure). This considerably improved her fuel economy, coal consumption during the 6-hour trial averaging 2.27lbs per ihp per hour, compared with 3.14 for *Thunderer*. She, and *Alexandra*, were the first battleships with vertical cylinders, saving deck area and made possible by the thick armour which protected the tops of the cylinders.

Auxiliary power was also increased and it was said that, on completion, she had thirty-nine engines and, by 1876, she also had an electric searchlight. Unfortunately, she also introduced a centreline bulkhead in the machinery spaces,

Somewhat similar in layout to the Devastation *was the Russian* Petr Veliki, *but the ship demonstrated the lack of design experience in Russia, completing nearly 750 tons over design weight. She was a bad seaboat, with a heavy roll, and unreliable machinery.* (CMP)

which would cause many of White's ships torpedoed in the First World War to capsize rapidly. Her impressive appearance maintained her reputation as a fighting ship long after she was obsolete.

Committee on Designs for Ships of War

The Board of Admiralty set up this committee in January 1871 under Lord Dufferin to examine specific designs in the light of the *Captain* disaster. The designs to be examined were: *Monarch*, *Fury*, *Cyclops*, *Glatton* and the unarmoured frigate *Inconstant*. The committee members included sixteen distinguished engineers, scientists and sailors representing a wide spectrum of opinion. There was considerable disagreement over the final report; two admirals refused to sign at all while several members dissented from specific sections.

In the general part of the report, they concluded, 'A perfect ship of war is a desideratum which has never yet been attained and is now further than ever removed from our reach. Any near approach to perfection in one direction inevitably brings with it disadvantages in another.' The main desirable features were seen as 'the power of sailing, steaming, and carrying both heavy guns and armour . . .' The increasing power of guns led to a corresponding increase in thickness and weight of armour making it impossible to combine all desirable qualities in one vessel. There is no evidence that they considered a drastic increase in size which would have permitted a combination of desirable qualities.

The committee continued saying that *Devastation* gave up the ability to sail while *Inconstant*

had no armour and then gave an unclear recommendation that different features should be emphasised in each class. They saw the *Devastation* as the most likely style for future seagoing battleships but thought thicker armour could be carried if coal stowage was reduced in battleships for home defence. They noted evidence from gunmakers that much larger guns would soon be available which would lead to demands for armour up to 24in thick and even this might be insufficient in the longer term. The Committee suggested that a possible way ahead might be very heavy armour over the vitals only, with close subdivision of the unprotected ends.

Their recommendations on specific classes were minor and most have already been mentioned. The unarmoured extensions to Reed's breastworks were desirable but not essential, except for the *Cyclops* class if they were likely to operate in long waves with a period of 10½ seconds or more which, from Froude's theory, would cause excessive rolling. However, they thought that the range of stability of future seagoing ships should not be less than 50 degrees and commended a guide to acceptable stability by Rankine. They asked that an inclining experiment be carried out on all new ships to measure their initial stability and that their roll damping should also be measured. The committee also commended Froude's experimental work on bilge keels and recommended deep keels for all ships.

They saw little value in ships such as *Monarch* or *Sultan* as being expensive with little fighting value. Second rate ships such as *Audacious* would be needed but they should have a single turret with two heavy guns. Such ships and also coast defence ships like *Glatton* should

have stronger bottoms to permit grounding without damage.

The committee report concluded with some important, detailed recommendations applicable to most new classes.

1. Much greater attention was needed to fireproof fittings.
2. Builders' measurement tonnage and nominal horsepower should be replaced by displacement and indicated horsepower.
3. Greater care was needed in insulating copper sheathing from iron hulls.
4. Ships should be given an apparatus for measuring their trim at sea and a continuous speed recorder should be fitted.
5. A trial of 'hydraulic propulsion' (water jet) should be carried out.
6. A mixture of protected and unprotected guns should be considered.
7. Ramming is so important that great attention should be paid to means of resisting it; *eg* cellular construction.

They also noted that compound engines seemed likely to reduce fuel consumption dramatically and that Froude's work on hull shape, both discussed later, gave promise of forms which were both more efficient and which could carry greater loads.

The immediate effect of the committee's report was small, the Board ordering the centre battery ships *Alexandra* and *Temeraire* of the type which they had condemned. Other navies must certainly have found the report, which was published, a most valuable guide to advanced warship design. However, the concept of *Inflexible* owed much to the committee's findings and, eventually, most of the technical recommendations were implemented. Above all, the confidence of the navy and people in their ships was largely restored.

Froude's work on powering

Until Froude's work was in regular use in the mid-1870s, estimates of power for new ships could only be made by careful comparison with previous similar ships with similar machinery. If there were no similar ships, this estimate might be very much in error either way. For some years Froude had been trying to use the results of model tests to estimate ship performance which, if successful, would enable a

Alexandra was the last central battery ship designed for the Royal Navy. Her double-decked battery had good theoretical arcs of fire thanks to hull topsides that were heavily cut back. She was originally fitted with a full sailing rig, but this view of her after a major reconstruction in 1889–91 reveals the shape of the battery very clearly. (CMP)

number of forms for a new ship to be tried, at little cost, and the best chosen. Many people had tried to use models but had found the results to be extremely misleading.

In the mid-1860s Froude tried three pairs of models of lengths 3ft, 6ft and 12ft; one of each pair had fine and the other bluff ends. These tests showed first that there was no one 'ideal' form as had generally been believed, the fine ends being better at lower speeds while those with bluff ends were better at the highest speeds. Froude also showed that if the resistance of models of different length but similar shape was compared at 'corresponding speeds' (*ie* the same values of speed/square root of length), then the resistance per unit displacement would be the same.

After some preliminary discussions, these results were sent to Reed at the end of 1868 together with a very detailed proposal for a ship model test tank which would cost £1000 to build and £500 a year to run, Froude offering his own services free. Despite the feuds in the Admiralty over the *Captain* design and Childers's way of doing business, Reed was able to obtain approval for what was then seen as quite a large sum in little over a year and construction of the world's first ship model tank began early in 1870. The first tests, in 1872, were of models of the sloop *Greyhound* whose resistance had been measured accurately in a trial directed by Froude. This showed that Froude's model tests, interpreted as he had shown, gave satisfactory estimates of the resistance of a full sized ship.

A year later, Froude designed an ingenious apparatus to measure the performance of model propellers, which remained in use until 1939, making it possible to design a propeller for a new ship matching speed with engine characteristics instead of relying on expensive

trial and error as before. The principles of Froude's work were published and there are now about 150 ship tanks worldwide using methods derived from his pioneer work.

HMS *Inflexible*

The 1873 estimates allowed for the building of one battleship, an improved *Fury*. The first design study was actually based on *Dreadnought* with the belt increased to 14in amidships stopping at thick bulkheads fore and aft of the turrets. The ends were given an armoured deck just below the waterline and were closely subdivided.

It soon became apparent that Woolwich would be able to offer a much more powerful gun than the 38-ton weapons fitted to *Dreadnought* – a 50-ton or even bigger gun. Armstrong had the contract to supply guns to the new Italian battleships, *Duilio* and *Dandolo*, designed by Benedetto Brin. Initially, these two ships would also have had 38-ton guns but

Armstrong offered first a 50-ton (15in) and then a 100-ton (17.7in) gun.

Armour to match these very powerful guns could not be arranged in a *Dreadnought* configuration. Both Brin and Barnaby adopted a different style and it has been debated if Barnaby copied Brin or vice versa but it seems more likely that both concepts derive from a passage in the report of the Committee on Designs, envisaging the consequences of exceptional guns and armour:

> The ships would then comprise a very strongly plated central citadel, surrounded and supported by an unarmoured raft, constructed on a cellular system, or containing some buoyant substance such as cork . . .

Armstrong was a witness before the committee and would ensure that Brin was aware of this suggestion.

Brin's ships were of about 11,000 tons full load and had the high top speed of 15kts. Their four 17.7in MLR fired a 1905lb projectile about once every 15 minutes and were mounted in two twin turrets, arranged en echelon, in an amidships citadel. The belt was 21½ in thick, of Creusot steel, with 17in steel over the turrets and upper citadel. Some steel was also used in the hull. The second ship had compound engines giving better fuel economy.

The Italian navy organised some very elaborate comparative tests of armour at Spezia for these ships and, as was the custom in those days, the results were published. Various guns, 10in, 11in and 17.7in, were fired against four targets. These targets had 22in of iron or steel, with backing, made by different manufacturers; two had armour in a single thickness and the others in two layers. The results were inconclusive and summed up in the *Engineer* magazine as that the steel plates were more likely to be destroyed by projectiles incapable of penetrating it than those of wrought iron whilst steel was slightly better at preventing a projectile from penetrating completely, including the backing.

Barnaby, assisted by White, saw the design of *Inflexible* as forming three blocks. Amidships there was an armoured citadel with two thicknesses of 12in iron armour which, together with 36in of teak weighed 1100lbs/sq ft. This citadel was long enough to contain the machinery, turrets and magazine and to remain afloat and upright if the ends were flooded.

At the ends there was a 3in deck just below the waterline. The spaces below the deck were closely subdivided and used for stores and coal, making it unlikely that they could ever be fully waterlogged. Above the armour deck there was a closely divided, cellular space, filled with cork at the sides. Above this, there was a light, fairly high structure for living quarters and to keep the ship dry and through which hatches and ventilation ran.

The turrets each weighed 750 tons and carried two 16in MLR (81-ton) guns with 16in compound armour in which a fairly thin, hard steel face was welded to a softer, wrought iron back. This had about 25 per cent greater resistance to penetration than wrought iron and was at least the equal of early Creusot steel. The guns were loaded hydraulically from outside and could fire a 1700lb shell every 2½ minutes if all worked well.

The arrangement of turrets en echelon, amidships was not very successful. It had been hoped that the outer gun in each turret could fire fore and aft but blast damage on the structure restricted firing to about 30 degrees off the axis. Cross-deck firing was also damaging.

Inflexible was a ship of 11,880 tons, with 8400 ihp and made 14.75kts on trial. The engines were three-cylinder, Elder compounds taking steam at 60psi (pounds per square inch) from cylindrical boilers and burning 2½lbs/hp/hour. She was full of novelties, with electric lighting, torpedo launchers, and anti-rolling tanks designed by Phillip Watts, formerly Froude's assistant (they were too small to be effective and were soon abandoned). *Inflexible* also carried a brig rig, intended for peacetime training and to be removed in war. It was actually removed quite quickly and replaced with a military rig with fighting tops.

In 1875, Reed visited Italy and, having inspected Brin's ships, declared that they were unsafe because, with the ends flooded, the armoured citadel would provide insufficient stability. This was denied by the Italians though they did not publish any evidence. Reed then made a similar charge against *Inflexible*.

A small committee was set up in 1877 under Admiral Hope to investigate the safety of *Inflexible*. The other members were Dr Wooley, expert on stability, William Froude and Mr Rendel, the engineer, and their report completely vindicated the design. They found that the chance of both ends being completely flooded ('riddled') and with all the stores and coal blown out ('gutted') was extremely small,

The Italian battleships Duilio *and* Dandolo *took to extremes the concept of small numbers of super-heavy weapons, having a sole gun armament as built of four 17.7in 100-ton muzzle-loaders in two closely spaced turrets* en echelon *amidships. This photograph of* Dandolo *was taken after the ship's reconstruction in 1895–98 when the armament was modernized and numerous smaller guns added.* (CMP)

The British, who had supplied the 100-ton guns for the Italian Duilio *class, were concerned not to be out-gunned in the Mediterranean and the result was the* Inflexible. *This ship was similar in concept but although the 16in guns were smaller than those of the Italian ships they were the heaviest muzzle-loading guns in any British ship.* Inflexible *also carried the thickest armour (24in) ever taken to sea. Originally completed with a brig rig for training, as shown in this photograph the ship was reduced to military masts in 1885. (CMP)*

even in a prolonged engagement. Even if this unlikely state was reached, the armoured citadel would provide enough buoyancy and stability to keep the ship afloat and upright in a calm sea, confirmed by Froude's tests with a one-ton model of the ship. It was also found that the waterlogged ends would act as very large and effective roll damping tanks and even in the extreme damaged state she would be safe in quite large waves. However, in this state she would have to be handled with great care as even running out the guns would cause a large heel.

The Battle of the Yalu River in 1894 provided some further evidence on the safety of

Inflexible. Two Chinese ironclads, built in Germany, smaller but with the same layout as *Inflexible*, were hit numerous times but remained afloat (although accounts saying they were hit 200 times are probably exaggerated).

Inflexible was a technical *tour de force* but, with very slow firing guns and poor arcs of fire, it seems unlikely that she would have been very effective in action. She was followed by two diminutives, *Ajax* and *Agamemnon*, which carried four 38-ton guns and 18in armour. They had *Inflexible*'s faults but, in addition, their citadel was too small to ensure their safety should the ends be flooded. Their stern lines were so bluff that the flow separated from the hull making their rudders ineffective. This was eventually cured, at least in part, by a small extension to the stern, designed following model tests by R E Froude, in charge of the Admiralty Experiment Works since the death of his father in 1879.

Two more ships of similar appearance followed, introducing breech-loading guns and steel hulls to the battlefleet. They are dealt with in the next chapter.

French development followed a very different line. The earlier, high freeboard ships with guns en barbette over a central battery gradually changed to heavier barbette guns and no battery. The Creusot works, using the open hearth (Siemens Martin) process had begun to make reliable steel and the French dockyards developed elaborate working practices for what was still a temperamental material. Barnaby and White, who had long been advocates of steel construction, visited both Le Creusot and *Redoutable* under construction during 1874 and were soon able to find suitable steel from the Landore works.

By 1877, the French style had evolved into *Amiral Duperré* with four 13.4in in single mounts and an unprotected battery of 5.5in guns. She had a continuous belt, 22in amidships and 10in at the ends but, even as designed, it extended only 18in above the waterline. With a small metacentric height (2ft), unprotected freeboard and considerable tumblehome reducing stability at large angles she would have been very vulnerable, as shown by somewhat similar forms at Tsushima.

CAPITAL SHIP DEVELOPMENT 1863–1878

Date is laying down; tonnage is load; scale is 1/1250

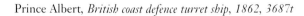

Prince Albert, *British coast defence turret ship, 1862, 3687t*

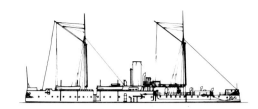

Hotspur, *British ironclad ram, 1868, 4331t*

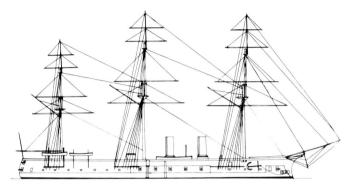

Bellerophon, *British central battery ship, 1863, 7551t*

Dreadnought, *British turret ship, 1870, 10,886t*

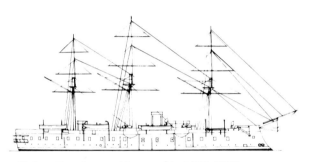

Océan, *French central battery ship, 1865, 7775t*

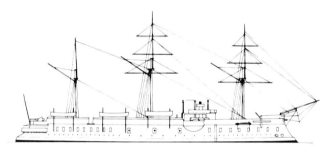

Colbert, *French central battery/barbette ship, 1870, 8750t*

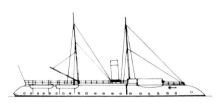

Cerbère, *French ironclad ram, 1865, 3532t*

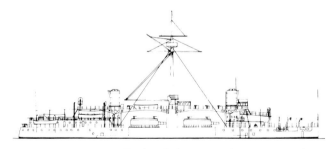

Duilio, *Italian turret ship, 1873, 12,071t*

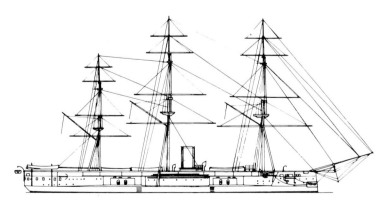

Captain, *British masted turret ship, 1867, 7767t*

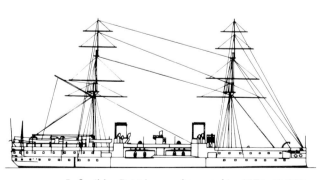

Inflexible, *British masted turret ship, 1874, 11,880t*

French warships of the later nineteenth century were very distinctive in appearance, with exaggerated features like excessive tumblehome (which seriously reduced stability at large angles of heel), a prominent ram bow and large funnels. This is Redoutable, *a central battery ship launched in 1876. Her main armament comprised eight 10.8in guns – one in each of the corners of the midships battery, and four unprotected on the upper deck (one under the forecastle, one aft and one on each beam in half barbettes – above the battery and behind the canvas screens in this view).* (CMP)

Cruising vessels and small craft

Cruisers and other small vessels can only be considered very briefly in the space available. Cruiser policy had been unclear since the introduction of the steam ship and remained unclear during the period under discussion. The depradations caused to Union trade in the American Civil War by *Alabama*, *Florida* and others showed the damage which could be caused by commerce raiders though the lessons drawn were flawed.

There were many real problems: fuel consumption was still very heavy, making sail essential for cruisers which had to stay at sea for long periods, and full rig would reduce speed under steam by at least 1½kts in a calm. There were no effective antifouling paints and copper sheathing was essential for ships which could not dock frequently. There was a failure to realise how many ships were needed to protect trade against even a few raiders and a failure to realise that there were very few fast merchant ships suitable for conversion to cruisers and these usually of limited endurance, though in some cases holds could be used to carry extra coal. In general, it was believed that merchant

Tension between Britain and the USA during the Civil War encouraged the latter to project a group of seven ultra-fast commerce raiders. Generally known as the Wampanoag *class, they were actually built to a variety of designs. They were very long, with a length:beam ratio of around 7.4:1 and had massively powerful engines. Both the name ship and* Ammonoosuc *achieved over 17kts on trials, but like so many extreme ships the one advantage was bought at the expense of many more practical qualities (evident in the aerial view of* Tennessee *ex- Madawasca in 1875). They were always controversial and those completed were soon laid up, condemned as 'over-engined'. This internal profile of (bottom)* Wampanoag *shows how the machinery dominated the design.* (US National Archives, by courtesy of Donald L Canney)

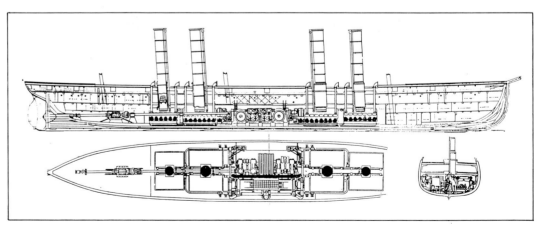

The British responded to the American Wampanoag *type with three large iron-hulled frigates, of which* Shah *(seen here) was the last. Although they did not have quite the trials speed of the US ships,* Inconstant *and* Shah *made over 16kts, but more importantly the speed was sustainable – the former logged 15.5kts over 24 hours. Crucial to a cruiser, they were also sprightly under sail, reaching 13.5 kts under canvas alone.* (CMP)

ships could be converted into cruisers for trade protection and many such schemes were worked out in some detail, usually with an armament of four 64pdr and one 40pdr BL.

Merchant ships of 1860–1880 were far more vulnerable than the armed merchant cruisers of the twentieth century. Few would remain afloat if even one large compartment was breached; their machinery was tall and exposed to gunfire; and in many cases their stability was inadequate to carry a topweight of guns. Losses, even in peacetime, were frequent and Barnaby and his staff worked closely with the Institution of Naval Architects to improve subdivision. Conversion might imply extra bulkheads, perhaps even a 6in armour bulkhead ahead of the machinery, ballast, coal bunkers arranged to protect the machinery and stiffening under the guns.

The US Navy reading of the lessons of the Civil War led them to design the fast cruisers of the *Wampanoag* class with a design speed of 17kts and with a wooden hull 335ft long, though with a good deal of iron stiffening. They were a total failure, with a weak hull and unreliable machinery. Furthermore, the concept was wrong: as shown in twentieth century wars, the best commerce raiders are medium speed merchant ships, undistinguished in appearance.

From their conception in 1865 until their faults were recognised about 1870, the *Wampanoag*s exerted a great influence on British and French naval thinking. The Controller envisaged a programme of six big, fast frigates and six corvettes only slightly inferior. Reed's frigate design, *Inconstant* with a speed of 16kts and heavily armed, was passed to the Controller in 1866. To reach the speed she had to be long (337ft) and hence had to have an iron hull; but an unarmoured iron hull was vulnerable to gunfire, particularly at long range, so she was given a 9in timber sheath to reduce the effect of the impact of shot and to insulate the hull from the copper antifouling.

Her main armament was ten 9in MLR, half on either beam. It appeared that she was intended to fight at 'long' range and destroy her enemies without much risk of damage. It must

be doubted if the mountings and the total lack of a gun direction system gave her big guns any greater effective range than smaller weapons. Technically *Inconstant* was a great success, making 16.2kts on trial (faster than any mail steamer of the day) and, at an economical speed of 6½kts, could steam over 3000 miles. She sailed well, too, making 13½kts under all plain sail. However, she was expensive at £213,000 (by comparison *Warrior* cost £270,000) and only two half-sisters were built. France built two similar ships, *Duquesne* and *Tourville*.

One of the British ships, *Shah*, together with the much smaller *Amethyst*, fought an action against the Peruvian rebel, near-pirate, turret ship *Huascar*. The latter carried two 10in MLR in a Coles turret with a 4½in belt, a formidable opponent for unprotected ships. *Shah* fired 280 rounds (and a torpedo), making about thirty hits, whilst *Amethyst* had a similar score. One 9in shell pierced the 3½in upper belt and caused a few casualties and that was all. *Huascar*'s slow firing guns, with untrained crews scored no hits. *Huascar* was captured by the Chileans and is preserved today with the only remaining set of Penn trunk engines.

Reed's corvette, *Volage*, was of just over 3000 tons and carried six 7in MLR and four 64pdr at 15kts, but at £130,000 she was still costly. There were considerable numbers of other, smaller corvettes, some wood hulled, some

iron and a few composite. Some steel was used in the *Comus* class and the later *Calypso*s were all-steel. The armament tended to consist of a number of smaller guns, 64pdr MLR in the earlier ships, 5in or 6in BL in the later. The two *Juno*s of 1866 were interesting in that their armament was reduced and, together with the crew accommodation, arranged in a covered upper deck, leaving the lower deck free for the carriage of troops. Though they seem to have been valuable in minor campaigns, the concept was not repeated.

Three armoured cruisers were built in 1873–76 with a short belt amidships and the ends protected by an armoured deck. The heavy guns were given forward firing arcs and the battery was protected only by a thick (8–9in) bulkhead at the fore end. They were too slow and had too little endurance for cruisers and were inadequately armed and protected to fight battleships.

In 1875 Barnaby and White commenced the design of a pair of ships, *Iris* and *Mercury*, which marked a major shift in cruiser policy although there were conflicting views on their role. They were very fast for the day at 17kts, with twin shafts, each driven by a four-cylinder compound engine giving greatly improved fuel consumption so that their token barque rig was soon removed. They had no armour but there were separate engine rooms for each shaft and two boiler rooms giving protection by duplica-

tion and coal bunkers were arranged to shield the machinery. Trials showed that 2ft of coal was equivalent in protection to 1in of iron. The hull shape was chosen after a number of model tests by Froude and was very successful. The initial propeller design was incorrect and *Iris* only reached 16.6kts on her first trial but following a considerable number of model tests and ship trials the design speed was exceeded, *Mercury* reaching 18.6kts with 7735ihp.

Iris and *Mercury* were the first British warships built of steel. Steel became available in quantity around 1860 from the Bessemer process and a few, commercial craft were built using it. Bessemer steel was still more expensive than iron and was seen as difficult to work and liable to unexplained, sudden failures, usually starting at rivet holes. Because of the greater strength of steel, main structure built from it was about 20 per cent lighter than in iron. Barnaby wrote a number of papers on the advantages of steel and of the problems to be overcome before it could be used with confidence. Bessemer saw this as a personal attack and denigrated him as a reactionary rather than the enthusiast which he was.

Following a visit by Barnaby and White to France in 1874, where they studied steel manufacture and construction, it was learnt that the

Landore works in Wales could make reliable steel using the Siemens open hearth process and the order was placed with them for the new cruisers' steel. A piece was cut from every plate and tested for toughness and more extensive tests were carried out on one plate from every fifty. Rules for working were carefully laid down in the Pembroke yard but, even so, there were still considerable difficulties in construction. However, both hulls had a long life so it appears that the difficulties were overcome.

During the period 1863–74, 26 corvettes, 17

sloops, 44 gun-vessels, 55 gunboats and 21 'flat iron' gunboats were built. They were the policemen of the growing Empire but the larger ones could deal with a converted merchant ship. Only a few had features of technical interest such as experimental engines and rudders but they were all reliable, easy to maintain and were seaworthy. The latter aspect was most clearly demonstrated in the Samoa typhoon of 1889 when the corvette *Calliope* got out of the harbour safely, leaving behind the wrecks of three American and three German warships as well as many merchant ships.

Two classes of gunboat deserve some mention as, though failures, their concepts were influential at the time. Three armoured gunboats with a 4½in belt and two 7in MLR were built in 1866, also testing different forms of propulsion. Two had twin screws (then novel), while *Waterwitch* had an internal pump discharging a water jet in either direction. She was

CRUISING SHIP DEVELOPMENT 1863–1878

Date is laying down; tonnage is load; scale is 1/1250

Unarmoured Ships

Armoured Ships

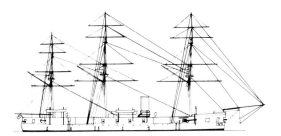

Favorite, *British central battery corvette, 1860 (modified during construction), 3232t*

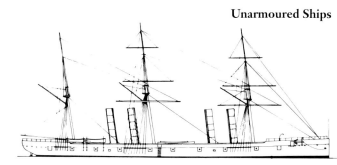

Wampanoag, *American wooden frigate, 1863, 4215t*

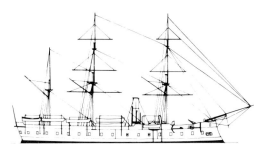

Alma, *French central battery ship, 1865, 3600t*

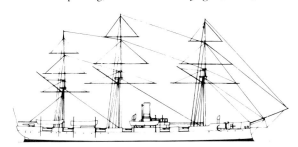

Fabert, *French wooden frigate, 1868, 2017t*

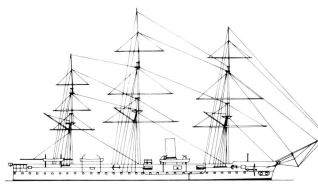

General Admiral, *Russian armoured cruiser, 1870, 5031t*

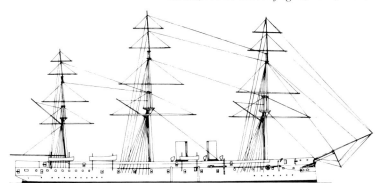

Shah, *British unarmoured iron frigate, 1870, 6250t*

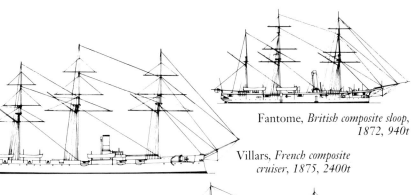

Fantome, *British composite sloop, 1872, 940t*

Villars, *French composite cruiser, 1875, 2400t*

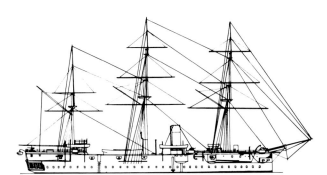

Shannon, *British armoured cruiser, 1873, 5670t*

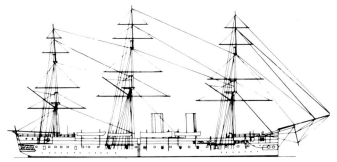

Bacchante, *British unarmoured iron corvette, 1876, 4070t*

a total failure, not exceeding 5–6kts in service and was never allowed out of sight of land.

Rendel developed a slightly more successful style of gunboat at much the same date. Armstrongs had built a barge for tests of big guns which was developed into the gunboat *Staunch* for the Royal Navy. She carried a single 9in MLR (10in in later boats) on an ingenious hydraulic mounting which allowed it to be lowered into the hold for passage and quickly raised for action. Hydraulic loading reduced the gun crew from sixteen to six. These 'flat iron' gunboats were highly manoeuvrable and were the first British warships without sail.

The idea was that these little craft could be used for coastal protection, working in shallow water, and using their heavy gun against an invading force. It is possible to use a heavy gun from a small craft only in a calm and later classes carried a more conventional armament of three 64pdrs. The combination of a big gun and low cost, about £13,000, appealed only to politicians. They were strongly built to take the recoil of their gun and several remained in use as lighters until after the Second World War and one or two exist in 1992.

Torpedo vessels

The Royal Navy bought its first batch of Whitehead torpedoes in 1870 following a

The invasion scares of the late 1860s and 1870s led the British to produce a series of small iron mastless gunboats to strengthen coastal defences. They were often called 'flatirons' because of their shape, or Rendel gunboats after their originator, Armstrong's chief naval architect. A variation on this theme was the Medina *class, which carried a barquentine rig and saw service on Chinese rivers. One curious requirement was that they should be capable of being towed at speeds of up to 13kts, so they could be deployed quickly off an enemy coast in wartime. This was a difficult problem but was solved by Froude using model tests. This 1882 photograph shows* Medina *herself with a conventional 'flatiron' beyond. (CMP)*

series of a hundred runs against the old sloop *Oberon*. Even though the charge was only 18lbs of dynamite and the speed 7kts, the potential of the torpedo was recognised. Most major warships were quickly fitted to launch torpedoes and the larger ships' boats were equipped for torpedo dropping. The latter scheme was extended into special 'Second Class' torpedo boats – larger and faster than normal ships' boats, they could be carried on big ships. In 1878 a merchant ship then under construction was requisitioned, initially as an auxiliary cruiser, but completed as a torpedo boat carrier and depot ship. *Hecla* carried six torpedo boats which could be launched at sea to attack the enemy in harbour.

The *Vesuvius* of 1873 was a much more novel approach. A small ship of 245 tons as opposed to the tiny torpedo boats, she had a speed of 9.7kts and relied on stealth to attack. She burnt coke to reduce smoke and even this was intended to be discharged underwater; she had a small silhouette and quiet engines. There was a single submerged bow tube with sixteen torpedoes. However, the torpedo enthusiasts were obsessed by speed and *Vesuvius* was soon relegated to training, but since most successful torpedo attacks in the nineteenth century (and even the twentieth) were carried out at low speed, she or derivatives could have been successful.

The *Lightning* of 1876 with a speed of 19kts and a displacement of 32 tons was the preferred approach, even though she was lacking in seaworthiness and could only make her speed in a flat calm. A number of variants on this theme were built but, up to 1880, these were mainly experimental. They were about the size of *Lightning*, a little faster, on trial, and carried two 14in torpedoes.

Polyphemus was another novel vessel, designed in 1878 by Phillip Watts under Barnaby's direction. She is usually described, even by Barnaby, as a ram, spoilt by the addition of five submerged torpedo tubes. However, the ships's 'Cover' (the compilation of documents relating to design history) makes it clear that she was intended as a torpedo vessel and it was the ram which was the afterthought. The cap of the bow tube was a bronze casting and formed the ram. *Polyphemus* displaced 2640 tons, had a largely submerged cigar-shaped hull, with the 4ft segment showing covered with 3in armour, making her almost invulnerable to gunfire. There was a small unprotected forecastle and a narrow superstructure for ventilation and navigation. With a speed of 18kts and eighteen torpedoes for her five tubes (two on each beam and one bow) she would have

been a formidable opponent in war but had little role in peacetime and the design was not repeated. Further details are given in Chapter 8.

Machinery development

An outline of engineering progress is given in Chapter 11, but a few specific points about machinery development in the 1860–1880 period are worth making here. Until the latter half of the 1870s there was not much change. In part, this was due to the very success of the simple, reliable engines built by Penn, Maudslay and Humphrys, which were gradually improved; there were also a number of more advanced designs tried, particularly compound engines, which proved unreliable, showing that there were still problems to be overcome.

In a compound engine the steam expands partially in one cylinder from which it passes to a second or even third where it expands further. The advantage in efficiency was obvious and an early version was tried in the frigate *Constance* (1862); it was complicated and unreliable though, when working, coal consumption was only 2.5lbs/hp/hour (pounds per horsepower per hour). Several corvettes were built with compound engines at the end of the 1860s getting down to 2lbs/hp/hour. By the early 1870s, the problems had been overcome and compound engines were universal.

Between 1860 and 1880 the consumption of coal by the Royal Navy doubled from 100,000 to 200,000 tons and this, together with the perceived need to do away with sails, encouraged the pursuit of more economical machinery. The way to a solution seemed clear, with higher pressure steam at 60psi, used in compound engines with at least two stages of expansion. Such an advance required fresh water in the boilers and a closed feed system with surface condensers, and all of these posed further problems, mainly of selecting and proving appropriate materials. It is common for major technical advances to depend on detail points and materials.

Box boilers were convenient to stoke and operate but higher pressures needed a cylindrical shape and a stronger shell. Pipes, too, had to be stronger and a suitable packing found for the joints. There were many metallurgical problems in condensers – hot water on one side, salt on the other – not fully solved until after the Second World War, while the need for extreme purity of the feed water took time to recognise and to achieve. The increase in piston speed led to problems with bearing materials, piston seals and with lubrication.

One may also note the rapid increase in the number of auxiliary engines driving capstans, turrets, ventilation fans and, eventually, dynamos.

Table 5/4: Auxiliary Engines

	Number	Total power of auxiliaries (hp)
Warrior	8	350
Devastation	16	880
Inflexible	82	1400

Most of these developments were initiated by industry but they were encouraged by a great civilian Engineer-in-Chief of the Royal Navy, Sir James Wright, who had followed Lloyd in 1860.

Cost

The cost of the ships described is not easy to identify as the method of calculating overheads changed several times. Overheads should include general costs such as the pay of senior staff and of people not working directly on the ship, such as cashiers, equivalent rate and rents, interest on capital etc. Estimates of the percentage to be allowed range from 12½ to 60. The figures below are for labour and materials only for the hull and equipment but include the machinery manufacturers' overhead. The cost of guns and stores is not included. Very precise figures are often quoted but they are meaningless; three-figure accuracy is enough to show the dramatic rise.

Table 5/6: Some Typical Costs

Ship	Cost (£ × 1000)
Warrior	377 (for comparison)
Bellerophon	356
Audacious	256
Alexandra	538
Monarch	354
Captain	335
Cerberus	118
Devastation	361
Dreadnought	619
Inflexible	812

Conclusions

The competition between gun and armour dominated warship design between 1863 and 1878. At the beginning, the 7in MLR fired a 115lb projectile which could pierce 7½in iron at 1000yds while twenty years on, the 16in MLR could fire a 1700lb shot through 22½in. This led to fewer guns and to thicker armour over the minimum length of ship to ensure flotation. The chance of hitting at more than 1000yds with slow firing, undirected guns on simple mounts must have been extremely remote, of the order of 1–2 per cent.

In Britain, the controversy over the introduction of turret ships, followed by the loss of *Captain* caused immense ill-feeling and many misunderstandings but led finally to the recognition that ship design is a matter for professionals. In general, the British Admiralty showed great willingness to experiment with new technology such as the turret in *Trusty*, hydraulic operation of guns, or jet propulsion, and were also active in sponsoring basic research. This willingness to experiment, coupled with lack of funds and of strategic thinking, meant that it was rare indeed for two major vessels to be identical. The Admiralty's clear interest in steel construction, while at the same time rejecting the quality of steel available in the UK, tends to support the widely held view that Britain's industrial lead began to disappear about 1860.

The changes in the theoretical base of naval architecture were dramatic with Barnes and Barnaby making it possible to examine stability at large angles of heel, Reed and White devising a rational and practical approach to the strength of ships, and William Froude making revolutionary advances, first in rolling and then in resistance, hull shape and propeller design as well as contributing to the design committees of the day. As Barnaby wrote of Froude in *Naval Developments of the Century*, '. . . to him the nineteenth century owes a very large part of its distinction.'

David K Brown, RCNC

Table 5/5: Machinery Particulars

Ship	Date (compl)	ihp (trial)	Boiler pressure (psi)	Wet weight (tons)	ihp/ton	Coal (lbs/ihp/ hour)	Floor area (sq ft/ihp)	rpm	Engine	Condenser	Boiler
Warrior	1861	5469	22	898	5.7	4–5	0.79	54	Penn trunk	Jet	Box
Bellerophon	1866	4708	30	988	4.8	–	0.79	74	Penn trunk	Surface	Tubular
Hercules	1868	8530	30	1210	7.2	3.1	–	71	Penn trunk	Surface	Tubular
Devastation	1873	6652	30	972	6.9	3.1–4.4	0.69	77	Penn trunk	Surface	Tubular
Shah	1873	7477	32	1270	5.9	3.2	0.64	65	Ravenhill, horizontal	Surface	Rectangular
Inflexible	1881	8433	60	1366	6.2	2.4–2.7	0.64	73	Elder, vert, compound	Surface	Oval

The Era of Uncertainty: Typical Vessels 1863–1878

Ship or class [type]	Nationality	Disp (load) (tons)	Dimensions (loa × breadth × draught) (feet–inches) (metres)	Armament	Armour (belt/battery or turret) (max, ins)	Speed (max,kts)	Launch dates	Numbers built
Centre battery ships								
ENTERPRIZE [Ironclad sloop]	British	1350	180–0 pp × 36–0 × 13–9 *54.9 × 11.3 × 4.2*	2–100pdr SB, 2–110pdr BL	4.5/4.5	9.9	1864	1
BELLEROPHON	British	7551	300–0 pp × 56 – 1 × 24 – 8 *91.4 × 17.1 × 7.5*	10.9in RML, 5–7in RML	6/6	14.2	1865	1

Ship or class [type]	Nationality	Disp (load) (tons)	Dimensions (loa × breadth × draught) (feet–inches) (metres)	Armament	Armour (belt/battery or turret) (max, ins)	Speed (max,kts)	Launch dates	Numbers built
AUDACIOUS	British	6010	280–0 pp × 54–0 × 22–7 85.3 × 16.5 × 6.9	10–9in RML, 6–20pdr BL	8/6	14	1869–70	4
RICHELIEU	French	8984	322–0 wl × 57–3 × 28–6 98.1 × 17.5 × 8.7	6–10.8in RML, 5–9.4in, 10–4.7in	8.7/6.3	13	1873	1
DEVASTATION	French	10,450	311–6 wl × 69–9 × 27–0 95.0 × 21.3 × 8.2	4–13.4in RML, 4–10.8in, 6–5.5in	15/9.5	15	1879	2
Turret ships PRINCE ALBERT [Coast defence ship]	British	3687	240–0 pp × 48–1 × 19–8 73.2 × 14.7 × 6.0	4–9in RML	4.5/10.5	11.3	1864	1
MONARCH [Masted turret ship]	British	8322	330–0 pp × 57–6 × 24–3 100.6 × 17.5 × 7.4	4–2in RML, 3–7in RML	7/10	15	1868	1
CAPTAIN [Masted turret ship]	British	7767	320–0 pp × 53–3 × 24–10 97.5 × 16.2 × 7.6	4–12in RML, 2–7in RML	8/10	15.3	1869	1
GROSSER KURFÜRST [Masted turret ship]	German	7596	316–10 × 53–1 × 23–6 96.6 × 16.3 × 7.2	4–26cm, 2–17cm	9/8	14	1873–75	3
Breastwork ships CERBERUS [Coast defence ship]	British	3344	225–0 × 45–0 × 15–4 68.6 × 13.7 × 4.7	4–10in RML	8/10	9.8	1868–70	2
DEVASTATION	British	9330	307–0 × 62–3 × 26–8 93.6 × 19.0 × 8.0	4–12in RML	12/14	13.8	1871–72	2
Turret ships DREADNOUGHT	British	10,886	343–0 × 63–10 × 26–6 104.6 × 19.5 × 8.1	4–12.5in RML	14/14	14.5	1875	1
INFLEXIBLE	British	11,880	344–0 × 75–0 × 25–6 104.9 × 22.9 × 7.8	4–16in RML	24/17	14.8	1876	1
DUILIO	Italian	10,962	358–2 × 64–9 × 27–3 109.2 × 19.7 × 8.3	4–17.7in RML	21.5/17	15	1876–78	2
Cruisers WAMPANOAG [Wooden frigate]	American	4215	335–0 wl × 48–0 × 18–6 102.1 × 14.6 × 5.6	3–5.3in RML, 10–9in SB	–/–	17.7	1864–65	3
INCONSTANT [Iron frigate]	British	5780	337–4 × 50–3 × 25–6 102.8 × 15.3 × 7.8	10–9in RML, 6–7in RML	–/–	16.2	1868	3
MININ [Armoured cruiser]	Russian	6136	295–0 wl × 44–6 × 25–5 89.9 × 15.1 × 7.8	4–8in, 12–6in, 4–3.4in	7/–	14	1869	1
VOLAGE [Iron corvette]	British	3080	270–0 × 42–0 × 22–0 82.3 × 12.8 × 6.7	6–7in RML, 4–64pdr RML	–/–	15	1869	2
DUQUESNE [Iron unarmoured cruiser]	French	5905	329–4 wl × 50–0 × 26–2 100.4 × 15.2 × 8.0	7–7.6in RML, 14–5.5in RML	–/–	16.8	1876	2
GENERAL ADMIRAL [Armoured cruiser]	Russian	5031	285–10 wl × 48–0 × 24–5 87.1 × 14.6 × 7.4	6–8in, 2–6in, 4–3.4in	6/–	12.3	1873	2
OSPREY [Composite sloop]	British	1130	170–0 × 36–0 × 15–9 58.8 × 11.0 × 4.8	2–7in RML, 4–64pdr RML	–/–	11.4	1876–80	14
Rams TAUREAU [Armoured ram]	French	2433	196–10 wl × 48–6 × 17–9 60.0 × 14.8 × 5.4	1–24cm	6/4.7	12.5	1865	1
AFFONDATORE [Turret ram]	Italian	4006	307–9 × 40–0 × 20–10 93.8 × 12.2 × 6.4	2–228mm	5/2	12	1865	1
HOTSPUR [Armoured ram]	British	4331	235–0 pp × 50–0 × 10–0 71.6 × 15.2 × 6.1	1–12in RML, 2–64pdr RML	11/10	12.6	1870	1

6

Warships of Steel 1879–1889

IN respect of warship design in general and battleship design in particular the period from the mid-1870s to the end of the 1880s continued the uncertainties outlined in the previous chapter. It was almost impossible to produce a universally approved design and any form of consensus as to either the design parameters or the tactical employment of major warships was non-existent. In battleships the large gun had increased in power until the only protection that could be provided against it was extremely thick armour which, because of its great weight, could only be applied to a minimal area. This combination of strong offensive qualities with weak defensive ones in what were regarded as expensive ships was the subject of much criticism and led many to call for an end to large ship construction in favour of more numerous smaller vessels. This was further compounded by the development of the torpedo which by the late 1870s had become a practical and powerful weapon and induced in some authorities a belief that the battleship was obsolete. Not only was the torpedo fitted in armoured and cruising ships, posing a substantial threat when ships were expected to fight at a comparatively close range, but in the new torpedo boats – small, high speed craft which, because of their cheapness, could be built in large numbers.

These difficulties, combined with politically generated economic restrictions and the claims and counter-claims of various theorists, resulted in an uncertainty amongst naval authorities which generated inconsistent design and construction policies. The most marked results were regular retrogressive steps into smaller, invariably unsatisfactory, battleship designs and the occasional abandonment of large ship construction altogether – the latter most marked in France where no new battleships were laid down between 1883 and 1889. In many ways these problems resulted from a clouding of the understanding of naval war resulting from a feeling that new technology had somehow negated the strategies and tactics of the past, a situation aggravated in the early part of this period by a lack of fleet manoeuvres designed to establish the best tactical use of modern ships and their relative values as fighting ships. Above all the modern theorists did not fully understand that torpedo boats, and small ships generally, were restricted in value by their limited seakeeping abilities and if any nation wished to maintain command of the sea then only ocean-going ships could provide the required security.

In all nations the size of battleships was held down by political and economic considerations so any possibilities for designers to ease their problems by increases in displacement were generally excluded. However, progress was made as a result of the savings possible from new technology. First among these was the substitution of steel for iron construction which, being lighter for the same strength, allowed for savings in hull weight which could be utilised elsewhere. Wrought iron armour was replaced with compound armour (a steel face on a wrought iron back) or all-steel armour which could provide for either weight saving for the same protection or improved protection for the same weight. Sailing rigs were abandoned in all battleships of this period, providing a further saving in weight, and machinery continued its steady advance towards higher speeds and improved economy. Despite all this, however, it was not until the arbitrary displacement limits were broken, at the end of the 1880s that satisfactory balanced designs were produced.

A point of some importance to this period is the length of time which separated the design of ships and their completion. British battleships averaged seven years under construction, a situation largely generated by delays in the production of their guns; in French and Italian ships ten years was the norm; Austro-Hungarian building times were five years and Russian ships varied between three and seven years. New designs, therefore, were usually being prepared without the benefit of the trial results or seagoing evaluation of immediately preceeding classes. By way of example, when the British *Inflexible* was completed in 1881, four similar central citadel turret ships were already under construction, and a new vessel,

Turret ship development in Britain progressed from the Inflexible, *via two reduced version in the* Agamemnon class, *to the* Colossus *and* Edinburgh *(illustrated here). Although similar in appearance to their immediate predecessors, the new ships were significantly improved by a largely steel hull, protected by compound armour, and the introduction of large calibre breech-loading guns. They also brought a substantial secondary armament to British capital ships for the first time, with five 6in guns adding to the four 12in in the two midships turrets.* (CMP)

the first of the new barbette ships – HMS *Collingwood* – had been laid down the year before. Thus before even the first vessel of the citadel type had been tried the design process had moved on to a new type, reducing to a great extent the value of information fed back to the designers and often producing a situation where newly completed ships were already rendered obsolescent by designs on the drawing board.

However, although speedier construction may have helped the design process, the nature of the warship itself was at this time involved in a rapid evolutionary process which did not lend itself to the production of a homogeneous fleet. Whenever warships gathered in any numbers, disparaging remarks were made about the odd collection of miscellaneous types which were now expected to operate as a co-ordinated unit and, although it must be admitted that many ships were retained as front line units well beyond the time when they should have been relegated, it is difficult to see how any other situation would have been possible in this age of experiment.

The introduction of steel

In Britain *Inflexible* was followed by two similar but smaller central citadel turret ships, *Ajax* and *Agamemnon*, laid down in 1876. With a lighter armament (four 12.5in MLR – muzzle-loading rifle – guns in place of four 16in MLR), thinner armour over a smaller area and a reduced speed, they displaced 8500 tons – over 3000 tons less than *Inflexible* – and were in almost all respects inferior to their predecessor. The only advantages they could claim were the provision of a single thickness of 16in compound armour (5.25in steel on 10.75in wrought iron) on the turrets in place of the sandwich arrangement of *Inflexible* and that they were designed without a sailing rig. Their greatest fault was that the hull protection was insufficient to ensure their stability with the unprotected ends destroyed and they thereby

abandoned what was supposed to be one of the primary requirements of the central citadel ship. They were also designed with a low length:beam ratio and, with an eye on possible service against Russia in the Baltic and Black Sea, a shallow draught. Although the form was checked by model experiments and seemed acceptable, after the ships completed in 1883 it was found that they steered very badly, requiring an excessive amount of helm to stay on a particular course and had the disconcerting habit of suddenly and unpredictably swerving off course, which often required the application of helm in the opposite direction to that previously in use! They were also bad sea-boats and although modifications were later made to the hull aft, which improved their handling, they were never popular ships in the fleet, particularly when operating in company, where their presence was regarded as dangerous.

The reduced dimensions of these vessels was in part due to a reaction against the size of *Inflexible* and a government-driven desire for economy. However, other factors were also at work in that the Admiralty was faced with a number of technical problems that made them reluctant to commit themselves to any substantial building programme. As a result, at a time when the French were in the process of increasing armoured ship construction, the British laid down no further armoured ships until 1879, a situation assisted by a general political and public indifference to the potential change in the balance of naval power. The first item of concern was the future of armoured ships and the correct balance of new designs with regard to stability, armour and armament and in particular their size and possibly whether they had any future at all. Added to this were several new developments all of which were related directly or indirectly to the use of steel in place of iron, namely:

1. the use of steel for ship construction;

2. improvements in the performance of guns and the relative merits of muzzle- and breech-loading;
3. the introduction of compound and all-steel armour.

Steel had been in existence for many years and was well known as a material which gave improved mechanical properties over iron and could allow for substantial savings in weight for the same strength. It was, however, much more expensive and was difficult to produce in consistent and reliable quality and was used only in limited amounts for relatively unimportant structures until the introduction of improved and large scale production methods in the 1870s. By the end of this decade iron for ship-building purposes, which was subject to a substantial premium on the cost to achieve the desired quality, was not much cheaper than steel (these materials were paid for by the ton which, given that less steel was required for the same structural strength, also improved the relative cost situation). Steel was first available in reasonable quantities in France where it was produced by the Siemens process and was first employed as the principal material of construction in the central battery ship *Redoutable*, laid down in 1873. However, there were still some problems in the control of the quality of steel and the outer bottom plating of this ship was constructed of iron and all subsequent French armoured ships of this period used mixed iron and steel hulls of this type. The cruiser *Milan* (laid down in 1882) had an all-steel hull, but this construction did not come into general use in French cruising ships until the mid-1880s.

In 1875 the British Admiralty also decided that the future lay in steel construction and contracted for the supply of Siemens material for the hulls of the Royal Navy's first all-steel ships – the despatch vessels *Iris* and *Mercury* laid down in 1875–76. All subsequent British con-

Britain's first steel warships were the Iris *and* Mercury, *completed in 1879. Officially rated as dispatch vessels, they emphasised speed over protection and armament,* Mercury *reaching 18.5kts, which made her the fastest warship of her day.* Iris, *shown here as built, may be regarded as the prototype of the modern British cruiser.* (CMP)

struction was all-steel with the exception of the use of composite hulls (iron and/or steel framing with wood hull planking) for small cruisers, a situation made largely possible by the production of large volume cheap steel in Britain as a result of the introduction of the Bessemer steelmaking process. Italy made a similar decision at about the same time by specifying steel for their new 13,000-ton battleships *Italia* and *Lepanto* laid down in 1876 and followed by starting on all-steel cruisers at the end of the decade. The few problems that occurred with steel in the early years were quickly overcome with improvements in the control of the production process and the introduction of new and improved grades, so that by the mid-1880s virtually all warship construction had changed over to this material.

Steel also provided a potential solution to fitting ships with adequate protection against the increasing power of modern guns. Steel could be manufactured in a much harder state than wrought iron and therefore had a much greater resistance to penetration; unfortunately it was also much more brittle and tended to crack and break-up when struck by projectiles. The initial solution to this problem was to weld a steel face onto a wrought iron back, the steel representing about 30 per cent of the thickness – the idea was that the hard steel face would provide the necessary resistance to penetration while the wrought iron would give resilient support to the steel and, if the latter cracked, would hold the pieces together. The first attempts to manufacture this compound armour in the late 1860s failed because of the inadequate welding of the two materials which resulted in the steel breaking up and falling off the wrought iron backing. However by the mid-1870s the British firms of Cammell and John Brown had solved these problems and produced compound plates which showed a superiority in resistance to penetration over wrought iron in the order of about 1.25:1. Plates from these manufacturers were tested at Shoeburyness in 1877 and resulted in the adoption of compound armour for the turrets of *Inflexible*, *Ajax* and *Agamemnon*. In 1879,

after further trials at Shoeburyness, the Admiralty decided to use compound armour for the vertical hull protection of all future battleship designs, including the recently begun *Colossus*, *Edinburgh* and *Conqueror*. Most other navies followed the British lead but the Italians and, partially, the French took a different course.

During the same period the French firm of Schneider based in Creusot were developing all-steel armour which was tested in comparative trials against iron armour at La Spezia in 1877. Although the steel plates were shattered they had greater resistance to penetration and the Italians decided to adopt this armour for the battleships *Duilio* and *Dandolo* (one of which had already been launched), which thus became the first warships with all-steel armour. Although this armour could be destroyed, it did keep out the first projectile, which expended its energy in cracking the plate; the danger was that a second projectile would strike in the same weakened area – the odds against this were obviously good and the Italians were willing to accept the risk in order to gain improved defence against the initial attack. However, they remained the only country totally dedicated to all-steel armour until the end of the 1880s.

In 1880 the French also carried out comparative trials, this time between all-steel and compound armour, and initially chose the latter but Schneider refused to accept orders for this material, wishing to continue its development of steel armour and the French authorities subsequently reversed their decision. However, Schneider did not have the capacity to supply all French requirements and, being the only supplier of high quality steel armour, it was necessary to make up the shortfall with compound armour from other sources. As a result French battleships carried an odd mixture of all-steel and compound armour which varied from class to class and from ship to ship within a class.

The passing of the muzzle-loading gun

In the manufacture of naval guns the principal players of this period were the British RGF (Royal Gun Factory) at Woolwich, which was under the control of the army, the French gun factories at Ruelle and Nevers, which were under the control of the Ministry of Marine, and the private companies of Armstrongs in Britain and Krupps in Germany. Armstrongs supplied the majority of the Italian navy's guns while Krupp designs were used by the Austrian and Russian navies. In the mid-1870s there was a considerable divergence of approach among these manufacturers. The RGF and Armstrongs were building MLR guns constructed with a steel tube over which were shrunk wrought iron hoops; the French were building BL (breech-loading) guns consisting of a cast iron body with a steel liner and outer steel hoops shrunk over the rear half only (1870 pattern), and an interrupted screw breech block; Krupps were building BL guns similarly built-up but of all-steel construction and with a sliding wedge breech block. In 1875 the French also changed to all-steel construction (1875 pattern).

Despite its apparent antiquity, the muzzle-loader originally compared well with its breech-loading rivals, either equalling or exceeding them in performance, but new developments in the late 1870s gradually made this weapon a much less practical proposition. Guns still used gunpowder to fire projectiles, which in its original form detonated and expended its energy virtually instantaneously. It was found that by manufacturing powder in larger grains this process could be slowed down thereby keeping the pressure behind the projectile for longer and increasing its velocity. This idea was further developed first by compressing powder into small pebbles, and then blocks of various shapes designed to burn from the outer surface inwards, and also by varying

France made a change from the centre battery ship to upper deck barbette mountings with the Amiral Duperré, *launched in 1879. This was followed by the generally similar* Amiral Baudin *class, laid down in that year but not completed until 1888–89. The second ship,* Formidable *(seen here) was slightly different in appearance. The main armament of three single 37cm (14.6in) guns on the centreline is clearly visible.* (CMP)

the basic composition of the powder. In addition it was found that chambering (providing an air space around the charge, by boring out the breech end of the bore to a larger diameter) further improved the ballistic performance. These developments had two major effects: first, slow burning powder produced a much lower initial pressure in the gun, which reduced the amount of strength, and therefore weight, required around the breech; second, to take advantage of the increased length over which the pressure of the charge could be maintained guns needed to be longer. Both increased length and chambering were applied to the MLR but the degree to which these could be successfully carried out was limited and towards the end of the decade new BL guns, particularly those of Krupps and Armstrongs were beginning to show marked advantages in performance and weight. The principal difficulty with chambering MLRs was in the physical limitations of machining the bores, which was comparatively easy with a BL gun, while the increased length created physical difficulties in loading, requiring either inconvenient loading arrangements external to the mounting and its protection or excessive amounts of room behind the mounting to allow the gun to be run in – both expensive solutions in terms of weight and space.

In 1878 Armstrongs, following experimentation with slow burning powder, re-embarked on the development of BL guns using a variation on the French interrupted screw breech block which, because it was provided with a firing mechanism that was locked-out unless the breech was fully closed, removed one of the Admiralty's chief objections to breech-loaders – a lack of safety. However, while succeeding in selling these weapons to Italy, they failed to interest the Admiralty, who decided in December 1878 that *Ajax* and *Agamemnon* would be armed with the 12in 38-ton chambered MLR manufactured by Woolwich. Shortly afterwards, in January 1879, one of the 38-ton guns in the fore turret of the battleship *Thunderer* burst while she was carrying out gunnery practice in the Sea of Marmora, killing eleven men and injuring thirty-five others. Initially this produced serious doubts about the existing

form of gun construction but the subsequent investigation revealed that the gun had been double loaded following a misfire. The lack of recoil had not been noticed because the guns were run in hydraulically immediately after firing. It was soon realised that such an accident was not possible with BL guns and in April 1879 the Admiralty set up a committee to investigate the relative merits of the two systems. In addition, Krupps carried out a series of extensive trials with their new BL guns at Meppen between May and August 1879, to which witnesses from most of the main European naval powers, with the principal exception France, were invited.

These trials created a considerable impression and the Admiralty eventually reversed its decision of the previous year, against the wishes of Woolwich who preferred to continue the manufacture of MLRs, despite the fact that it was becoming increasingly clear that the only remaining merit of these guns was cheapness. In August 1879 BL guns were approved for the recently begun battleships *Colossus, Edinburgh* and *Conqueror* and an experimental 12in 43-ton BL gun was ordered from Armstrongs. At the same time Woolwich, who were still the Admiralty's chief supplier of heavy ordnance, began work on a 12in 43-ton BL of their own design utilising the Armstrongs breech mechanism. Unfortunately considerable technical problems were encountered in the production of Woolwich guns during the 1880s, which resulted in inferior weapons (in terms of quality rather than performance) and excessive delays in supply which in turn delayed the completion of the ships in which they were to be mounted. At the end of the decade, following the expression of dissatisfaction with the situation both officially and publicly, the Admiralty regained

control of its ordnance from the army and thereafter ordered the majority of its guns from private companies, usually Armstrongs or Vickers.

The French barbette ships

The preferences of French designers in seagoing battleships varied markedly from those of Britain. The evolution of designs was fairly steady and showed only limited signs of the sudden changes which characterised policy across the channel. Although this produced ships which appeared to give a regularity of type to the French navy they had serious weaknesses in protection and were generally under construction for so long that their potential value was greatly reduced by the time they joined the fleet. High freeboards and narrow, full-length waterline belts were favoured which, given stability requirements, did not lend themselves to the heavy turret mounted gun. At the same time there was a need to provide the few heavy guns now required with wider angles of fire and a higher command. To achieve these objects M Sabattier, the Director of Material (Chief Constructor) of the Ministry of the Marine, abandoned the central battery and its armour in favour of mounting the main armament entirely in barbettes on the upper deck. The advantages were substantial in that it promised to allow the efficient operation of the guns in all but the most severe weather but, with no protection above the shallow belt, except for the barbettes and their ammunition tubes, these high-sided ships were extremely vulnerable to gunfire.

The first ship of this type was *Amiral Duperré* laid down in 1877 and completed in 1883. Basically, she was a modified version of the

Courbet class central battery ships with the main armament of four 34cm (13.4in) guns raised one deck, two being mounted athwartships, forward in an elongated barbette to fire either side of the fore mast and two in individual barbettes on the centreline amidships and aft. Compared with the earlier ship, the belt was increased in thickness from 15in to 21.6in of wrought iron to take account of the increasing penetrating power of modern guns, the top being covered by a 3in steel protective deck 18in above the load waterline. Above this, armour tubes of 4in plating protected the ammunition supply to the barbettes which were little more than shallow parapets of 12in armour. One of the disadvantages of the barbette – that it was open topped, leaving the gun crew vulnerable to splinters and light fire from the tops of an enemy ship – was partially overcome by fitting steel splinter shields around the guns. However, the gun itself, projecting above the armour was always more vulnerable to damage than those of turret ships. *Amiral Duperré* was designed with a full sailing rig but this equipment was abandoned before the ship was completed; she retained all three masts, despite the fact that they obstructed the guns' arcs of fire. Like all the French barbette ships, and unlike contemporary British vessels, she carried a substantial secondary broadside battery on the main deck but, being completely unprotected, its value was limited.

Contemporary with *Amiral Duperré* were the *Bayard* and *Turenne*, virtually small versions of the same design with the after barbette omitted and the armament and armour proportionally reduced in line with a displacement reduction from 11,000 to 6000 tons. These, like other similar vessels of this period, are usually classed as armoured cruisers but could better be regarded as cheap, second class, armoured ships for foreign service. They had no speed advantage over their larger contemporaries – a prime requirement for cruisers – but did have a sailing rig and a wooden hull (albeit with a steel superstructure), which placed them in the colonial cruiser category. Two very similar vessels, *Duguesclin* and *Vauban*, were laid down in 1878–79 but were constructed with steel hulls, sheathed in wood and copper for tropical service. They were the last vessels of this type to

be laid down in France until the advent of the true armoured cruiser at the end of the 1880s.

Amiral Duperré was followed by the four ships of the *Terrible* class (*Caiman*, *Indomptable*, *Requin* and *Terrible*) laid down during 1877–78. These were second class battleships of 7500 tons which could best be described as enlarged coast defence ships. They were the only French ships to follow the British and Italian trend towards monster guns, carrying two barbette-mounted 42cm (16.5in) guns on centreline, one forward and one aft of a central superstructure. Their small size and heavy armament precluded a high freeboard but they were still better in this respect than contemporary British designs particularly because the barbette gun was by its very nature positioned well above the deck. The 19.7in belt, steel in *Terrible* and compound in her sisters, with a 3in steel deck followed closely the pattern set in *Amiral Duperré* but the protection to the guns was much improved, with 8in thick ammunition tubes and 18in barbettes.

At the end of 1879 two improved versions of *Amiral Duperré*, *Amiral Baudin* and *Formidable*, were laid down, in which the features of the earlier ship were modified to give a higher speed and better protection to the armament. As they were designed without a sailing rig there was no fore mast to obstruct the forward gun position and this was reduced to a single centreline barbette which saved weight, reducing the ahead fire to one gun but retaining the same broadside of three. The guns were larger calibre 37cm (14.6in) weapons protected by 16in compound armour barbettes and 16in steel ammunition tubes. The waterline was protected by a 22in steel belt and 3in–4in steel

deck but the height of the side armour was reduced and projected only 1ft above the load waterline. The ships did not complete until 1888–89.

In 1881 the French departed from their set pattern with the commencement of *Hoche*, an unusual vessel with a single 34cm (13.4in) gun mounted in a turret forward and aft and a 27cm (10.8in) gun in a barbette on either beam amidships. The turrets necessitated a low freeboard fore and aft but a high freeboard was retained amidships and it seems that this was an attempt to combine the best features of the turret and barbette systems in one ship. The turrets were of a design markedly different from those of other navies and provided a style which, in later years, was to become a distinctive feature of French ships. Instead of being low profile structures with the guns close to the deck they were tall, of minimum area (to save weight) and carried their guns high which compensated to some extent for the low freeboard and reduced the chances of water entering through the gunport in heavy weather. In other respects the design followed that of earlier ships with some small improvements, including an increased speed, a larger secondary armament and some minor changes in protection such as the raising of the main belt so that it projected 2ft above the load waterline.

In the same year France laid down *Marceau*, a vessel of similar design but with the turrets replaced by barbettes and, consequently, a uniform high freeboard. In addition the guns in the wing barbettes were increased in calibre to give a uniform main armament of four 34cm (13.4in) guns. The mountings for these guns were provided with all-round loading, thus ob-

Alongside the larger capital ships, France continued to favour smaller coast defence types, like the four ships of the Terrible *class, laid down in 1877–78 but not completed until ten years later. The single 42cm (16.5in) guns in the barbettes fore and aft are evident in this view of* Requin *taken about 1891. These ships inspired the British 'Admiral' class. (CMP)*

viating the need to bring the guns to a fixed loading position and increasing the rate of fire, but the system had a number of mechanical problems which reduced their efficiency. She was followed by two sister ships, *Neptune*, laid down in 1882, and *Magenta* (originally to have been a sister ship of *Hoche*), laid down in 1883. *Marceau* had compound armour for her belt and barbettes, in *Neptune* the barbettes were of steel, while in *Magenta* the belt was also changed to steel. Like the previous vessels these last four ships were extensively delayed during construction and did not complete until 1890–93 by which time the type was virtually obsolete.

Magenta brought the era of the French barbette ship to an end; she was also the last French battleship to be laid down until the end of the decade as a result of the influence of the *jeune école* – a group of influential naval officers who believed among other things that the day of the large ship was over and advocated the construction of small specialised ships and torpedo craft. Despite the high freeboard, most of these barbette ships were poor sea-boats and handled badly. Moreover, one of the marked features of French ships, a pronounced tumblehome, which helped in the reduction of topweight, did little to assist their stability or to limit their propensity for heavy rolling. However, in the form of gun mounting they did provide the pattern which all the major naval powers were to follow and during the 1890s the barbette, with the addition of an armoured gunhouse, became the standard method of mounting heavy guns. Oddly enough, when the French themselves returned to battleship construction in 1889 they abandoned the barbette for the turret mounted gun which they retained in all subsequent ships until the advent of the dreadnought period in the next century.

Italia

The first country to adopt the French barbette system in a seagoing battleship was Italy, although this was achieved in their own individual way in two remarkable and unusual ships. *Italia* and *Lepanto*, laid down in 1877–78 were designed by Benedetto Brin with the intention

of providing the Italian navy with the most powerful ships afloat. Mounting four Armstrongs 17in, 100-ton BL guns in pairs at opposite ends of an elongated barbette, or redoubt, fitted diagonally across the midships section of a high freeboard, steel hull, they were at the time the largest, most heavily armed and fastest battleships in existence. However, despite a displacement of 13,500 tons, well in excess of what other nations regarded as an acceptable size, these features were achieved at the expense of the vertical hull protection which Brin abandoned entirely on the basis that modern guns were so powerful that belt armour was no longer effective and it would in any case absorb so much weight that it could not be included without seriously limiting the other requirements of the design. Instead he adopted 3in thick, curved protective deck over the entire length with its outer, lower, edge 5ft 6in below the waterline. In the space between this and the deck above, 6ft above the waterline, protection of the stability and floatation was provided by a cellular layer. This consisted of longitudinal bulkheads and cofferdams fitted down each side of the ship, between which was an intermediate deck which divided the remaining volume into a minutely subdivided upper section and a lower section employed as coal bunkers. The space between the cofferdams and the ship's sides was filled with cork while the cofferdams themselves were accessible from the deck above so that the space could be utilised for damage control (by filling with hammocks, wood etc) in the event of the side being pierced at the waterline. The only substantial armour in the ships was provided for the guns, the 7ft 6in high barbette being of 19in armour with, unlike the French, sloping sides which increased the relative thickness to horizontal fire. The ammunition supply was protected by a single, central 9ft diameter tube of 18in plating and the funnel

uptakes by 16in armour from the protective deck to about 3ft above the waterline.

One of the requirements of the design was that they could serve as troop transports for 10,000 men, and it seems likely – given Mediterranean weather conditions, the vulnerability of the hull structure and the weight involved – that the high freeboard of 25ft (giving a gun height of 32ft) was more to do with providing accommodation than seakeeping qualities. They were designed for a speed of 16kts with 15,000hp which, at the time they were laid down, was only exceeded by the British despatch vessels *Iris* and *Mercury*, but by the time the ships completed in the mid-1880s the speeds of battleships generally had increased, and although they achieved around 18kts on trial their superiority in speed was to last only a few years. Like many Italian ships they showed technical brilliance but debatable military value and very soon after entering service they were outmoded by new developments, particularly the introduction of the medium calibre quickfiring (QF) gun which would have played havoc with their unprotected hulls.

The *Italia* design was heavily criticised as employing an unproven protective system and being wasteful of Italy's limited financial and shipbuilding facilities, a view that was endorsed by the Navy Minister, Vice-Admiral Fernando Acton. Consequently, the next class of Italian battleships reverted to smaller dimensions with an improved version of the *Duilio* class. Designed by Giuseppe Micheli the new vessels, *Ruggiero di Lauria*, *Francesco Morosini* and *Andrea Doria* were laid down in 1881–82. Compared with *Duilio* they were of the same size and proportions and employed the same system of hull protection, but gained the advantages of newer technology in adopting barbette mounted 17in BL guns in place of turret mounted MLRs and more powerful machinery giving an increase in speed. They were,

After a period of great innovation under the auspices of Benedetto Brin, the march of Italian warship design faultered. The three ships of the Ruggiero di Lauria *class represented a return to moderate characteristics, and were little more than slightly improved* Duilios. *Since they did not completed until 1888–91, they were effectively obsolescent by the time they entered service.* Andrea Doria *is depicted here in April 1899. (CMP)*

however, retrograde in character and, by the time they completed during 1888–91, they were of outdated design.

In the early 1880s Benedetto Brin, who was soon to replace Acton as Navy Minister, set to work on reinstating his own ideas and produced a design which combined the layout of the British 'Admiral' class with the protective system and speed of *Italia*. The resultant *Re Umberto* class, *Re Umberto*, *Sardegna* and *Sicilia*, laid down during 1884–85 were again much larger than foreign contemporaries but abandoned the 17in gun in favour of the more moderate but faster firing 13.5in and a heavier secondary battery. Protection to the hull originally followed the *Italia* pattern except that the protective deck was positioned higher, with its outer edge about 3ft below and its centre projecting above the waterline. While the ships were under construction the medium calibre quick-firing gun made its appearance and Brin, conceding that their unprotected sides were insufficient to meet this new threat, added 4in side armour between the protective and main decks, extending from the fore side of the forward barbette to the aft side of the after barbette. This additional weight increased the displacement and reduced freeboard but as the barbettes were comparatively tall with the guns well above the deck, this was less of a disadvantage than might otherwise have been the case. The main armament guns could be loaded at any angle of training and 4in gun shields were fitted over the top of the barbettes which, although insufficient to keep out heavy shells as later gunhouses were intended to do, were a great improvement on the splinter shields and bullet-proof plating previously employed. The ships were designed for a speed of 18kts but actually achieved 20kts on trials and they were to remain the fastest if not the best protected battleships in the world for several years. The third ship of the class, *Sardegna*, was an additional unit ordered after Brin became Navy Minister and differed from her sisters in being the first Italian ship fitted with triple expansion engines. *Re Umberto* did not complete until 1893, while her two sisters followed in 1895, by which time their value as fighting ships had greatly diminished.

The 'Admiral' class

After a three-year break the Admiralty laid down three battleships in 1879. The first two, *Colossus* and *Edinburgh*, were slightly enlarged versions of *Ajax* and *Agamemnon* and the third, *Conqueror*, a turret ram similar in concept to the earlier *Rupert*. None of these ships was particularly outstanding but they did introduce all the major material developments of the time, being the first British battleships constructed of steel, the first to carry the new BL guns and the first to have compound armour protection to the hull. *Colossus* and *Edinburgh* had a larger citadel than their predecessors and increased stability, giving a better chance of surviving with extensive damage to their unprotected ends but they rolled badly and while increased length improved their handling they were still less than perfect in this respect. Although they ran trials in 1883–84 they did not enter service until three years later owing to the delayed completion of their guns. *Conqueror*, too large for coast defence and too small for efficient operation at sea, was not a success. A sister ship, *Hero*, was laid down five years after *Conqueror* but before the latter was completed.

The decision to change to BL guns, made after *Colossus* and *Edinburgh* were designed, made it possible for the British to fulfil a desire to follow the French barbette system, this hav-

ing been impractical with muzzle-loading guns. Initially, in keeping with existing political desire for small, inexpensive ships, the French *Terrible* class were taken as a model, but the Director of Naval Construction, Barnaby, soon found that it was not possible to provide for British requirements within such a limited displacement and the final design was some 2000 tons heavier. This ship, *Collingwood*, was laid down in 1880 and carried four 12in guns mounted in two barbettes, one forward and one aft giving good all-round arcs of fire – with one exception it was to remain the standard main armament disposition for all British battleships for the next twenty-five years. Although the freeboard fore and aft was low, limiting the ability to maintain speed in a seaway, the gun axes were 22ft above the load waterline, about 10ft higher than in the turret ships, which enhanced her value as a seagoing fighting ship. Also following the French pattern, she was designed with a secondary gun battery of six 6in BL guns equally disposed on each side of the upper deck amidships. Unlike the French model, however, these weapons were not entirely unprotected, having 6in armour screens at the ends of the superstructure as a defence against raking fire. This armament was intended for defence against torpedo craft and for attack on unprotected portions of enemy ships, and again was in part made possible by the change to BL guns which required less space to accommodate than muzzle-loaders. This innovation was also made retrospectively to the turret ships then under construction but, due to the physical limitations of the superstructure in those ships, could not be arranged in quite so convenient a manner.

The heavy citadel armour followed the practice of the earlier turret ships except that, having no turret bases to protect, the height was reduced by one deck, saving a substantial amount of weight but increasing the amount of vulnerable structure. The barbettes had sloping walls like those in *Italia* while the undersides were protected by a 3in floor and the tops covered with bullet-proof plating. The mountings, designed by George Rendel of Armstrongs, had fixed loading arrangements at the rear of the barbette which, in consequence, was pear shaped. The ammunition supply was protected, as in the French ships, by an armoured trunk between the rear end of the barbette and the citadel. Fore and aft of the citadel between the lower and main decks the hull was heavily subdivided and coal and patent fuel formed part of the defensive system but, unlike the earlier turret ships, no provision was made for cork or other water-excluding devices. The ship was to be heavily criticised, particularly in the service, for lack of protection but she was a broad ship with fine ends so the hull volume beyond the citadel actually represented a small proportion of the whole. *Collingwood* was the first ship to be designed with forced draught

for her boilers which were intended to give 9000hp for a speed of 16kts, a 2kt advantage over the designed speed of *Colossus* and *Edinburgh*. However, the latter achieved 16kts on trial while *Collingwood* made 16.6kts with natural draught and gained only a quarter of a knot when forced. Despite the advantages gained in adopting the barbette, her low freeboard was to prove a major disadvantage; having fine ends she pitched heavily and, combined with a heavy roll, this produced a tendency to ship large amounts of water over the forecastle, seriously limiting the working of the main armament.

Five similar ships were laid down in 1882–83 which together with *Collingwood* became the 'Admiral' class, the first homogeneous, if not entirely identical, group of battleships to be provided for the Royal Navy since the *Audacious* class of 1867. The first two, *Howe* and *Rodney*, were repeats of *Collingwood* except for the substitution of 13.5in guns for the 12in and some minor changes to the protection. These alterations added 800 tons to the displacement and increased the draught, and the immersion of the armour belt, by 18in. In order to correct the latter and provide for further improvements the next three ships, *Anson*, *Camperdown* and *Benbow*, were made 5ft longer and 6in wider, the displacement increasing by another 300 tons to 10,600 tons. The principal additions were an increase in the thickness of the barbette armour, the lengthening of the citadel by 10ft and an increase in the power of the machinery to compensate for the modified

hull form. In 1883 one last variation occurred, partly as a result of the problems being experienced at Woolwich in the production of BL guns, when it was decided to modify *Benbow* to carry two Armstrongs 16.25in, 110-ton guns; it was to be the last of the British excursions into the monster gun craze. Weight and space considerations meant that only one gun could be mounted in each barbette giving an overall weight saving which was utilised to increase the secondary armament from six to ten 6in guns. The 16.25in gun proved a limited success and suffered from various problems including muzzle droop and a high wear rate. Considering the limitation of the number carried by *Benbow* and its slow rate of fire the four 13.5in guns of the other ships of the class gave a better balanced design. All six ships of the 'Admiral' class were delayed in completion while waiting for their guns and eventually entered service during 1887–89.

The end of the sailing era

In 1881 Britain laid down *Imperieuse* and *Warspite*, two armoured cruiser contemporaries to *Collingwood* with a full two-masted brig rig. Their design followed even more closely the French barbette ships, having the same armament layout as *Marceau* but with four 9.2in guns in shallow barbettes and a pronounced tumblehome – a necessity to give the wing guns clear, blast free, arcs of fire. Hull protection followed the *Collingwood* pattern but was of reduced dimensions and thickness except that the protective deck, fore and aft, was increased to 3in. Additions and poor weight control during construction resulted in an increase in displacement which almost completely submerged the belt armour, making it virtually useless and an unnecessary burden on the design. In addition, the trials of *Imperieuse* revealed her sailing qualities to be extremely poor and the report of her captain pointed out that his ship would be greatly improved if her masts and yards, which had proved to be so much dead weight, were removed. This advice was followed and both ships were refitted with a single military mast amidships which partially compensated for their overweight condition.

Warspite, one of a pair of armoured cruiser equivalents of the 'Admiral's. Designed primarily as flagships for foreign stations, they originally sported a brig rig – reckoned to be useful for peacetime training – but this was soon removed, as shown here. The curiosities of the hull-form – the convex tumblesome, the midships 9.2in sponson and the ports for the secondary 6in guns – can be seen to advantage. (CMP)

Even so they were not a successful design and their main claim to fame is that they were the last fully rigged warships, apart from a few sloops and smaller vessels, to be designed for the Royal Navy.

In battleships sail power had already been abandoned by all the major naval powers and during the 1880s the same pattern was followed with cruisers, although some full rigged designs were still to be seen into the early 1890s. This was particularly so in Russia which was the only country other than Britain to continue the construction of armoured cruisers during the 1880s. In all, five such ships were laid down during this time, all rigged and generally outdated – one, *Admiral Nakhimov*, was virtually a copy of the British *Imperieuse*, while the others were simple broadside ships. The last of this group, *Rurik*, attracted some attention but this was largely because of her 11,000-ton displacement. The last British armoured cruisers of this period, the *Orlando* class, are discussed later.

The Royal Navy's last turret ships

The design of the 'Admiral' class did not find favour in the Navy, the principal objection being the apparent weakness of the hull protection. Changes in the Board of Admiralty in the early 1880s also brought a change of policy with regard to the mounting of heavy guns and the barbette was abandoned in favour of the turret with its improved but weighty protection. Initially there was also a desire for reduced dimensions, which led to the laying down of *Conqueror*'s sister ship, *Hero*, in 1884 and a request for an improved version of this ship as a follow up. It soon became clear, however, that the inclusion of all the design requirements in such a limited displacement was impossible and the end result, after the consideration of several other layouts, was a substantially enlarged version of *Hero*. Two ships to this new design, the 10,500-ton *Victoria* and *Sans Pareil*, were laid down in 1885 and completed in 1890–91. Like *Benbow* they carried two 16.25in guns but in this case they were concentrated in a single turret forward, thus minimising the weight required for their protection. Unfortunately, while this arrangement may have been acceptable for a coast defence ship or a ram, it was hardly suitable for a first class battleship – it seriously restricted the all-round arcs of fire and hence tactical use of the ships and concentrated the main armament, which was thereby in danger of being put out of action by one hit.

The turret was constructed of 17in compound armour and was mounted over an 18in oval redoubt which protected the turret base and ammunition supply between the upper deck and the citadel. Despite the criticism of the protection of the 'Admiral' class, the remaining armour was almost identical in design to that of the previous class, except that the citadel was 12ft longer and 1ft deeper and the protective deck at the ends was increased to 3in thickness. To compensate for the ships' lack of astern fire a single 10in gun was fitted at the after end of the superstructure but, as this weapon was completely unprotected, its value was negligible. *Victoria* and *Sans Pareil* were the first British battleships fitted with triple expansion engines and on trials achieved over 17kts with forced draught and 16kts without.

Victoria subsequently achieved notoriety when she was accidentally rammed and sunk by *Camperdown* during fleet manoeuvres in the Mediterranean on 22 June 1893. Although this started the usual debate on the lack of stability of the central citadel ship the subsequent inquiry showed that the loss was due to progressive flooding resulting from the fact that the ship was not fully closed-up. As a result the regulations with regard to the closure of watertight doors and hatches were tightened, and improvements were suggested with regard to future ship design, including the omission of doors in bulkheads below the protective deck.

In 1885 Nathaniel Barnaby resigned his position as the Admiralty's chief designer and William White, a former member of the Admiralty design staff and then the manager and chief designer of the Armstrongs shipyard, was invited to take his place. At the same time there was a change of Government and a new Board was appointed with Admiral Sir Arthur Hood as First Sea Lord. This officer was an advocate of turrets and heavy armour and, before White took up his appointment, he set the Admiralty's design team to work on a modern version of the turret ship *Dreadnought*. Although the design subsequently received White's official approval, it was not to his liking, showing a bias towards protection which did not represent a careful utilisation of the available weight. To meet the requirements of the heavy protection it was finally accepted that an increase in size would be necessary and, with the advantage of a return of political and public interest in the Navy, the displacement was raised to 12,000 tons.

The resultant ships, *Nile* and *Trafalgar*, laid down in 1886, followed the same general layout as the 'Admiral' class but with the barbettes replaced by turrets and the unprotected space between the upper deck and the citadel filled by an 18in–16in redoubt extending around the turret bases and then angled out to the ship's side where it formed an upper belt. The citadel itself was of increased dimensions and thickness, being 20in amidships and reducing to 18in and 14in towards the ends. The result was an exceptionally well protected ship

Russia built four barbette ships for the Black Sea Fleet in the 1880s. The six 12in guns were disposed in three twin mountings in a triangular pattern around the central redoubt, two abreast, forward and one aft. In Ekaterina II, *the name ship of the class, they were fitted on hydraulic disappearing mountings, so are almost invisible, hidden under the superstructure in this view. (CMP)*

in which a third of the displacement was absorbed by the armour but one which still retained the inherent defect of the turret ship – a low freeboard. The designed secondary battery was six 5in BL guns but during the ships' construction these were replaced by the newly introduced Armstrongs 4.7in QF gun and, as a defence against the same weapon, the battery was fitted with 4in side armour as well as 5in screen bulkheads. These and other changes during construction raised the displacement of the completed ships to 12,590 tons, increasing the draught and reducing the freeboard by 1ft. The two ships completed in 1890–91.

When the construction of *Nile* and *Trafalgar* was officially announced in Parliament it was stated that they were expected to be the last such ships that would be built for the Royal Navy. Like the French, the British had concluded that the torpedo and the improving qualities of the vessels built to carry it would soon render the battleship obsolete. It was soon realised, however, that this was not to be the case and after a three-year break the big ship was to return with a vengeance with the onset of the pre-dreadnought era.

Russia

Although nominally the third naval power of this period, Russia did not commence any new seagoing battleships throughout the 1870s and

it was not until 1883 that the country embarked on a new construction programme. During the next eight years the Russians laid down ten battleships but, although this restored their quantitative position among the naval powers, the ships were generally uninspiring and somewhat behind their contemporaries in design. The Russians were more reliant on foreign expertise for guns, armour and machinery than the other major naval powers and also had to contend with the difficult strategic problem of providing fleets for both the Black Sea and the Baltic. Nevertheless, the Russian fleet was a force to be considered and at this time the Royal Navy viewed a combination of France and Russia as the most serious threat it could face.

Russia never showed any interest in the monster gun and all the ships of the 1880s were fitted with 12in guns of Krupp design but manufactured in Russia. The numbers carried varied considerably from six in the *Ekaterina II* class to one in the small *Gangut*, but by the end of the decade a standard arrangement of four,

mounted in pairs fore and aft, had been adopted. The earlier ships tended to follow the French pattern with full length waterline belts, high freeboards and barbette mounted guns, but the later ships, *Navarin* and *Tri Svititelia*, laid down in 1889 and 1891 respectively, followed the layout of the British *Trafalgar* class with low freeboard, turret mounted guns and heavy central citadel armour. The most interesting of these ships was, however, the first group – the 11,000-ton *Ekaterina II*, *Tchesma* and *Sinop* laid down in 1883 and completed in 1889–90. They carried their six guns in three pairs at the corners of a large triangular redoubt – two pairs mounted abreast forward and one on the centreline aft – which gave the ships good all-round arcs of fire. The redoubt also extended right down to the top of the belt, greatly improving the protection over that normally available from the barbette system. Applied to a single mounting this arrangement was to become the standard barbette design of the next decade. The *Ekaterina II* carried her guns on disappearing mountings and the *Sinop* was the first battleship to be designed with triple expansion engines. A fourth ship of this class, *Georgi Pobiedonosets*, was laid down in 1889 but differed from the earlier vessels in having all-steel armour in place of compound and in abandoning the full length belt armour for a central citadel arrangement. Most of the ships that followed the *Ekaterina II* class were of limited displacement, except the above-mentioned *Tri Svititelia*, which was designed for 12,500 tons and completed at 13,300 tons.

Navarin of 1889, *a Russian turret ship similar in layout to the* Trafalgar. *The ship was well protected and survived considerable damage before succumbing to mines at the Battle of Tsushima in 1905. Note the four funnels that caused the ship to be nicknamed 'The Factory' in the Russian navy. (CMP)*

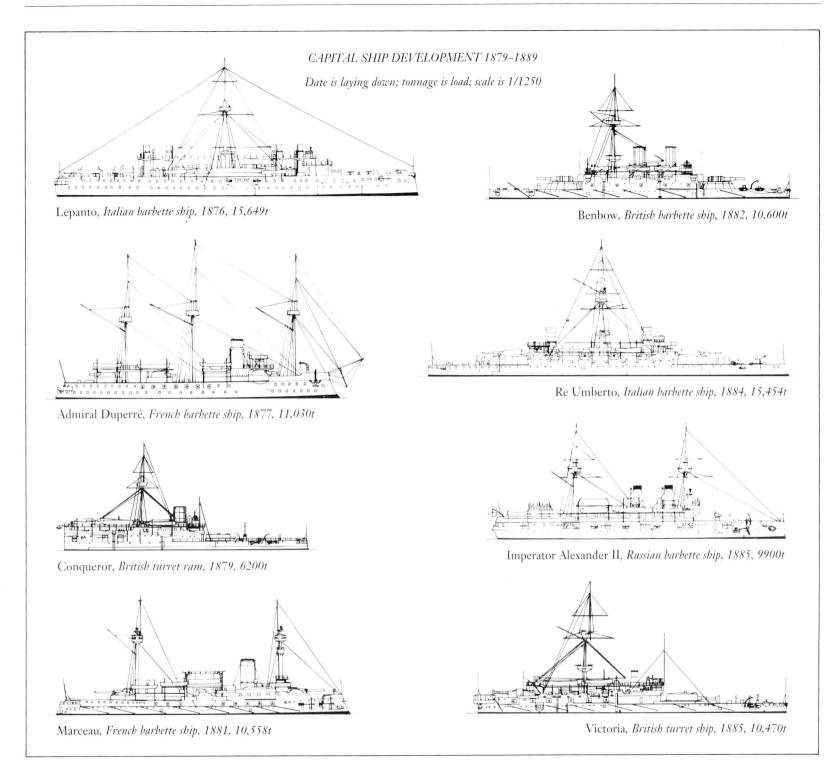

CAPITAL SHIP DEVELOPMENT 1879–1889

Date is laying down; tonnage is load; scale is 1/1250

Lepanto, *Italian barbette ship, 1876, 15,649t*

Benbow, *British barbette ship, 1882, 10,600t*

Admiral Duperré, *French barbette ship, 1877, 11,030t*

Re Umberto, *Italian barbette ship, 1884, 15,454t*

Conqueror, *British turret ram, 1879, 6200t*

Imperator Alexander II, *Russian barbette ship, 1885, 9900t*

Marceau, *French barbette ship, 1881, 10,558t*

Victoria, *British turret ship, 1885, 10,470t*

Cruising ships

Until the end of the 1870s the design of cruising ships (frigates, corvettes, sloops, gunvessels and gunboats), although provided with the latest types of machinery and ordnance, showed little variation in general layout and basic concept from those of the pre-ironclad period. The majority were constructed of wood and although some, particularly the larger vessels, were iron hulled, the only marked variation was to be found in the construction of armoured cruisers which, as previously mentioned were, in their early form, little more than second class ironclads. The reasons for this apparent lack of development were both practical and technical. The building of ironclads absorbed much of the available expertise in design and construction, which tended to concentrate attention on the individual characteristics of these vessels. This, together with the absence of any major naval war or any form of fleet manoeuvres designed to reproduce the possible strategies and tactics for war, resulted in a general lack of consideration of the development of the fleet as a whole.

The requirements for cruisers were well understood but how they were to integrate with the ironclad fleet was not. In some ways this was not surprising, for given the bulky steam machinery then available it was not possible to provide cruisers of moderate dimensions with a margin of speed over the modern battleship. Without this the full requirements of a fleet or trade cruiser could not be fulfilled, principally because they could not escape from more powerful adversaries. The problem could and sometimes was solved by an increase in size, but cruisers also needed to be available in large numbers and this was therefore an impractical solution for economic reasons. Even in engaging each other cruisers would have had serious problems since, being unprotected, they were extremely vulnerable to modern ordnance. Any attempt to solve this with the existing methods of vertical armour protection would have absorbed too high a percentage of the available weight in a medium sized ship and still further diminished the speed.

All this principally applied to the provision of ships for war, but cruisers also enabled the main colonial powers, Britain and France, to extend their peacetime power and influence to distant parts of the world; for this purpose existing cruisers were more satisfactory. The main requirements were for economic vessels, cheap both to build and operate, powerful enough to deal with minor conflicts and local disturbances, to carry out police duties and show the flag. For this, sail power was essential, because steam machinery alone was for many years insufficiently reliable for service in areas where docking and repair facilities were few. It also took some years to establish a world-wide system of coaling stations and the ships themselves had insufficient endurance to undertake extended voyages on steam alone. Improvements in ship and machinery design were to reverse this situation during the early 1880s as sail power, although requiring no fuel, was expensive in terms of weight and manpower and was moreover a dangerous encumbrance in action. It was abandoned by most navies during the 1880s but survived in some cruisers into the next decade, and for even longer in the smaller gun-vessels, which effectively became a separate type from the modern cruiser and specifically intended for colonial police work.

In the mid-1870s the British Admiralty began to examine the requirements for future cruiser development and concluded that the essential high speed could be obtained by a change in the balance of hull weight and engine power. This resulted in the construction of the experimental despatch vessels *Iris* and *Mercury* in which a steel hull, light armament

An innovation in the armouring of cruisers was the protective deck designed to cover the machinery spaces. This was introduced in the steel corvettes of the British Comus *class, laid down during 1876–79. Two improved versions were added in 1881, one of which was the famous* Calliope, *seen here, which was the only ship of the international squadron to escape from Apia during the hurricane of March 1889. (CMP)*

and reduced rig were utilised to save weight for the installation of a 6000hp twin-screw machinery arrangement which, together with a fine hull form, was intended to give a speed of 17kts. All previous cruisers, except the large armoured ships of the *Nelson* class, had single-screw machinery and this addition of a second set of engines not only improved performance but avoided the possibility of total disablement due to a single machinery breakdown. The initial trials of *Iris* in 1877 were disappointing as she achieved only 16.6kts but after the fitting of new propellers she made 17.89kts with 7330hp. *Mercury* did even better, achieving 18.57kts with 7735hp, which made her the fastest warship in existence for several years. The cost of this achievement was fairly light – steel, although expensive in this case, was soon to become much cheaper and the light armament of ten 64pdrs had been established by experiment as at the lower end of the ideal range for cruisers, whose liveliness in a seaway mitigated against the successful working and loading of heavy guns. Although described as despatch vessels they were ideally suited to scouting and attacks on trade but for defensive purposes their light armament and lack of protection (apart from the provision of deep coal bunkers on each side) was insufficient, and for the British the defence of trade was a primary requirement.

The problem of protection was partially overcome in the 2400-ton *Comus* class, designed by Barnaby and contemporary with *Iris* and *Mercury*. These ships had a flat 1½ in protective deck fitted over the machinery and magazines with the space above, which was abreast the waterline, subdivided into water-tight compartments. Six ships of this class were laid down in 1876, a further three in 1878–79

and two modified versions, with slightly improved protection in 1881. The protective deck not only served to defend the machinery and magazines from the splinters of projectiles detonating overhead but to preserve the buoyancy and stability. Unfortunately, these ships were in other respects conventional cruising vessels with a full rig and a speed of only 13kts. They were successful ships, well armed and among the best of the colonial cruiser types but they were not fleet cruiser material.

The answer was to fit the protection of *Comus* into a ship of similar design to *Iris*: and this was done with the next design of cruiser for the Royal Navy, the *Leander* class, the four ships of which were laid down in 1880–81. These ships were originally classified as despatch vessels but were redesignated Second Class cruisers before completion in 1885–87. Although larger than *Iris* they adopted less powerful machinery for a speed of 16.5kts in order to accommodate the additional weight of the protection, a heavier armament and an increased coal supply for a greater endurance. The protection was similar to that of the *Comus* class, except that the protective deck was raised to a position just below the waterline and its outer edge sloped down to a position 4ft below the waterline. This arrangement, while keeping the deck and hence the protected volume high, stopped projectiles from going under the deck if they struck near the waterline. The armament of ten 6in BL guns was fitted with 1.5in shields as protection against machine-gun fire and splinters.

The development of the *Leander* type was completed with the four ships of the *Mersey* class laid down in 1883–4, which stabilised the basic features of the Second Class protected cruiser. These ships, on a lighter displacement,

In parallel with the traditional looking sloops for colonial service, the Royal Navy developed a more modern form of cruiser from the dispatch vessels Iris *and* Mercury. *The first stage comprised the four ships of the* Leander *class laid down in 1880–81. Although they had a good steaming radius of 11,000nm at 10kts, they were fitted with a light barquentine rig which, as this photo of* Leander *shows, was retained until the late 1890s. These were followed by the* Mersey *class in which the sail rig was abandoned completely.* (CMP)

provided a substantial increase in protection and an increase in speed, while abandoning the sailing rig and accepting a small reduction in endurance. The protective deck was 2in thick on the flat and 3in on the slope and was extended to the full length of the ship. The level of the flat part was raised above the waterline producing a triangular space between the protective deck and the ship's side which was intended to restrict any flooding resulting from a hit on the waterline. They were also equipped with an armoured conning tower (9in) and 2in gunshields. The armament, influenced by the designs of Armstrongs for other navies (see below) was strengthened by the addition of an 8in gun on the forecastle and poop, but an increase in the 6in battery would have produced a better balanced design and no later British Second Class cruiser carried guns larger than 6in.

The Elswick cruisers

Although the Admiralty had initiated the development of the modern cruiser, it was a private company, Armstrongs, which provided the lead in cruiser design in the 1880s; their influence was to be seen directly in Italy, Japan, the United States and many minor navies, and indirectly in numerous others. The first of these ships was the 3000-ton *Esmeralda*, laid down at

After a period of very little construction in the 1870s, the USA launched what came to be called the 'New Navy' with a small programme of four ships authorised in March 1883. Sometimes called the 'ABCD' ships, because their names happened to begin with the first four letters of the alphabet, the 'C' was represented by the protected cruiser Chicago, *an undistinguished 4500-ton ship completed in 1889. The barque rig shown in this photograph was the original configuration.* (CMP)

Armstrongs' Elswick shipyard in 1881. Designed by George Rendel for Chile, she was a light, fast, heavily armed ship with no rig and the first vessel of the type to adopt a full length protective deck. The latter was 1in thick (2in over the magazines) reducing to 0.5in at the ends and was arched with the crown just below and the sides 4ft below the waterline. The space between this and the deck above was subdivided as in the *Leander* class but in addition a cork-filled cofferdam was fitted along the sides. This protective system was of basically the same principle as that employed in *Italia* and it is probable that that ship was its inspiration.

Esmeralda carried an armament of two 10in, on the centreline fore and aft, and six 6in, equally disposed on each broadside. All these guns were mounted on the upper deck in single, shielded, centre pivot mountings. With a speed of 18kts, she was on paper one of the most powerful medium sized warships in existence but her great advantages were gained at the expense of endurance, seakeeping qualities and a double bottom. In addition, the provision of two heavy guns, which was to become a standard feature of many Elswick and other cruisers, including the British *Mersey* class, did not prove successful in practice as they were too heavy to load and operate efficiently in a seaway in ships of this size. These limitations were to be found to a greater or lesser extent in the majority of the Elswick cruisers but they were nevertheless remarkable and advanced ships for their time and led the way in many of the improvements in cruiser design. Armstrongs went on to build cruisers for Italy, Japan, China, Argentina, Austria and the United States. George Rendel was followed as Armstrongs' senior designer by William White in 1883 and Phillip Watts in 1886; both were former Admiralty designers and subsequently returned there as Directors of Naval Construction.

Led by the Royal Navy and Armstrongs, cruiser design followed a similar general pattern throughout the 1880s, progressing from the old slow types to modern high speed ships in this one decade. The protective system of cruisers, other than the armoured types, changed from the partial, flat, submerged pro-

CRUISER DEVELOPMENT 1879–1889

Date is laying down; tonnage is load; scale is 1/1250

Armoured Cruisers

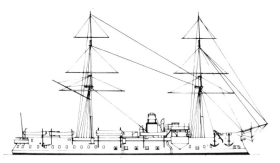

Vauban, *French small barbette ship, 1879, 6112t*

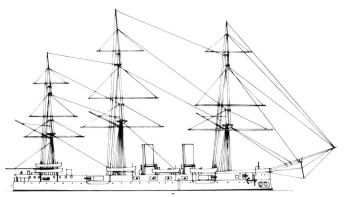

Vladimir Monomakh, *Russian armoured cruiser, 1880, 6000t*

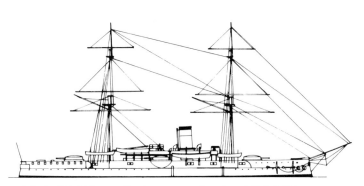

Admiral Nakhimov, *Russian armoured cruiser, 1884, 8524t*

Orlando, *British armoured cruiser, 1885, 5600t*

Unarmoured or Protected Cruisers

Comus, *British steel corvette (protected), 1876, 2380t*

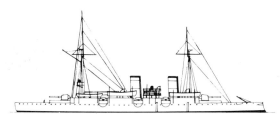

Idzumi (*ex-Esmeralda*), *'Elswick' cruiser, 1881, 3000t*

Milan, *French unarmoured cruiser, 1882, 1707t*

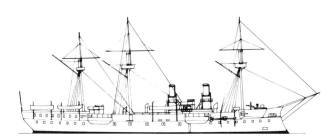

Sfax, *French protected cruiser, 1882, 4561t*

Mersey, *British protected cruiser, 1883, 4050t*

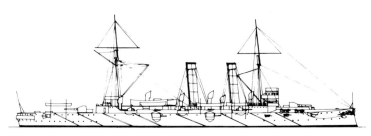

Blake, *British protected cruiser, 1888, 9150t*

The first French protected cruisers were the Sfax *of 4500 tons (in the background) and the larger* Tage *of 7500 tons. Laid down in 1882 and 1885 respectively, they retained a full sailing rig longer than equivalent British ships.* (CMP)

tective deck and cellular layer to the full length arched or sloped deck, sometimes with (but more often without) the cellular layer. Machinery power increased, to raise speeds from around 16kts to over 20kts while improved efficiency helped to save weight and enhance endurance. Engines changed from the horizontal to the more efficient vertical type which, because they could be mounted side by side, instead of fore and aft, saved length and hence weight, while the associate problem of having the cylinders projecting above the waterline was solved by fitting an armoured sloping glacis on the protective deck around the cylinder heads.

The introduction of steel boilers of improved design and, towards the end of the decade, evaporators which provided for the continuous supply of fresh feed water pushed steam pressures up from around 60psi (pounds per square inch) in 1880 to 155psi by the end of the decade. The use of forced draught – the pressurising of the stokehold to drive additional air through the furnaces – also gave a substantial improvement in boiler performance but it was soon found that excessive forcing rates caused rapid deterioration of boiler tubes, resulting in breakdowns and expensive repairs. Subsequently, stokehold pressures were limited to more reasonable levels and higher speeds obtained by increasing the machinery power. Inspired by more efficient machinery, sailing rigs were abandoned generally around the middle of the decade, although Russia retained this feature in all her cruiser designs of the 1880s.

Among the last developments of the decade was the introduction of the Armstrongs medium calibre QF gun which was first fitted in the Elswick cruiser *Piemonte*, built for Italy during 1887–89. This ship carried six 6in QF and six 4.7in QF, was designed for a speed of 22kts, and was protected by a full length deck of 1in on the flat and 3in on the slope, all on a displacement of 2400 tons. The high rate of fire of the QF gun effectively rendered the BL armed cruiser obsolete although this was later remedied in many ships by simply rearming them.

In France the introduction of the modern cruiser came later than in Britain but was less gradual. Before 1882 the majority of French cruisers were unprotected, rigged ships with wooden hulls, but in this year they laid down

Milan and *Sfax* – the former, a small unprotected cruiser but with a steel hull, no rig and a speed of 18kts; the latter, the first French protected cruiser, had an iron hull with steel frames and a full length 2.4in steel deck. *Sfax* was followed by two similar but larger vessels, *Tage* and *Amiral Cécille*, in which the speed was increased from the 16.5kts of *Sfax* to 18kts. It was, however, *Milan* that provided the basis for subsequent cruiser design, first in the six ships of the *Forbin* and *Troude* classes, laid down during 1886–87. These 2000-ton ships were designed for a speed of 20.5kts, carried four 5.5in guns and were fitted with a full length 1.6in protective deck. The design was further developed in the larger *Davout* (3000 tons), *Suchet* (3300 tons) and the *Alger* class (4000 tons), in which the increased dimensions were utilised to strengthen the armament and thicken the protective deck.

The primary purpose of these ships was attacks on trade: in fact in 1885 the French had officially stated that in any future war it was their intention to avoid fleet actions and concentrate on the crippling of the enemy by attacks on his seaborne trade. This was also the primary purpose of Russian cruisers, although these were all large and few in number – during the 1880s she laid down four armoured and one protected cruiser. Naturally, this was of particular concern to Britain whose empire and world-wide trade made her particularly vulner-

able to a war on commerce. To counter this threat she laid down the seven armoured cruisers of the *Orlando* class during 1885–86. These ships were true armoured cruisers, basically enlarged versions of *Mersey* with the addition of a shallow 10in armour belt amidships and a heavier armament. They were originally designed as 5040-ton ships but during construction the machinery and armament were improved and the nominal coal capacity increased which, together with other additions, increased the displacement by over 500 tons. The resultant increase in draught submerged the belt at load displacement, rendering it an almost useless appendage whose weight could have better been utilised on other features of the design. As a result of this experience the Admiralty concluded that the provision of a satisfactory arrangement of side armour was not possible in a cruiser and for the next thirteen years built nothing but protected cruisers. In other respects the *Orlando* class were reasonably successful ships, although they were soon to be outclassed in both speed and armament.

One of the first tasks facing William White when he returned to the Admiralty in 1885 was the preparation of new cruiser designs. His earlier ships, Second and Third Class cruisers, were not particularly outstanding, largely because of their limited size, but in the design of the First Class protected cruisers *Blake* and *Blenheim*, laid down in 1888 and completed in

1891–92, he truly fulfilled the Royal Navy's requirements for a well armed and protected, long range, high speed cruiser, with good sea-keeping qualities, capable of serving as both a fleet vessel and for trade protection. As always there was a price to pay, in this case a substantial increase in size to 9000 tons – largely necessary to accommodate the machinery.

The armament was the same as that fitted in the *Orlando* class except that the 6in guns were QF and distributed more widely, with two guns on each side moved down to the main deck and fitted in 6in armour casemates. This wider distribution, a feature also applied to the smaller cruisers, was intended to reduce the effect of losses among the guns and their crews if the ships were subjected to the fire of QF guns. The casemates were intended as a more positive defence against the same weapon and were to become a standard feature in future large cruiser and battleship designs, not only in Britain but in the majority of the principal navies.

They were too expensive in weight to be employed in smaller ships, where splinter shields had to suffice, but although providing a good level of protection they proved something of a mixed blessing. The main deck casemate (later ships also carried casemates at upper deck level) was generally too close to the waterline for the gun to be operated satisfactorily in anything other than calm weather; in any sort of sea they were in constant danger of being washed out and with the guns so low their sighting was also subject to severe limitations.

Blake and *Blenheim* had an unusual machinery arrangement in which, in order to accommodate the required power, two triple expansion engines were fitted in tandem to each of the two propeller shafts. It was designed to provide a speed of 20kts with 13,000hp at natural draught and 22kts with 20,000hp at forced draught. Endurance was to be 15,000 miles at 10kts. Unfortunately, neither ship proved capable of achieving these high figures as the extreme forcing rate, as previously mentioned, proved impractical and the machinery as a whole less reliable or economic than expected. The endurance was actually 10,000 miles at 10kts. However, both ships achieved over 21kts on trial at forced draught and proved capable of maintaining 19kts for extended periods under natural draught. Whatever the shortcomings of the machinery, which it should be mentioned were not the fault of the designer, *Blake* and *Blenheim* set the pattern for the future design of British First Class cruisers for the next decade and influenced the development of ships in other navies.

John Roberts

Warships of Steel: Typical Vessels 1879–1889

Ship or class	Nationality	Disp (load) (tons)	Dimensions (loa × breadth × draught) (feet–inches) (metres)	Armament	Armour (belt/turret or barbette/deck) (max, ins)	Speed (max, kts)	Launch dates	Numbers built
Battleships								
AMIRAL DUPERRÉ	French	11,030	319–10 wl × 66–11 × 27–8 97.5 × 20.4 × 8.4	4–13.4in RML, 1–6.4in, 14–5.5in	22/12/3	14	1879	1
ITALIA	Italian	13,678	409–0 × 74–0 × 28–8 124.7 × 22.5 × 8.8	4–17in, 7–5.9in, 4–4.7in	–/19/4	17.5	1880–83	2
COLOSSUS	British	9420	325–0 pp × 68–0 × 25–10 99.1 × 20.7 × 7.9	4–12in, 5–6in	18/16/3	16.5	1882	2
CONQUEROR	British	6200	288–0 × 58–0 × 23–6 87.8 × 17.7 × 7.2	2–12in, 4–6in	12/14/2.5	14	1881–85	2
TERRIBLE	French	7530	271–6 pp × 59–0 × 26–2 82.8 × 20.0 × 8.0	2–16.5in, 4–3.9in	20/18/3.2	15	1881–85	4
COLLINGWOOD	British	9500	325–0 pp × 68–0 × 26–4 99.1 × 20.7 × 8.0	4–12in, 6–6in	18/11.5/3	16.5	1882–86	6
EKATERINA II	Russian	11,200	339–6 × 69–0 × 28–0 103.5 × 21.0 × 8.6	6–12in, 7–6in	16/12/2	15	1886–92	4
TRAFALGAR	British	12,590	345–0 pp × 73–0 × 28–6 105.2 × 22.3 × 8.7	4–13.5in, 6–4.7in	20/18/3	16.5	1887–88	2
MARCEAU	French	10,558	323–6 pp × 66–0 × 27–0 98.6 × 20.1 × 8.3	4–13.4in, 16–5.5in	18/16/3.5	16	1887–90	3
RE UMBERTO	Italian	13,673	418–7 × 76–11 × 30–0 129.6 × 23.4 × 9.3	4–13.5in	4/14/3	18.5	1888–91	3
Armoured cruisers								
VAUBAN	French	6112	265–10 × 57–4 × 25–0 81.0 × 17.5 × 7.5	4–9.4in, 1–7.6in, 6–5.5in	10/8/2	14	1882–83	2
IMPERIEUSE	British	8500	315–0 pp × 62–0 × 26–10 96 × 18.9 × 8.2	4–9.2in, 10–6in	10/8/4	16.5	1883–84	2
ORLANDO	British	5600	300–0 pp × 56–0 × 22–6 91.4 × 17.1 × 6.9	2–9.2in, 10–6in	10/–/3	18	1886–87	7
PAMIAT AZOVA	Russian	6674	384–6 × 56–6 × 26–11 117.2 × 17.2 × 8.2	2–8in, 13–6in	6/–/2.5	17	1888	1
Cruisers					(deck/gun shields)			
IRIS	British	3730	333–0 × 46–0 × 22–0 101.5 × 14.0 × 6.7	13–5in	–/–	17	1877–78	2
COMUS	British	2380	225–0 × 44–5 × 19–3 68.6 × 13.6 × 5.9	4–6in, 8–64pdr	1.5/–	13	1878–81	9
ESMERALDA	Chilean	2950	270–0 pp × 42–0 × 18–6 82.3 × 12.8 × 5.6	2–10in, 6–6in	2/2	18	1883	1
SFAX	French	4561	300–5 wl × 49–2 × 25–2 91.6 × 15.0 × 7.7	6–6.4in, 10–5.5in	2.4/–	16.5	1884	1
MILAN	French	1705	302–0 × 32–10 × 15–7 92.1 × 10.0 × 4.8	4–3.9in	–/–	18	1884	1
MERSEY	British	4050	315–0 × 46–0 × 19–6 96.0 × 14.0 × 5.9	2–8in, 10–6in	3/–	18	1887–89	4
FORBIN	French	1935	311–8 × 29–6 × 17–2 95.0 × 9.0 × 5.2	4–5.5in	1.6/–	20	1888	3
PIEMONTE	Italian	2443	321–0 × 38–1 × 16–0 97.8 × 11.6 × 4.9	6–6in, 6–4.7in	3/4.5	22	1888	1
BLAKE	British	9150	399–10 × 65–0 × 24–0 121.8 × 19.8 × 7.3	2–9.2in, 10–6in	6/4.5	20	1889–90	2
ALGER	French	4313	344–6 pp × 42–7 × 20–0 105.0 × 13.0 × 6.1	4–6.4in, 6–5.5in	4/2	19	1889–91	3

7

The Pre-Dreadnought Age 1890–1905

THE inconsistency in naval development that had characterised the period prior to 1889 contrasted markedly with the designs of the 1890s. Warship construction, although still occasionally the subject of controversy, stabilised dramatically and showed a regularity of development which had not existed since the introduction of the ironclad. This progress was, moreover, largely a matter of detailed technical developments, the ships themselves being of generally similar specification, lending themselves more readily to the co-operative tactical requirements of fleet operations. Although the challenge from new navies was growing, the era was still dominated by the Royal Navy, which had gained an unprecedented level of public support and consequently a substantial level of political and financial backing. This advantage not only allowed for the construction of large numbers of ships but also for the increases in the size of individual ships which were necessary to improve the balance of the designs. This was particularly so with battleships, these being larger on average than those of other countries where the usual political/economic restraints continued to prevail until the turn of the century. Thereafter, not only warship design but the entire strategic situation began the gradual change which saw the emergence of Germany, Japan and the USA as new naval powers and was to lead to the *Dreadnought* era and the First World War.

Capital ship development

The 1890s also saw an improved understanding of the strategic and tactical use of naval power and, although France continued to plan for war with Britain on the basis of attacks on trade, both countries returned to battleship construction in 1889. This resulted from the final acceptance that torpedo boats were not as serious a threat as had been originally expected; this revision followed the evaluation of tactical exercises and a combination of anti-torpedo boat developments. Chief among the latter was the introduction of the medium calibre QF gun for, although the light QF gun and the machine-gun had been widely used since the early 1880s as an anti-torpedo boat armament, it was not until the introduction of these larger weapons that a gun with both a high rate of fire and the stopping power to seriously counter a massed torpedo boat attack became available. On a lesser scale, the use of torpedo nets (curtains constructed of steel rings which could be suspended on booms around a ship at anchor or when moving very slowly) and searchlights had removed some of the dangers of being attacked in harbour and at night.

Subsequently, the introduction of the first successful anti-torpedo boat vessel, the 'torpedo boat destroyer', in 1893 provided the battlefleet with a suitable defensive escort and the final vessel required for the balanced fleet of the future. The destroyer was, however, armed with both guns and torpedoes and effectively combined a defence against and a means of delivering torpedo attacks in a vessel more seaworthy than its predecessor. Although the torpedo therefore remained a potent threat, it was one that could be effectively countered given a good fleet organisation and well rehearsed tactics, the dangers being no greater than those to be expected when battleships faced each other.

Guns and armour

All the major manufacturers of heavy ordnance had by the early 1890s overcome the more serious problems encountered in the construction

The Naval Defence Act of 1889 marked something of a renaissance for the Royal Navy in numbers of new ships but also in the quality of the new designs. The battleships of the Royal Sovereign *class were particularly successfully, departing from previous designs in the high freeboard which helped to make them very seaworthy. They formed the basis for British battleship development over the next fifteen years, during the whole of the so-called 'pre-dreadnought era'. This is* Empress of India *in 1902. (NMM)*

of all-steel guns, and these continued to improve steadily in performance and accuracy along the already established lines of development. The only country to introduce a major change was Britain, which officially adopted wire-wound guns in 1890. This system consisted of winding steel ribbon wire around the gun's interior tubes and then shrinking the exterior tubes over it. This process added substantially to the gun's radial strength and its resistance to internal pressure, providing both a stronger and lighter gun. Its major disadvantage was that it reduced longitudinal rigidity leading to the possibility of the gun bending under its own weight (muzzle droop) but those weapons most susceptible to this – the large guns – were still comparatively short and it was several years before this became a serious problem. The wire gun was not new and had been tried experimentally by the French and by Armstrongs in the 1870s but had been abandoned as too expensive for the limited gain. Woolwich began experimenting with wire guns in 1883 and produced a highly successful 9.2in wire gun in 1887, which led to the decision to adopt this form of manufacture. It was to remain the standard British system of gun manufacture until the 1930s.

The major advance of this period was not, however, in gun manufacture but in the improvement of internal ballistics. For several years research had been in progress to find a chemical 'smokeless' powder to replace the organic gunpowder-based charges used for firing projectiles. The latter produced voluminous clouds of smoke, obscuring the view of gunners and creating undesirable environmental conditions on board. Two types were ultimately developed – nitro-cellulose, which was first introduced in France in 1886, and cordite, a nitro-glycerine based powder, introduced in Britain in 1890. Both generated greater power than existing charges, were slow burning and gave much improved ballistic performance and regularity, opening the way for the production of lightweight high velocity guns. The new charges were completely consumed on firing, leaving no residue in the gun so making it unnecessary to sponge them out and, although they still produced smoke, it was at a much lower level. Due to their being chemical compositions both types could deteriorate in time and required care in storage. Of the two, cordite was the more stable and, being more powerful, required a lighter charge but it was less regular in performance and produced a higher wear rate in the bore of the gun. Subsequent developments were to reduce these shortcomings and eventually there was little to

choose between the two types. Nitro-cellulose was adopted by the French, Russian and US navies and nitro-glycerine types by the British, German, Italian, Austrian and Japanese.

To take full advantage of the new powders it was again necessary to produce longer guns and between 1890 and 1905 there was a steady increase in the length, penetrating power and range of naval ordnance. There was, however, no substantial shift in the calibre of heavy guns, which remained at an average 12in throughout the period – mainly because the gain available from a larger weapon (greater hitting power) was outweighed by the disadvantages (increased weight of guns, mountings and ammunition; increased space for magazines and shell rooms – or reduced stowage; slower rate of fire, etc). There were also substantial improvements in the design of projectiles and their armour penetrating qualities. Steel shells had been in use in the majority of navies since the early 1880s or before, although Britain continued to use cast iron shells right up to the end of that decade. In 1886 the French company of Holtzer introduced a chrome steel projectile and by the early 1890s projectiles of this type had been generally adopted. Subsequently the composition and quality of the steel was further improved, armour-piercing caps introduced and more powerful bursting charges developed, which added greatly to the penetrating power and destructive effect of the heavy gun.

That these developments in gun power did not completely outclass the battleship's defensive abilities was due initially to the introduction of counter-balancing improvements in the quality of armour. In the late 1880s Schneider began to manufacture steel armour with nickel added to its composition, which greatly improved its toughness and resistance to cracking. Shortly after this an American engineer, H A Harvey, developed a method of treating these nickel-steel plates to provide a superhard face on a tough, resilient back. This was achieved by carburising or cementing the face of the plate (increasing the steel's carbon content and hence its hardness by covering the face with a carbon-rich material and heating it for an extended period) and then hardening it by first heating and then rapidly cooling it with water. The process was completed by annealing to give the required toughness. Armour of this type, which became known as Harvey armour, was first tested in 1891 and was adopted for the new ships, including many already under construction, of all the principal navies about two years later.

This improvement had, however, been ap-

plied to few ships before Krupps had still further developed and improved the process, producing even greater toughness and resistance to penetration. This was achieved by modifying the composition of the steel, principally the addition of chrome which improved both the quality of the steel and the depth of cementation, and the use of differential heating for the hardening process, where the face of the plate was heated to a higher temperature than the back. Again this process was adopted by all the major navies and became known as Krupp cemented or KC armour (non-cemented plates were also produced by this process principally for armour 3in thick and less, this being designated Krupp non-cemented – KNC). Compared with compound armour, Harvey plates showed a 60 per cent improvement and KC plates a 100 per cent improvement in resistance to penetration and at first this advantage was used to reduce the thickness and increase the area of armour.

As gun power continued to improve, armour thicknesses had again begun to increase when another factor intervened to balance the gun-versus-armour battle that had been in progress since the 1860s. With the improving quality and accuracy of guns, ships could fight at longer ranges and at longer range the velocity and hence penetrating power of projectiles was much less, reducing the need for heavier armour. With earlier technology the maximum range at which battleships were expected to engage was about 2000yds, not because guns were limited to this range but because they were not expected to be able to hit anything beyond this distance except by luck. By 1900 this figure had doubled and was set to steadily increase in the new century as telescopic sights, rangefinders and fire control instruments were introduced to take advantage of the improving qualities of guns and their mountings.

Machinery development

Although the development of machinery was to see initial increases in speed during the 1890s, from around 17kts to 18kts in battleships and from 20kts to 23kts in cruisers, the majority of new technology was directed toward reductions in machinery weight and improved economy in fuel consumption. The latter was employed either to reduce fuel stowage to save weight or to increase endurance, depending on the requirements of the design. The most important step in achieving these objects was the adoption of the water-tube boiler which, compared with the cylindrical type, could operate at much higher steam

The Naval Defence Act provided for no fewer than forty-two cruisers, including eight ships of the Astraea *class of which* Bonaventure *(seen here) was the first. British ships of this generation showed a renewed emphasis on seaworthiness: although 25 per cent larger than the preceding* Apollo *class, the* Astraeas *showed little obvious increase in fighting qualities or speed (a fact much criticised at the time) but the extra superstructure deck made the ships drier and ensured that the guns could be effective in any fighting weather.* (CMP)

pressures, was lighter (principally because it contained less water), and could generate steam at a faster rate. Against these were the facts that they were more difficult to operate and, if not handled and maintained well, suffered serious deterioration in performance. The first, and initially the most popular, of these was the French Belleville boiler, which first appeared in its modern form in the French despatch vessel *Voltigeur* in 1879. It was followed by many other designs, principally those of Lagrafel-D'allest and Niclausse in France, Thornycroft and Yarrow in Britain and Babcock and Wilcox in the USA. By the mid-1890s the Belleville had been adopted by the majority of the major navies, the principal exception being the USA, which continued to specify cylindrical boilers for its new ships until 1900 when the Babcock and Wilcox boiler was adopted. At first, although the Belleville performed well on trials, the installations were very troublesome, partly because of poor manufacture and partly due to inexperience in their use. These problems were eventually overcome and in the long term the Belleville proved durable and efficient but by 1900 it had suffered such a loss of reputation in Britain that they were abandoned by the Royal Navy for the more reliable and easier to operate boilers of Yarrow and Babcock and Wilcox.

Oil fuel also came into general use in this period and mixed firing – coal and oil – was taken up first by Italy, then by Germany and France and finally by Britain and the USA. It allowed for a substantial increase in the generation of power and provided a means of producing that power more quickly than was possible by simply adding more coal to the furnaces.

The triple expansion engine, introduced during the 1880s, remained the principal form of motive power throughout this period, the only major change, outside the general improvement of design, being the adoption of four-cylinder engines in large ships as a means of taking more steam without an excessive increase in piston diameters. In general twin-screw installations were favoured but both France and Germany introduced triple-screw

machinery for battleships and armoured cruisers, which had the advantage of using three smaller, and therefore lower, engines which were easier to fit under the protective deck. They also gave improved steering qualities, due to the fact that the centre screw was immediately forward of the rudder, and improved security in the case of machinery breakdown. Against this the triple screw arrangement occupied a larger area, was of greater weight and was generally more complex.

The Naval Defence Act

The events that were to lead to the Royal Navy's major expansion of the 1890s began in 1884 when a series of critical articles entitled 'The truth about the Navy' appeared in the *Pall Mall Gazette*. These stirred up an interest in naval affairs in the press generally, a situation later exploited by naval officers, politicians and others with an interest in the improvement and expansion of the fleet. Within a few years the political and public attitude to the Royal Navy had shifted from one of indifference to one of great discontent that such an important service, the principal defence for Britain's all important world-wide trade and empire, should be in such a moribund state. Criticisms were levelled at the ill assortment of ships the Navy possessed, the lack of cruisers for trade protection, the poor state of the dockyards, the delays in gun supply, the shortage of personnel and the lack of stores and preparations for war in general. A good deal of this criticism was

unjustified, particularly that directed at ship design, as the Admiralty, despite its faults, was already aware of most of the problems it faced but had for many years been prevented from making improvements by financial restrictions. It was, however, a willing victim – having to publicly defend itself was a small price to pay for the political and financial backing it then received.

The first sign of the effect of the agitation for improvement appeared in 1885 when William White, the new Director of Naval Construction, was given the task of reorganising the Royal Dockyards with a view to increasing their efficiency and reducing construction times and costs. Although receiving some initial resistance, his proposals were accepted in 1886 and in a few short years the dockyards were transformed into the fastest and cheapest battleship builders in the world. White was also made responsible for changes in the Controller's Department, where a considerable tightening up of warship design procedures was adopted – in particular the strict control of the weights allowed to be added to a design once it had received Board approval. This included the provision of an allowance for additions (known as the Board margin) as part of the design – an allowance that could not be exceeded without express Admiralty approval. These reforms, and several others, including the formation of a naval intelligence department, were not achieved without resistance, some from within the Admiralty itself, but by 1888 much of this had been overcome and the

CAPITAL SHIP DEVELOPMENT 1890–1905

Date is laying down; tonnage is load; scale is 1/1250

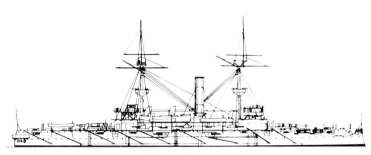

Royal Sovereign, British battleship, 1889, 14,150t

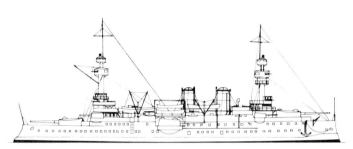

Jauréguiberry, French battleship, 1891, 11,637t

Sissoi Veliki, *Russian battleship, 1892, 10,400t*

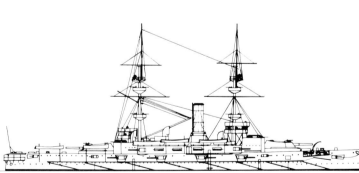

Majestic, *British battleship, 1895, 14,700t*

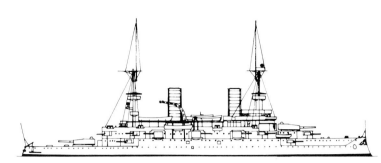

Kaiser Friedrich III, *German battleship, 1895, 11,599t*

Henri IV, *French battleship, 1897, 8807t*

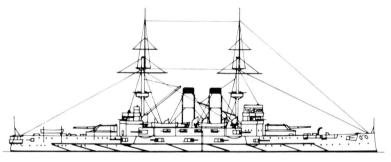

Mikasa, *Japanese battleship, 1899, 15,140t*

Arkansas, *American coast defence ship, 1899, 3225t*

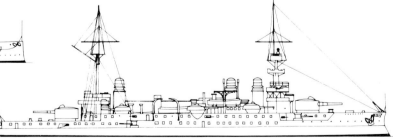

Justice, *French battleship, 1903, 14,860t*

way was open for the naval expansion that the country now demanded.

At this time White placed before the Admiralty plans for the steady replacement of the existing fleet and the disposal of obsolete vessels, together with his own analysis of the types of ships required. This formed the basis of the recommendations the Admiralty made to the Government for a future construction programme, which in turn resulted in Parliament passing the Naval Defence Act on 7 March 1889. This set the required size of the Royal Navy as equal to the combined strength of any other two navies, by which was meant the two largest – at this time the French and Russian. To achieve this 'two power standard' the act provided an unprecedented £21,500,000 for a five-year construction programme of seventy ships consisting of:

8 First Class battleships (*Royal Sovereign* class and *Hood*)
2 Second Class battleships (*Centurion* class)
9 First Class cruisers (*Edgar* class)
29 Second Class cruisers (*Apollo* and *Astraea* classes)
4 Third Class cruisers (*Pallas* class)
18 torpedo gunboats (*Sharpshooter* class)

During 1886–88 few ships were laid down for the Royal Navy, partly because of the changes taking place in the dockyards and partly because the Admiralty were in the process of enquiring into the best form for future ships. For this purpose reports on the performance of existing vessels were obtained both from recently instituted annual fleet manoeuvres and from sea officers in general. In addition, the first full scale trial of the effects of torpedoes on a ship's structure were carried out in 1886 against the old ironclad *Resistance*. These trials, which were initiated by White, were principally intended to provide information on defensive systems, in particular the protective value of coal, and the general effects of shellfire and underwater explosions.

White began work on battleship designs in 1888, following instructions from the Board to produce an improved version of *Trafalgar*. He presented several outline sketches for both barbette and turret ships but forcefully argued for the former on the basis that this was the only type that could satisfactorily incorporate a high freeboard, and it was the lack of this feature which recent enquiries had shown to be the most serious fault in existing designs. This view received general acceptance and provided the basis for the design of the *Royal Sovereign* class of the Naval Defence Act. However, the First Sea Lord, Admiral Hood, still favoured the

heavily armoured, low-freeboard turret ship and in deference to his authority one of the eight First Class battleships of the new programme was modified to a turret design. This ship, appropriately named *Hood*, was basically the same as her half-sisters but was reduced by one deck fore and aft to maintain stability requirements. She served to prove the correctness of White's views, for while the seven ships of the *Royal Sovereign* class were excellent all-round ships which set the pattern for future battleship design over the next fifteen years, *Hood* was spoilt for lack of good seakeeping qualities and stability.

In order to fully meet the Admiralty requirements for the *Royal Sovereign* design, White had to go to the substantially increased displacement of 14,000 tons and it says much for the changed atmosphere of the time that this was accepted by both the Board and the Government. As already stated, the principal improvement was the provision of a high freeboard, which placed the gun axis 23ft above the load waterline compared to 14ft in *Trafalgar* and 17ft in *Hood*. In other respects the design was basically an enlarged and improved version of the *Admiral* class. The citadel armour was similarly arranged but was more extensive being deeper (8ft 6in, compared with 7ft 6in, of which 3ft 6in was above water) and covering a larger proportion of the length. There were, however, some important additions to the protection: in particular the fitting of an upper belt, closed at the ends by screen bulkheads, of 4in nickel-steel (Harvey steel in three of the class) between the top of the main belt and the main deck as a defence against QF guns; and the extension of the barbette armour down to the top of the protective deck, thereby substantially improving the defence of the gun mountings and their loading gear.

The main armament of four 13.5in guns was the same as that of *Trafalgar* and the 'Admirals' but the secondary armament consisted of the new Armstrongs 6in QF gun of which ten were carried – three on each side of the upper deck on shielded mountings and two on each side of the main deck in 6in armour casemates. As in White's earlier cruisers of the *Blake* class, the latter arrangement was intended to give maximum dispersion to reduce the likelihood of more than one gun being put out of action by a single hit. Apart from a heavy roll, subsequently corrected by the addition of bilge keels, they proved to be good sea-boats and were very successful ships whose well balanced and pleasing appearance contrasted markedly with the designs of the previous twenty years.

The seven ships of the class were laid down during 1889–91 and completed in 1892–94, three being built by Royal Dockyards and the remainder by private shipbuilders. Construction time averaged about four years, although Portsmouth Dockyard built the lead ship in only two years and eight months.

The two Second Class battleships of the Naval Defence Act, the 10,500-ton *Barfleur* and *Centurion* (laid down in 1890 and completed in 1894), were reduced editions of *Royal Sovereign* with thinner armour and the armament reduced to a 10in main battery and a 4.7in QF secondary. The only important change was the addition of an open-backed 6in Harvey armour gunshield on the barbettes, a feature to be expanded in later ships into the fully enclosed armoured gunhouse. They were primarily intended for service on the China and Pacific stations, where they could be employed as flagships and, in time of war, provide a defence against interference by foreign armoured cruisers.

An improved vessel of this type and the last such vessel to be built by Britain, *Renown*, was laid down in 1893 and completed in 1897. She was 2000 tons larger than her predecessors and incorporated a number of improvements to her protection that were later adopted in First Class battleships. She was the first British warship to employ all-steel armour, Harvey plates being used, which allowed for a more even distribution of the protection and, in particular, an increase in the thickness of the upper belt to 6in. In addition, the entire secondary armament, which was the same as that of *Royal Sovereign*, was mounted in armoured casemates while the protective deck was arranged in similar fashion to that of protected cruisers, with an outer sloped edge – in this case extending down to meet the bottom of the main belt. The latter arrangement created a triangular enclosure behind the belt which meant that any shell that penetrated the belt also had to pass through the slope of the protective deck to reach the ship's vitals. It also improved security in the case of splinters from shells exploding just inside the belt armour and would limit flooding should the side be pierced near the waterline. It is interesting to note that the first two of these 'second class' ships were of a size that a decade earlier was regarded as the maximum for battleships, while *Renown* considerably exceeded it.

The Spencer Programme

By 1893 concern was being expressed about the lack of a follow-on programme to the Naval

The layout of the British battleship, with four 12in guns in twin 'turrets' fore and aft and secondary armament in casemates, was finalised with the Majestic *class of 1893. Thereafter development was steady but unspectacular until the introduction of intermediate armament in the ships immediately preceding the* Dreadnought. *The photograph depicts* HMS Implacable *of the three-ship* Formidable *class, launched in 1899.* (CMP)

Defence Act, particularly as French construction appeared, incorrectly as it turned out, to be keeping pace with that of Britain. Despite Government reluctance to increase naval expenditure, overcome largely by a threat by the Board of Admiralty to resign en bloc, a programme of even greater proportions than that of 1889 was passed by Parliament on 8 December 1893. Referred to as the 'Spencer Programme', after the current First Lord of the Admiralty, it provided for the expenditure of £31,000,000 on another five-year programme to cover the construction of 159 vessels. Of these seven were to be First Class battleships and thirty cruisers, the remainder being principally destroyers and torpedo craft, but the programme was later modified with the battleship numbers increased to nine and the cruiser requirement reduced.

The battleships were to become the *Majestic* class, the largest single class of battleships ever built, all of which were laid down during 1893–95. By this time the dockyard reforms were well established and only two were placed with private shipbuilders; all were constructed in good time, completing during 1895–98, the lead ship, *Majestic*, again going to Portsmouth Dockyard, where she was built in the record time of twenty-two months. Many regard them as the first true pre-dreadnoughts, although all the elements of their design were already established. In essence they combined the basic features of *Royal Sovereign* with the improvements in protection already adopted in *Renown* – namely Harvey armour, a sloped protective deck and all the secondary 6in guns fitted in casemates. There were, however, some important changes apart from a general increase in the level of protection appropriate to the change from a Second to a First Class battleship. The upper and lower belts were combined into a uniform belt of 9in thickness, 16ft deep, giving a much improved level of protection over that of *Royal Sovereign* and, with the exception of the soft ends, vastly superior to that of contemporary French ships. In addition, the main armament was provided with a fully enclosed armoured gunhouse, thereby eliminating one of the major disadvantages of the barbette system as thus far applied to Brit-

ish ships. Almost inevitably the gunhouse was eventually to be referred to as a turret and although the barbette/gunhouse arrangement had little connection with the original turret form it was later to become accepted terminology.

The main armament of the *Majestic* class consisted of the newly introduced 12in 35-calibre Mk VIII wire-wound gun which exceeded the performance of the old 13.5in in everything but shell weight. This calibre of main armament was to remain the standard for all British battleship designs for the next sixteen years. The mountings were similar to those of *Royal Sovereign* with elliptical barbettes and fixed loading positions, but the provision of an auxiliary rammer in the gunhouse allowed all-round loading with a limited supply of ready-use ammunition. However, two of the later ships of the class, *Caesar* and *Illustrious*, were fitted with a new model mounting which had a central hoist and all-round loading allowing the use of lighter circular barbettes – a system that became standard in all later British battleships, ultimately with the refinements of a split hoist, to improve the safety of the supply arrangements, and all-angle loading.

The *Majestic* class in effect refined the *Royal Sovereign* design and during 1896–1901 a further twenty battleships of the same basic configuration were laid down. The following group, the *Canopus* class, introduced Krupp armour and Belleville boilers, the advantages gained being used to reduce displacement and increase speed. They were principally intended for service on the China station to counter Japanese naval expansion and were somewhat under-protected compared with their contemporaries. However, their 6in KC belt was in

fact only marginally inferior to the 9in Harvey belt of *Majestic* and they had the advantages of a second protective deck across the top of the belt and an extension of the waterline protection in the shape of a 2in splinter belt between the citadel and the stem. The following ships of the *Formidable* and *London* classes were generally similar, but had the belt increased to 9in KC (equivalent to about 11½in Harvey), the waterline protection extended to the stern as well as the stem and adopted the 40-calibre 12in gun. These improvements pushed the design displacement up to 15,000 tons. Finally, the *Duncan* class again sacrificed protection for a reduction in displacement and an increase in design speed from 18kts to 19kts. They were built to counter increased construction programmes in France and Russia, the higher speed being adopted in response to a report that the Russian ships were to be fast vessels; in fact the latter proved to be false and the construction programmes much less than expected.

The need for Britain to have built such a large number of ships is a debatable point as in 1900 she had completed or had under construction 36 modern First Class battleships compared with 11 in France and 13 in Russia, a superiority of 3:2. There followed a marked reduction in the laying down of new ships, two further vessels of the *London* type being started in 1901 before the last of Britain's true pre-dreadnought classes, the eight ships of the *King Edward VII* class, were commenced during 1902–4. These ships showed the first changes from the basic *Majestic* design, having an intermediate battery of four 9.2in guns mounted in single turrets at the corners of the superstructure. In addition, the 6in guns were mounted in a box battery on the main deck instead of in casemates, the 7in armour of which effectively increased the height of the side protection amidships by one deck. In order to save weight the main belt was again split, with a 9in lower and 8in upper strake, but they still showed a substantial increase in size, the design displacement being 16,350 tons. As a result of the abandonment of the Belleville boiler the class carried a mixed installation of Babcock and Wilcox (Niclausse in one ship) and cylindrical boilers following the recommendations of a committee set up to enquire into the problems with earlier types. The mixed arrangement, which varied from ship to ship for trial purposes, was intended to provide the best features of both types but the use of cylindrical boilers proved an unnecessary addition to the weight and the arrangement was not repeated.

France

The advantages gained by the British were not repeated on the other side of the channel where financial restriction continued to limit battleship size and, together with inefficient shipyards, generated lengthy construction times. The battleship design process simply continued with the established philosophy of the 1880s, employing shallow full-length waterline belts and unprotected upperworks and it was not until the early 1900s that French battleships began to match those produced for the Royal Navy. Problems were also created by low stability levels and ships completing overweight, reducing the effectiveness of their side protection, a problem solved by the British whose ships were generally completed below design weight as a result of the strict controls introduced by White. French designers did, however, enjoy some advantages in that their ships were not expected to travel far from their bases, which reduced the requirements of endurance and hence coal stowage. Both France and Britain assumed that war between them would take the same form as earlier conflicts, with the British closely blockading the French fleet in its own harbours. The French answer to this was to slowly erode the blockade with torpedo craft, the battleship being held in reserve as local defence until such time as the opposing forces were more evenly matched. In the meantime the principal function of the

The battleship Brennus *was a departure from French practice in a number of respects, including the turret mountings for the 34cm (13.4in) guns which replaced the barbettes preferred for earlier ships. She was the first capital ship with Belleville water-tube boilers and also abandoned the ram bow. (CMP)*

navy was to be attacks on British trade using cruisers, which, again as in the past, were not expected to have any difficulty in evading a blockading force in order to reach the open sea.

Battleship construction recommenced with the 11,000-ton *Brennus*, laid down in 1889 and completed in 1896. She followed the protective system of earlier ships with the addition of an upper belt of 4in steel armour but, unlike that of *Royal Sovereign*, it extended to only half the height of the deck above, about 4ft 6in, although it did have the advantage of extending over the full length of the ship. The main armament consisted of three powerful 13.4in, 42-calibre high velocity guns mounted in a twin turret forward and a single turret aft. The adoption of these centre pivot turrets in place of the barbette system was the principal design change from previous ships. To maintain the high freeboard and stability, weight was saved by keeping the turret and ammunition hoist protection to minimum dimensions – they were in effect a reverse of the British gunhouse/barbette arrangement with the turret armour overlapping a much smaller diameter barbette, the major difference being that the gun mounting was entirely within the turret, the barbette containing only the ammunition hoist. The secondary armament of *Brennus* showed a major improvement on earlier practice, the ten 6.4in QF being fully protected by 4in armour. Four were mounted in single turrets on the upper deck and the remainder in a box battery on the main deck which added to the depth of the hull protection amidships. This arrangement did, however, concentrate the secondary armament in such a way as to increase the danger of several guns being disabled by a single hit. *Brennus* was also the first battleship to be fitted with water-tube boilers,

in this case thirty-two Bellevilles, and was well ahead of foreign contemporaries in this respect.

In 1891 a new construction programme began that was ultimately to push the British into the Spencer Programme. It was to be the last attempt by the French to challenge British dominance in battleship construction. By 1895 it was realised that there was little chance of matching Britain's growing naval power or the efficiency and speed of her shipbuilders. Naval policy returned to the ideas of the *jeune école* with a reliance on torpedo craft, cruisers and war on commerce. Other factors were also at work in that Germany's increasing power was beginning to become a more serious threat, prompting a transfer of finance from naval to military expenditure. As a result battleship construction slowed considerably in the last five years of the century and although it revived slightly in the early 1900s France never regained her position as the second world naval power.

Three battleships were laid down in 1891, *Charles Martel*, *Carnot* and *Jauréguiberry*, which although differing in detail were of generally similar design. They reverted to the main armament layout of *Marceau* with turrets in place of barbettes, having a single 12in gun mounted fore and aft and a single 10.8in on each beam. Although this arrangement did not compare well in numbers and distribution with foreign ships, Britain's in particular, the guns were again powerful weapons, both being 45-calibre high velocity types, while their mountings provided efficient all-round loading, giving a higher rate of fire than was possible with the fixed loading system. These mountings were of a new electrically powered design and eliminated most of the problems of earlier installations which also had all-round loading but had

proved inefficient and mechanically troublesome. Particular care was taken to keep the weight of these mountings as low as possible, which allowed for the fore turret to be raised one deck, giving an increase in freeboard forward by the addition of a forecastle deck that extended to the after end of the superstructure. Unfortunately these advantages were lost in an extended construction time of six years and by the time the ships completed they were almost obsolete.

The secondary armament of eight 5.5in QF, also electrically operated, was entirely mounted in single armoured turrets (twin in *Jauréguiberry*) but was positioned in such a way that they were subject to serious blast interference from the main armament. The protection was similarly arranged to that of *Brennus* but with the addition of a splinter deck formed by extending the inner bottom up and under the protective deck. The space between the two was subdivided to form a cellular layer but the distance, about 2ft 6in, was insufficient to give adequate splinter protection. Two similar ships, *Masséna* and *Bouvet*, were laid down in 1892 and 1893 respectively and differed from the earlier vessels in introducing the three-shaft machinery arrangement to battleships. *Bouvet* was also the first French battleship to adopt Harvey armour, previous vessels having nickel-steel protection. Presumably because of her poor relations with Germany the Harvey process remained in use in French ships for several years and was not superseded by Krupp armour until the designs of 1901.

The next three battleships, the *Charlemagne* class (*Charlemagne*, *St Louis* and *Gaulois*), laid down in 1894–96 and completed in 1899–1900, are generally regarded as the first true pre-dreadnoughts of the French navy, since they adopted the standard configuration of twin turrets fore and aft. However, in most other respects they followed the general pattern of earlier ships and again were limited by low displacement and a narrow waterline belt. Some improvement was achieved by deepening the cellular layer which occupied the space between the 3in cambered protective deck, laid across the top of the belt, and a 1½in splinter deck, positioned at the base of the belt, the space between having a minimum height equivalent to the belt depth (6ft 8in).

The laying down of these ships was followed by a lapse in battleship construction until 1898 when *Iéna*, a slightly larger version of *Charlemagne*, was commenced. She was followed in 1899 by *Suffren* which showed the first sign of acceptance that the size limit on earlier ships was too low. Displacing 12,500 tons, the increased dimensions were utilised to improve protection and increase the size of the secondary battery to ten 6.4in QF, compared with eight in *Iéna*. Six of these guns were again mounted in turrets, three on each side of the upper deck, and the remainder in main deck casemates. It was, however, with *République* and *Patrie* that France finally reached a size that allowed her designers to produce a reasonably well balanced ship. These 14,600-ton vessels, laid down in 1901–2, were faster, better pro-

tected and better armed than any of the previous ships. The main belt of 11in KC armour was 12ft 6in deep, of which 7ft 6in was above water. The cellular layer system was retained, but the increase in belt height allowed the upper and lower (splinter) protective decks to be raised by one deck level and the outer edge of the lower protective deck to be sloped down to meet the bottom of the belt. In section this was virtually the same as the arrangement in contemporary British ships, except that the latter did not have a cellular layer. The secondary armament was substantially increased to eighteen 6.4in QF, twelve of which were mounted in twin turrets, three on each side of the upper deck and widely distributed. They were broader than earlier ships, had a much reduced tumblehome and consequently a greatly improved level of stability.

They were followed by the four similar ships of the *Liberté* class (*Démocratie*, *Justice*, *Liberté* and *Verité*), laid down in 1902–3 in which the only major difference was an increase in the calibre of the secondary armament to 7.6in, the number carried being reduced to ten. Unfortunately these greatly improved ships came too late, the first pair being completed at the same time as the British *Dreadnought* at the end of 1906 and the *Liberté* class in 1908, by which time they were out of date.

One other French battleship should be mentioned, the large coast defence ship *Henri IV* built during 1897–1903. She had a monitor type hull with only 4ft freeboard, protected by a full length belt with a maximum thickness of 11in covered by a 3.2in deck. However, above this was a high superstructure which extended forward to blend with the bows and form a high freeboard forecastle, the whole producing a ship that was both seaworthy and of high stability. The main armament of two 10.8in guns was mounted on the superstructure well above water, the forward turret being three decks above the main hull. Her principal claims to fame are that she was the first ship to incorporate an underwater protection system against torpedo attack and the first to adopt a superfiring turret arrangement. The latter was aft where one of her secondary 5.5in guns was fitted in a turret firing directly over the after 10.8in mounting. Unfortunately, blast effects on the sighting hoods of the lower turret prevented the successful operation of the 10.8in gun when the 5.5in was fired on after bearings. The underwater protection system consisted of extending the splinter deck downward to meet the inner bottom effectively producing a longitudinal protective bulkhead. Again this was not fully successful as it was too close to the outer bottom to be effective.

Russia

The design of Russian battleships originally followed the British pattern but as the 1890s progressed they began to show a marked French influence, albeit with some advantage as their later ships were rather larger than those of France and were generally constructed in a shorter time. They also abandoned the Krupp gun in favour of manufacturing guns to Schneider-Canet designs and adopted the French style turret mounting. Although their designs were somewhat inconsistent in development and did not normally compare well with foreign contemporaries, the Russians

were quick to adopt new ideas and generally kept pace with the changes in armour, ordnance and machinery design. The decade started in a haphazard manner with 7 battleships laid down in 1892 (including 3 coast defence types), one coast defence battleship in 1894 and 4 battleships in 1895. However, in 1898 a seven-year construction programme was initiated which included provision for 8 battleships as well as 17 cruisers, 20 destroyers, 30 torpedo boats and a number of auxiliaries. Owing to the limited construction facilities in Russia several of these ships were ordered from shipbuilders in France, the United States and Germany. The proposed increases in the Russian fleet were viewed with some concern in Britain but these were principally directed toward the increasing rivalry with Japan which was ultimately to bring disaster in the Russo-Japanese war of 1904–5.

The ships begun in 1892 were *Sissoi Veliki*, a small ship similar to the earlier *Navarin* but with increased freeboard, three 4000-ton coast defence battleships of the *Ushakov* class (a fourth vessel was begun in 1894) and the three First Class battleships of the *Petropavlovsk* class. These last, the 11,000-ton *Petropavlovsk*, *Poltava* and *Sevastopol*, completed in 1894–95, resembled reduced editions of *Royal Sovereign* with a lighter scale of protection and a 12in armament. The principal difference from the British ship was the turret mounted main armament and the concentration of the secondary armament amidships in French fashion – eight of the twelve 6in guns being mounted in twin turrets on the upper deck and the remainder in main deck casemates. All these ships had Harvey armour except *Veliki* in which it was nickel-steel.

The 1895 ships consisted of *Rostislav*, a Second Class battleship of 8800 tons and *Peresviet* and *Osliabia*, which showed a marked increase in displacement to 12,600 tons. The first ship was similar to *Petropavlovsk* but was armed with 10in instead of 12in guns following closely the concept of the British Second Class vessels of this period. The other two ships were definite

French derivatives with a high freeboard and heavy tumblehome, but the secondary armament was mounted entirely in casemates and the narrow waterline belt of Harvey armour stopped just short of the bow and stern. Although the first ships of the Russian navy to be fitted with Belleville boilers (which provided for the high speed of 18kts), they carried only 10in guns for the main armament and proved inferior in armament, protection and stability. They did not complete until 1901. A third ship of the class, *Pobieda*, was laid down in 1898, completing a year later than her sisters.

Two other battleships were laid down in 1898, *Retvisan* and *Kniaz Potemkin Tavritcheski*, the latter subsequently gaining notoriety for the mutiny that took place onboard her in 1905 (after which she was renamed *Pantelimon*). The 12,500-ton *Potemkin* was a substantial improvement on the previous class with better stability and a return to the 12in gun main armament. She had a distinctive appearance with three funnels, raised forecastle and low quarterdeck which owed little to either British or French influence. Protection was similar to that of *Peresviet* but employed KC armour, which increased its relative resistance, and an improved arrangement of protection for the secondary armament, twelve of her 6in guns being fitted in an armoured battery on the main deck and the remaining four in individual casemates on the upper deck. *Retvisan* was built by Cramp in the United States and completed in 1901, two years before *Potemkin*. She was of the same basic design and appearance as the Russian built ship, except for having a flush full length upper deck, but had a speed of 18kts, compared with *Potemkin*'s 16.5kts, a main belt that extended to the full length and a secondary battery of twelve guns instead of sixteen.

Despite the fact that *Retvisan* was probably the best Russian battleship of the period, future development followed from the battleship *Tsessarevitch*, a French designed and built ship laid down in 1899 and completed in 1903. She followed closely French design practice but was somewhat larger than contemporary

The three Russian battleships of the Petropavlovsk *class showed a degree of French influence in the tumblehome of the hull and the type of turrets. They were laid down in 1892 and all three were at Port Arthur at the outbreak of the Russo-Japanese War in 1904. All were sunk in the course of the conflict, although the Japanese later raised and refitted the* Poltava. Sebastopol *shown here was scuttled at the fall of the port after suffering extensive damage during the siege. (CMP)*

The USA returned to capital ship construction in the 1890s. The Kearsarge *class authorised in 1895 adopted an unusual arrangement with pairs of 8in guns mounted above the 13in main turrets but unable to train independently. This gave a number of theoretical advantages in the use of space and maximising broadside firepower, but these were more than offset by practical difficulties and the vulnerability of the whole unit to a single hit.* (US National Archives)

French navy ships at 12,900 tons which allowed for the provision of deeper side protection, with a 10in main and 8in upper belt. In addition, she was the first major battleship to be fitted with a protective bulkhead as defence against torpedoes. It followed the pattern of that fitted in the *Henry IV* but the 1½in splinter deck was in this case curved down further inboard, about 6ft 8in from the ship's side, and extended vertically down to meet the inner bottom rather than being an extension of it. The *Tsessarevitch* design was copied by the Russians in the five ships of the *Borodino* class constructed during 1899–1905 but despite being 600 tons larger they were slower, fitted with thinner belt armour of reduced depth and showed little sign of any gain except for a slight increase in endurance. The next and last pair of true pre-dreadnoughts, *Evstafi* and *Ioann Zlatoust*, reverted to the *Potemkin* design from which they varied little in either appearance or particulars. They were, however, modified during construction as a result of experience during the Russo-Japanese war, to include some additions to the protection and an intermediate battery of four 8in guns in place of the upper deck 6in.

The new naval powers

The United States

In 1883 the United States Congress authorised the construction of three cruisers and a despatch vessel which were intended as a first step in the replacement of the US Navy's old and obsolete vessels dating from the Civil War or earlier. This initiated the construction of what became known as the 'new navy', and during the remainder of the 1880s the United States laid down a further eleven cruisers and two small turret ships, *Texas* and *Maine*. These ships were authorised as a result of the realisation that the extensive coastline of the United States was extremely vulnerable to attack from the sea and that the navy was insufficient to

defend either this or American interests in the Caribbean and Pacific. Particular concerns were expressed at the expansion of South American naval forces and the fact that no ship capable of dealing with such vessels as the Brazilian turret ships *Riachuelo* and *Aquidaban* or the Chilean cruiser *Esmeralda* existed in the US fleet.

This need for coastal defence was generally accepted but a strong desire also existed both in the navy and elsewhere to build a first class seagoing fleet, one in keeping with the country's growing wealth and industrial power. However, there was also a strong body of opinion in Congress and in the country generally that saw no need for extravagant expenditure on an oceanic navy, which was strongly associated with imperialist Europeans. In 1890 a special board was set up to report on future naval development. It recommended a fifteen-year construction programme for 192 ships, including ten First Class battleships and twenty-five Second Class battleships, the latter intended to protect the US coastline. This ambitious plan was thrown out by Congress which authorised only three 'seagoing coast defence' battleships, one cruiser and a torpedo boat.

The three battleships, the 10,000-ton *Indiana*, *Massachusetts* and *Oregon*, were laid down in 1891 and completed in 1895–96. They typified what Congress expected and continued to expect for the next seven years – medium sized ships, heavily armed and protected but of moderate endurance, capable of fighting within a reasonable distance of the American coast – seagoing but not oceangoing. They were low freeboard ships which resembled the British turret ship *Hood* but differed in one major respect from European designs in having an intermediate gun battery of eight 8in mounted in four twin turrets at the corners of the superstructure. This was to remain a consistent feature of US battleship designs, being omitted

from only two of their nine pre-dreadnought classes. The main armament of four 13in was mounted in two circular turrets but these were in turn mounted inside a barbette which allowed them to be raised clear of the deck. In fact the arrangement was much closer to the barbette/gunhouse system of later British ships than the true turret, as the barbette protected the lower part of the mounting and a central hoist which allowed all-round loading.

Unfortunately, the mountings were not centrally balanced and when trained abeam caused the ship to heel toward the point of aim, increasing the submergence of the main belt and reducing the available elevation of the guns. The problem was solved by counter-weighting the rear of the turrets but the mountings, which suffered other mechanical defects, were never entirely satisfactory. Like the earlier *Texas* they were fitted with Harvey armour, but rather than taking advantage of its improved qualities to give a more extensive area of protection it was fitted in thicknesses equivalent to those used for earlier armour (18in belt, 17in barbettes, 15in turrets) and arranged in similar fashion to that of *Royal Sovereign* with a central citadel, soft ends, full depth barbettes and a 5in upper belt. Given their small size and low freeboard, nobody expected them to be exceptional sea-boats but they rolled excessively as first built, a problem later improved by the addition of bilge keels (originally omitted owing to docking restrictions).

In *Iowa*, laid down in 1892 and completed in 1897, the design of *Indiana* was recast to produce a much more satisfactory design. To improve seaworthiness a forecastle deck was added running aft as far as the after turret and to reduce weight a 12in gun was adopted for the main armament. The thicknesses of armour, although still heavier than European standards, were generally reduced, allowing for an increase in the length of the citadel, the speed and endurance. The result was a vessel 1000 tons larger than her predecessors but with greatly improved seakeeping qualities which for its size proved an excellent all-round design. Despite this success the next two ships to be constructed, *Kearsarge* and *Kentucky*, reverted to a flush deck, low freeboard and introduced another dubious feature. In order to save weight and cure the problems created by blast interference from the intermediate gun battery, the 8in guns were fitted in twin gunhouses mounted on the roofs of the main armament turrets. These mountings were fixed and could not train independently of the 13in guns; they complicated the main turret's ammunition supply arrangements and required an increase in the strength of the supporting structure. In addition, the dangers of a large proportion of the armament being put out of action by a single hit were increased and the added topweight was one of the reasons for their not having a raised forecastle. In protection they were similar to *Iowa* but the belt was increased from 14in to 16½in and extended to the stem with 4in plating. The secondary armament of fourteen 5in QF (RF for rapid-fire in US terminology) was equally disposed on each side in a 6in armour box battery which effectively extended the citadel armour to the top of the first superstructure deck. As with the *Indiana* class they were poor sea-boats and bad gun platforms.

In the next class the 8in battery was omitted altogether, the secondary armament being increased to 6in calibre in partial compensation, and the raised forecastle of *Iowa* re-adopted. In other respects the design was little altered, except for the installation of new 13in gun mountings and a wider distribution for the 6in guns with eight on the main deck and four on the upper deck. The three ships of this design, *Illinois*, *Alabama* and *Wisconsin* were laid down in 1896–97 and completed in 1900–1901. While they were under construction the Spanish-American war broke out following the loss of the turret ship *Maine*, which blew up and sank in Havana Harbour on 15 February 1898. Although certainly the result of an accidental magazine explosion the Spanish authorities were accused of sabotage and the incident was used as an excuse for the United States to declare war.

The real reason was a long-standing dispute over the future of Cuba and American support for the rebels that had been fighting for independence from Spain for many years. In the ensuing conflict the US Navy outfought the inferior Spanish squadrons at the Battles of Manila Bay and Santiago, leaving the Spanish possessions isolated and open to attack by sea-borne forces. The war was ended by the Treaty of Paris on 10 December 1898 and although Cuba became an independent state, she was effectively a protectorate of the United States. In addition, America found itself in possession of the Spanish islands of Puerto Rico, Guam and the Philippines; having also annexed the Hawaiian Islands and Midway, the United States became a colonial power in all but name, with responsibilities stretching from the Caribbean to the far side of the Pacific. It was soon realised that a seagoing navy was required to protect these interests, together with coaling and base facilities in the newly acquired territories, and with a new enthusiasm generated by the successful outcome of the war, Congress became much less of an obstacle to naval expansion. The war also provided much valuable experience, revealing weaknesses in both ships and the organisation of naval supply and command. In the subsequent reorganisation a General Board was set up as an advisory council on all naval matters including ship design and was soon to recommend a long term construction programme intended to provide the United States with a fleet second only to that of Britain by 1919.

Shortly after the outbreak of the Spanish war Congress authorised the construction of three more battleships which were originally intended as repeats of the *Illinois* class. The design was, however, modified to accommodate a 2kt increase in speed to 18kts and improved endurance, the expanded machinery power being provided by the adoption of water-tube boilers and a 1000-ton increase in displacement. Armour thicknesses were also reduced but as KC armour was employed there was only a marginal loss in the protective value. They also adopted a new generation of high velocity guns employing smokeless powder and carried four 12in 40-calibre and sixteen 6in 50-calibre weapons of considerably greater power than those of earlier ships. The first ship of the class was named *Maine* in honour of the vessel lost at Havana, she and her two sisters, *Missouri* and *Ohio*, being built during 1899–1903. As completed they were overweight to varying degrees and had an exceptionally high level of stability, making them very stiff and consequently poor gun platforms.

The first vessels to fully reflect the lessons of the Spanish-American war were the five ships of the *Virginia* class which were laid down in 1901–2 and completed in 1906–7. For the first time these were true First Class battleships of almost 15,000 tons, with a high-freeboard flush deck, a substantial endurance and a speed of 19kts. In the distribution of armament and ar-mour they were generally similar to the *Maine* class but had two important innovations. First, the armoured deck instead of being laid flat across the top of the belt adopted the sloped edge common to European practice. The slope, as usual, terminated at the base of the belt and was of 3in thickness. Second, the intermediate 8in battery was reinstated, these weapons having proved of some value during the war with Spain. Unfortunately, four of the eight guns were mounted in the same unsatisfactory manner as in *Kearsarge* in fixed gunhouses on the roofs of the main armament turrets, the remaining guns being mounted in standard twin turrets on each beam amidships. This mistake was not repeated in the following *Connecticut* and *Louisiana* which were improved versions of the *Virginia* class with all eight 8in guns mounted in wing turrets. In addition, 7in guns were substituted for the 6in, a new 45-calibre 12in gun was adopted for the main armament, and the endurance further increased. They displaced 16,000 tons but it was still necessary to compensate for the additions and the engine power was reduced, lowering the speed to 18kts. They were excellent ships which could stand comparison with any foreign design and were repeated, with only minor modification, in the four ships of the *Vermont* class constructed during 1903–8.

America's last pre-dreadnoughts, *Mississippi* and *Idaho*, were retrograde in character following Congressional and some naval opposition to what were regarded as excessively large ships. Displacement was reduced to 13,000 tons, weight being saved by reductions in speed, endurance and the secondary battery. The end result, as usual in such cases, was ships of limited value – both were sold to Greece in 1914 only six years after completion.

In addition to their battleships the United States completed a small number of monitors during this period. Initially this was a means of extracting funding from a reluctant Congress, as the earlier monitors were in theory 'repairs' of incomplete Civil War vessels. In fact, they were effectively new ships – or they would have been were it not for the extremely protracted construction times of twenty years or more which resulted from the need to disguise the building costs. The first such ship, *Puritan*, was originally laid down in 1876 and launched in 1882. Work on her recommenced in 1890 and she completed in 1896 as a 6000-ton vessel armed with four 12in guns. The smaller *Amphitrite* class, armed with four 10in guns, followed a similar path, although one of the four, *Miantonomah*, completed in 1891. With some naval officers and congressmen still supporting

Double turrets were again employed in the five-ship Virginia *class of 1899–1900. Improved firing rates of the 8in guns made for interference with the slower-firing 12in, and the concept was not tried again. This view of* Nebraska *shows another American innovation, the 'basket' or 'cage' mast, designed to combine light weight with strength and resistance to damage. However, it had a tendency to flex in a seaway or when the ship fired a salvo – this was far from ideal as fire control equipment became more sophisticated but cage masts survived into the 1930s.* (US National Archives)

the monitor type another five of modern design were laid down in 1889 – the 4000-ton *Monterey* and the 3200-ton *Arkansas* class. Unlike the earlier 'repairs', these ships carried only one twin 12in gun mounting. Apart from *Monterey*, completed in 1893, their construction times were also extended and they did not enter service until 1902–3. All these monitors, like their namesake, had raft hulls, with little freeboard and were very slow. They were of scant use except in harbour defence, where shore fortifications and torpedo craft would have given better service, but their construction was not a total loss as several were later used as submarine tenders, in which role their low freeboard was a positive advantage.

Japan

The Japanese began their modern naval expansion at the same time and in a similar manner to the United States with an increase in their cruiser force. They did not at this time have

the industrial facilities of the Americans and therefore obtained most of their ships from either Britain or France with, eventually, a marked preference for the former. In the meantime they began to develop their own industrial base and by the beginning of the century had sufficient shipbuilding expertise to take over the majority of their own construction. The initial impetus for naval expansion came from a conflict with China over Korea and the realisation that the small Japanese fleet was outmatched by its potential adversary.

Under the influence of the teachings of the *jeune école*, the Japanese at first concentrated on cruisers and torpedo craft but in 1893 ordered two battleships from British yards for what was now regarded as the inevitable clash with China. The new ships were too late, however, as, following military intervention in Korea by both Japan and China, war broke out in July 1894. The Chinese fleet was defeated a few weeks later on 17 September in the Battle of the Yalu, leaving the way open for the Japanese army to fully occupy Korea and then invade the Chinese province of Manchuria. With the Japanese threatening Peking the Chinese sued for peace in 1895, the terms of which included the surrender of the Liaotung peninsula in Manchuria, which contained the naval base of Port Arthur.

This prospect did not please Russia, which had its own designs on the area, and with the backing of France and Germany they forced Japan to relinquish its claim. Later, in the

European scramble for 'spheres of influence' in China, Russia herself found a pretext to occupy Liaotung and Port Arthur. It caused considerable resentment in Japan and generated an even greater determination to increase the country's naval and military power. In 1896 a major ten-year construction programme was authorised which provided for the addition to the fleet of four battleships, twelve cruisers and eighty-six destroyers and torpedo boats. At the same time plans were made to increase construction and base facilities and to build up home based ordnance, armour and steelmaking plants.

The battleships ordered in 1893 were *Fuji* and *Yashima*. Laid down in 1894 and completed three years later, they were very similar to the *Royal Sovereign* design but were smaller and fitted with a more modern main armament of 12in guns, which were covered with an armoured gunhouse. They were also faster than the British ships, being capable of 18kts, a speed that was to remain standard in all the Japanese battleships of this period. The four ships ordered in 1896, *Shikishima*, *Hatsuse*, *Asahi* and *Mikasa*, again all British built, were broadly similar to each other but differed in detail, only the first two being sister ships. They were about 2500 tons larger than *Fuji*, averaging 15,000 tons, and were very similar in design to the British *Majestic* class. Like *Majestic* they had a 9in Harvey belt but, unlike that ship, this was not extended to the upper strake of side armour which reduced to 6in. Instead the main belt was continued to the stem and

Among the new naval powers of the nineteenth century was Japan, which began to purchase modern warships from the late 1860s. Her first battleships were two Fuji *class ships ordered from Britain in 1893. They were modifications of the* Royal Sovereign *but with more modern 12in gun mountings. This is the name ship of the class. (CMP)*

stern at reduced thickness. *Mikasa*, the last of the group, employed KC armour and also abandoned the casemate protection of all but four of her 6in guns in favour of an upper deck box battery of 6in armour similar to that which was to appear later in the British *King Edward VII* class. These six battleships, the last of which was completed in 1904, formed the core of the fleet that was to face the Russians in the war of 1904–5. Anticipating the coming conflict Japan initiated another construction programme for three battleships and five cruisers in 1903 but none of these vessels was available in time.

The war was initiated by Japan, without declaration, on 8 February 1904 with a torpedo boat attack on Port Arthur and before the end of the year they had effectively defeated the Russian naval forces in the area. In answer to this the Russians despatched the bulk of the Baltic fleet, under the command of Admiral Rozhestvenski, on an 18,000-mile voyage to the Far East. During its final approach to Vladivostok this fleet was intercepted by the Japanese under the command of Admiral Togo with his flag in *Mikasa*. In the ensuing Battle of Tsushima, on 27/28 May 1905, the Russian fleet was almost completely destroyed. Peace followed soon after, Japan gaining Port Arthur and the lower half of the Island of Sakhalin, immediately north of Japan, and adding a large number of captured Russian ships to its fleet.

In all Russia lost seventeen battleships, eleven cruisers, twenty-one destroyers and fourteen other craft during the war; the Japanese two battleships (*Yashima* and *Hatsuse*) and three cruisers – all of which were mined – and a few smaller vessels. Tsushima was the only major naval battle of the pre-dreadnought era and as such its lessons would have been of great use but occurring as it did on the eve of the dreadnought period their value was limited by the rapid changes in naval technology that were about to take place.

The rise of Germany

The newly united German States initially developed their navy as a coast defence force and up to the mid-1890s showed little sign of competition with the major naval powers. The combination of an ambitious emperor, Kaiser Wilhelm II, and an equally ambitious naval officer, Admiral Alfred von Tirpitz, generated a growth in the German navy intended to match the country's growing industrial power and to reinforce the desire to build a colonial empire. In 1897 Tirpitz was appointed Secretary of State for the Navy and in the following year the first Navy Law was passed which provided for the construction of nineteen battleships, eight coast defence vessels and forty-two cruisers. Two years later the second Navy Law expanded this programme to thirty-eight battleships, forty-eight cruisers and ninety-six destroyers, all of which were to be completed by 1920.

A large part of the reasoning behind this massive programme was based on Tirpitz's 'risk theory' which evolved around a deliberate interference with Britain's 'two power stand-

Germany, a new country and a new naval power, built its own warships from the late 1860s, but since the country had no overseas pretensions at the time these tended to be relatively small ships. The eight 3700-ton ships of the Siegfried *class, laid down between 1888 and 1892, were designed to defend the seaward approaches to German harbours; they had an unusual arrangement of two single 24cm (9.4in) abreast forward and one aft.* Hagen *displays the original appearance of most of the ships, although the last two were different in details. (CMP)*

The first German seagoing battleships were five Brandenburg *class ships laid down in 1892. They were not entirely successful, the midship mounting requiring a short 35-calibre version of the main 28cm (11in) guns to allow it to train on either beam. This is* Wörth *about 1900.* (CMP)

ard'. It was thought that Britain would not be willing to risk a naval war involving a strong German fleet because, even though it would probably win such a war, the losses involved would seriously weaken the Royal Navy and Britain would then be open to attack by France and Russia. Britain would not therefore risk confrontation with Germany and would instead give support to German ambitions in Europe and abroad. The 1900 Navy Law did indeed cause serious concern in Britain, not least because it might cause further expansion in the French and Russian navies, but the result was far removed from that expected. Britain and France in face of a common threat were driven into friendlier relations, which together with a Treaty signed between Britain and Japan in 1902, enabled the Royal Navy to concentrate its main forces in home waters. The Russo-Japanese War effectively removed Russia from the equation, which eventually left only Britain and Germany in direct naval competition.

The development of the new German navy began in the late 1880s with the construction of a few cruisers and the small coast defence battleships of the *Siegfried* class. Completed between 1890 and 1896 the eight ships of the latter group were small 3700-ton ships of slow speed, lightly protected and armed with three 9.4in guns. During the same period work began on a much larger design, the 10,500-ton *Brandenburg* class which, although smaller than foreign contemporaries, were seagoing vessels with a reasonable endurance. They were unusual ships in carrying an armament of six 11in guns in three twin turrets all positioned on the centreline – one at each end and one amidships. The four ships of this class were begun in 1890 and completed in 1893.

Germany's first true pre-dreadnoughts, the *Kaiser* class, provided the basis for future development, the outline design being enlarged and improved upon in each successive class. One ship of the class was laid down in 1896, another in the following year and finally two more in 1898; they completed in 1898–1902. Of 11,600 tons, they did not compare well with foreign ships, being under-protected and under-gunned. They had a shallow waterline belt of 12in KC armour extending from the stem to the after turret, covered by a flat 2½in

deck above which the hull was completely unprotected. In armament they more closely resembled an armoured cruiser than a battleship, having four 9.4in guns mounted in twin turrets and eighteen 5.9in of which six were mounted in turrets and the remainder in casemates. The 9.4in gun was, however, a 40-calibre high velocity QF weapon employing fixed ammunition and had an excellent performance for its size. These ships employed a three-shaft machinery arrangement, already in use in the larger German cruisers and subsequently to become standard in the majority of the country's large warships.

The following *Wittelsbach* class of five ships, the first to be constructed under the 1898 Navy Law, were of generally similar design to the *Kaiser* class but with the displacement increased to allow for the improvement of protection. The main belt was reduced to 9in but was extended to the full length of the ship while the protective deck was sloped down behind it where its 3in plating compensated for the reduction in the thickness. In addition a 5½in upper belt was fitted between this and the main deck where a 5½in box battery, for ten of her 5.9in guns, effectively extended the side armour amidships to the upperdeck. The only other change of note was the provision of a flush deck in place of the cut down quarterdeck of the *Kaiser* class. The next ten battleships, equally divided between the *Braunschweig* and *Deutschland* classes, represented the beginning of the major naval expansion provided under the 1900 Navy Law, which was subsequently brought to a temporary halt by the construction of *Dreadnought*. Averaging 14,000 tons the ships of these two classes were generally similar, the increased displacement

allowing for an increase in the calibres of the armament to 11in and 6.7in and an increase in speed to 18.5kts. The 11in gun was to become a standard calibre for German capital ships and reflected a bias toward protection in the balance of gunpower and armour. The *Deutschland* class differed from the *Braunschweig* in having thicker side armour and in abandoning the use of turret mountings for some of the secondary armament. Although none of these ships managed to match their British contemporaries, they showed a distinct pattern of rapid improvement which was to beome even more noticeable in the later German ships of the dreadnought era.

Semi-dreadnoughts

At the beginning of the twentieth century the conditions which would eventually produce the all-big-gun *Dreadnought* were already at work. Guns had improved in accuracy and fire control equipment was under development which would enable their use at greater ranges. In addition, the torpedo was improving in power and range, forcing a need to accept greater fighting ranges. In this situation the normal secondary armaments of battleships were likely to be ineffective and the need for an increase in the power of these weapons was perceived. The first signs of change were the provision of intermediate batteries, as had been standard in US battleships for many years, but the process was leading toward the provision of a uniform battery of larger guns and few ships of this intermediate type were built before the *Dreadnought* brought the evolutionary process to a premature conclusion.

The first country to produce a design of this

After ten years or more of stability in battleship design, the consensus among the naval powers began to break down after 1900. Italy once again showed willingness to innovate with the fast 21kt battleships of the Regina Elena *class (this is the name ship running trials in 1907). Being derived from a proposal for a large armoured cruiser, their protection was weak, but besides the two main 12in guns, they had a powerful intermediate armament of twelve 8in guns. (CMP)*

type was Italy which laid down only three battleship classes during the 1890s. The first of these classes, consisting of *Ammiraglio Di Saint Bon* and *Emanuele Filiberto*, was little more than a cut down version of the earlier *Re Umberto* design with the main armament reduced to four 10in guns. The second group, *Regina Margherita* and *Benedetto Brin*, were larger ships of 13,000 tons but showed the usual Italian preference for speed and gunpower at the expense of protection, being 20kt ships with only 6in side armour. The armament consisted of four 12in and twelve 6in but they also carried an intermediate battery of four 8in guns. The last vessels, and the ones that best fit the process described above, were the four ships of the *Regina Elena* class, which were designed by Vittorio Cuniberti, one of the first naval architects to propose an all-big-gun armament for battleships. In 1899 he was asked to produce a design for a battleship faster than contemporary French and British ships but powerful enough to deal with armoured cruisers. The result was a 12,500-ton ship with a speed of 21kts, well protected for its size and carrying an armament of two 12in guns, in single turrets fore and aft, and a remarkable secondary battery of twelve 8in guns, mounted in three twin turrets along each side. In essence this was a precurser of the battlecruiser concept, although these ships were better protected than the original British ships of this type. The four ships of the class, *Regina Elena*, *Vittorio Emanuele*, *Roma* and *Napoli*, did not complete until

The movement towards a substantial intermediate armament culminated in the British Lord Nelson *class – Agamemnon is shown here – which replaced the 6in secondary guns with ten 9.2in, all in turrets. However, before the two ships could be completed the all-12in* Dreadnought *had ushered in a new era in battleship design, overshadowing what was in itself a substantial step forward. (CMP)*

1907–8 by which time they had been outclassed and did not cause the stir they might otherwise have done.

The first country to apply the intermediate battery principle to a First Class battleship was Britain with the *Lord Nelson* and *Agamemnon*, laid down in 1905 and completed in 1908. In these ships the main deck 6in gun battery that had become a standard feature of British battleships was entirely omitted leaving the ships' sides completely clear of casemates and gunports. In their place they carried ten 9.2in guns disposed in two twin and one single turret on each side of the upper deck. They also had substantially thicker armour than earlier British ships, which included a 12in main belt, an 8in upper belt and an 8in redoubt to the bases of the 9.2in turrets – the latter carrying the side armour to the full depth of the hull amidships. They were excellent ships, one of the best predreadnought designs ever produced, but like all the ships of this period they were of obsolete design by the time they completed.

Two similar vessels were produced by Russia, *Imperator Pavel* and *Andrei Pervoswanni*.

Begun in 1903–4, their design was modified as a result of the lessons of the Russo-Japanese war, in particular the fact that larger guns had proved more effective and that protection needed to be more extensive. These ships carried a secondary armament of fourteen 8in guns, eight in twin mountings at the corners of the superstructure and the remainder in a central armoured battery. The entire hull above the waterline was covered in armour and unpierced by gunports or side scuttles. However, in order to provide for this degree of coverage the maximum thickness was limited to 8½in, with a 5in upper strake and the ends reducing to 4in. Speed was moderate but even so they were over 1000 tons larger than *Lord Nelson* at 17,400 tons. They did not complete until 1910. France and Japan were to take the semi-dreadnought type still further but these ships were constructed later and blend more readily into the early dreadnought period.

Cruisers

The cruisers of the 1890s fall broadly into three overlapping groups of large, medium and small vessels – by British designations First, Second and Third Class cruisers. The early part of this period saw some interest in ar-

CRUISER DEVELOPMENT 1890–1905

Date is laying down; tonnage is load; scale is 1/1250

Armoured Cruisers

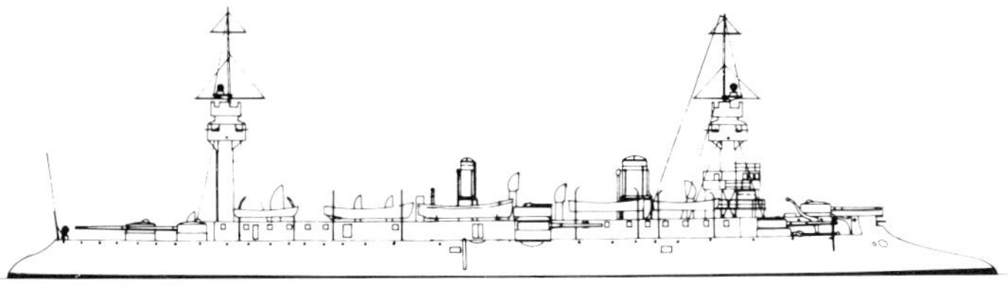

Dupuy de Lôme, *French, 1888, 6676t*

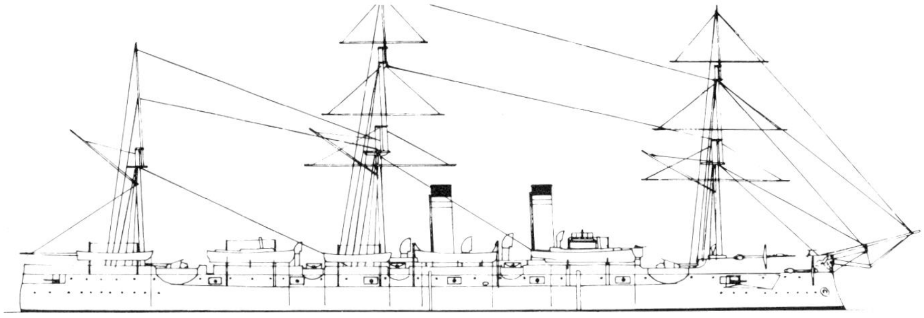

Rurik, *Russian, 1890, 11,690t*

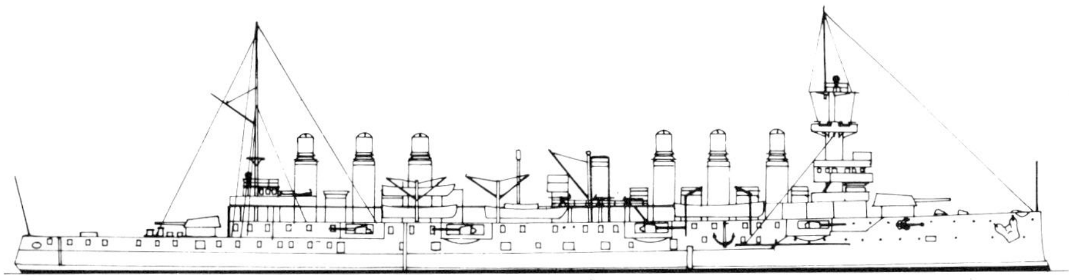

Jeanne d'Arc, *French, 1896, 11,092t*

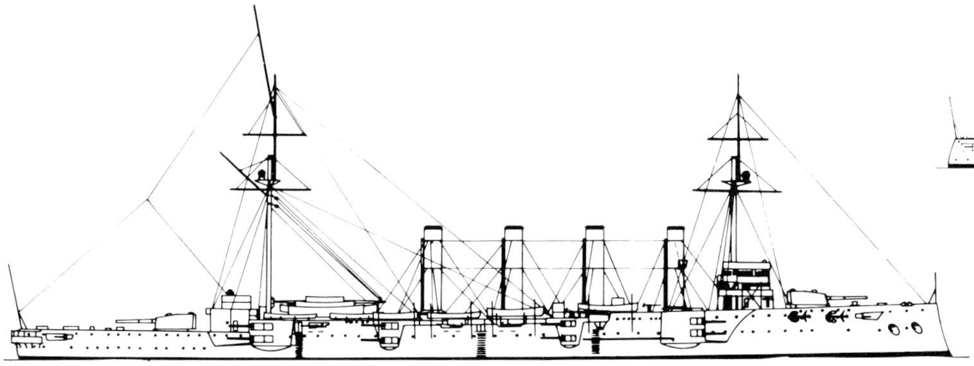

Drake, *British, 1899, 14,150t*

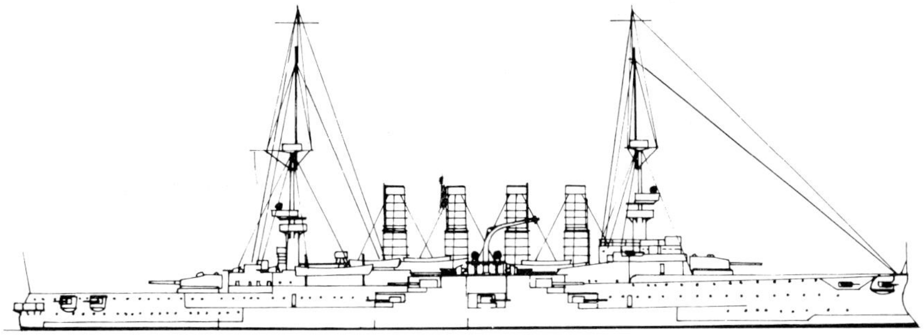

Scharnhorst, *German, 1905, 12,781t*

Protected Cruisers

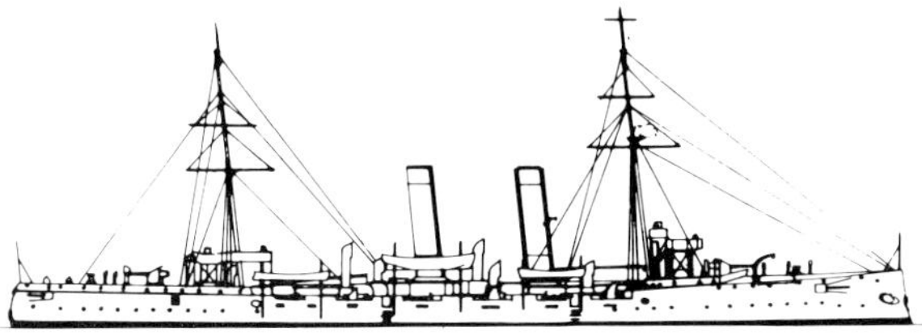

Sirius, *British, 1889, 3600t*

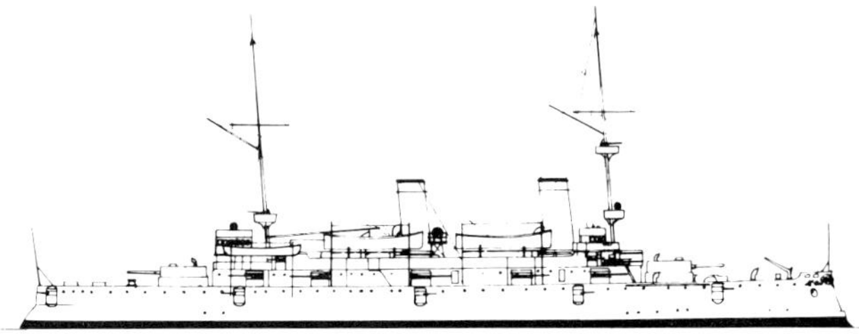

Olympia, *American, 1891, 6558t*

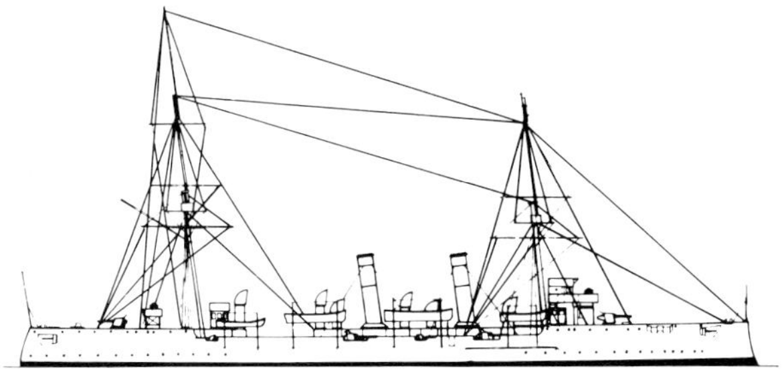

Pelorus, *British, 1895, 2135t*

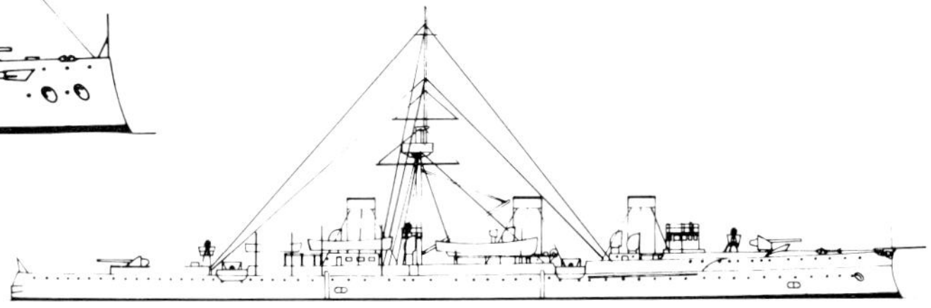

Novik, *Russian, 1898, 3080t*

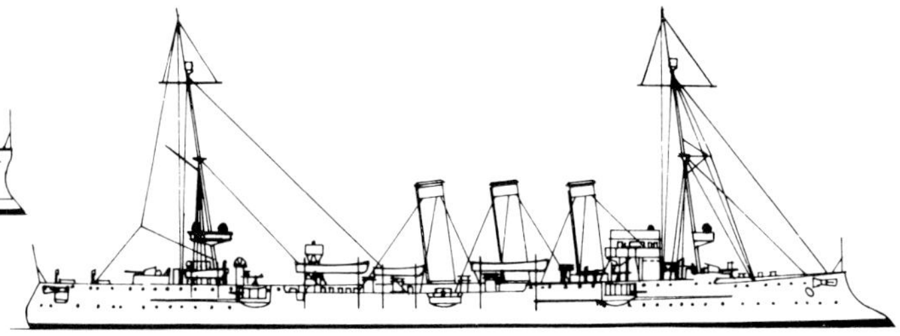

München, *German, 1903, 3756t*

moured cruisers, particularly in France, but generally the protected cruiser was favoured until first Harvey then Krupp armour made it possible to provide side armour over a large area without an excessive increase in displacement. From 1895 onward development was dominated by the armoured cruiser and despite its large size and cost, and consequent restriction in numbers, it almost completely supplanted the construction of small cruisers in most of the major navies. These ships paralleled closely developments in battleship design in their respective countries and generally followed the same basic layouts of armour and armament and, particularly in the United States and Germany, often closely resembled them in appearance. The ships of this period were usually designed with a particular bias towards either trade, fleet or colonial duties but all were expected to serve as multi-purpose vessels. The French and some Russian ships were primarily intended for raids on commerce, while the British generally constructed replies often on a ship-for-ship basis. Many of the later armoured cruisers were also intended to operate with the fleet, serving as a fast wing in conjunction with the battleships where their superior speed would, it was hoped, both enable them to out-manoeuvre an enemy and keep out of trouble. After a short spell of building at the beginning of the decade the small cruiser was abandoned by the majority of the major navies but again revived towards the end of the 1890s.

The first armoured cruiser of the new era was the French ship *Dupuy de Lôme*, laid down in 1888 but not completed until 1895 owing to

an accident to her boilers during trials in 1893. She was an extraordinary ship, having her entire hull from 4ft 6in below water to the upper deck covered in 4in steel armour. Displacing 6600 tons, she had a speed of 20kts and carried an armament of two 7.6in guns, one on each side, and six 6.4in guns which were grouped in threes at each end – all were fitted in single turrets. Her appearance was also somewhat unusual with a long plough bow, heavy tumble-home and a sloping stern. The design was repeated in the smaller *Amiral Charner* class and *Pothuau* but with less extensive and thinner protection. All these ships lacked seaworthiness and, as the protection was insufficient to cope with the medium calibre QF gun, France reverted to the construction of protected cruisers. Nine such ships, averaging 4000 tons, were laid down during 1891–94 and generally followed the design of the earlier *Alger*. They were typical of the medium cruisers of the period with a speed of 19–20kts, a mixed armament of 6.4in and 3.9in QF guns in single shielded mountings and a full length curved protective deck of about 3in thickness. These were followed by three much larger ships, *D'Entrecasteaux*, *Guichen* and *Châteaurenault*, all of around 8000 tons. The first ship was an enlarged version of the previous cruisers with the armament increased to two 9.4in mounted in turrets and twelve 5.5in but the other two were lightly armed commerce raiders with speeds of 23.5kts and 24kts respectively.

During 1896–97 France laid down her last four protected cruisers – two small 2400-ton ships (*D'Estrees* and *Infernet*), the last ship of the earlier 4000-ton group and another com-

merce raider, *Jurien de la Gravière* of 5600 tons. From this point on, under the influence of the *jeune école*, France built no ships smaller than armoured cruisers or larger than destroyers. The first of her new armoured cruisers was the 11,000-ton *Jeanne d'Arc*, laid down in 1896 and completed in 1902. She carried two 7.6in guns in single turrets fore and aft and fourteen 5.5in in shielded mountings equally disposed along each side. Her 3in full length side protection was reinforced by the addition of a waterline belt of 6in Harvey armour over the length of the machinery spaces with, as in the battleships of this period, an upper and lower protective deck forming the boundaries of a cellular layer. She had triple-screw machinery, first introduced in *Guichen*, and a centrally positioned engine room which split the boilers and funnels into two widely spaced groups, an arrangement that was to give all the French armoured cruisers their distinctive appearance. Between 1897 and 1906 a further eighteen cruisers of broadly similar type were laid down. Initially size was reduced in the 7500-ton *Dupleix* class but then steadily increased to over 13,000 tons in the last four ships. During the process of development there was an increasing use of turret mounted guns, although a few were always mounted in casemates, and the armament progressed from eight 6.4in guns in the *Dupleix* class, through mixed 7.6in and 6.4in guns in the intervening classes to a uniform fourteen 7.6in guns in the last two ships – the *Edgar Quinet* class. At the same time speed increased from 21kts to 23kts, and with the introduction of KC armour the area of the side protection was substantially increased.

Following the lack of success of the *Orlando* class belted cruisers, Britain showed no interest in armoured cruisers for several years, concentrating on the construction of a large number of First, Second and Third Class ships derived directly from White's designs of the late 1880s. The Second Class cruisers were initially the more popular and were built to cover trade protection, to police the empire and as fleet scouts in that order. The first of these, the twenty-one ships of the *Apollo* class, were 3400-ton ships, armed with two 6in and six 4.7in guns. They were not successful ships as they lacked seaworthiness and were under-gunned, so in later designs displacement was increased

Bruix, one of four small armoured cruisers that followed the revolutionary Dupuy de Lôme *in 1889–90. France expended considerable energy and resources on the armoured cruiser, which was regarded as an effective commerce raiding weapon, a tactic much advocated in any war with the numerically superior British fleet.*

One of the great export successes of the late nineteenth century was the so-called 'Elswick cruiser', built by Armstrongs at their Tyneside yard of that name. These small but heavily armed ships found favour with a number of navies, including the Japanese, who acquired the original ship Esmeralda *from Chile in 1894, and ordered the* Takasago *(seen here) in 1896. (CMP)*

sembled the *Eclipse* class and carried the same armament, but they had a specially reinforced stem and were given a hull form to enhance their manoeuvring qualities. The last British Second Class cruisers, three ships of the *Highflyer* class and two ships of the *Challenger* class, laid down during 1897 and 1900–1901 respectively, were repeats of the *Eclipse* class but with the armament altered to a uniform eleven 6in guns (the *Eclipse* class itself was modified to this standard in 1903–5).

The First Class cruisers of the Naval Defence Act, the nine ships of the *Edgar* class, were of much the same design as the earlier *Blake* but were smaller at 7350 tons. They carried the same armament but had reduced engine power and a slight reduction in the thickness of the protective deck. Nevertheless, as *Blake* did not come up to expectations with regard to speed they did in fact prove to be almost equal to the earlier ship. While these ships were under construction the Admiralty

first to 4300 tons in the eight ships of the *Astraea* class, then to 5600 tons in the nine cruisers of the to *Eclipse* class. The increased displacement was used principally to increase freeboard, speed and endurance which were, unfortunately, not obvious advantages and the ships were greatly criticised for being under-gunned for their size (*Astraea* had two more 4.7in and *Eclipse* three more 6in than the *Apollo*s). All these ships were laid down during 1889–95, after which Britain, like France, began to concentrate on larger cruisers. However, three more classes, of considerably reduced numbers, were laid down before the type was abandoned altogether. The first, the four ships of the *Arrogant* class, were unusual in being designed to operate as rams in conjunction with the battlefleet. They closely re-

Parliamentary pressure and public opinion often forced the Royal Navy to reply to foreign vessels with exact counters, some of which bore little resemblance to traditional British requirements. The results were often costly and bizarre, as in the case of the huge protected cruisers Powerful *and* Terrible *launched in 1895 as answers to the Russian* Rossia *and* Rurik. Terrible *is shown here as completed, but the funnels were later raised to improve draught to the boilers. (CMP)*

Varese, an Italian armoured cruiser of the Garibaldi *class, represented another cruiser type that achieved considerable export success, being operated by Argentina, Spain and Japan as well as the home country. They had a heavy, if mixed armament, and were designed to serve in the battle line in an emergency. (CMP)*

became increasingly concerned by the production of large foreign cruisers and in particular the 11,000-ton Russian cruiser *Rurik* which had been laid down in 1890. This ship was reported as fast and heavily armed and it was imagined that she could cause havoc once loose among British shipping on the high seas. In fact her design was very dated – an 18kt belted cruiser with a shallow 10in belt and an armament of four 8in and sixteen 6in equally disposed along each side and protected only by shields. To counter this vessel the British laid down *Powerful* and *Terrible* in 1894. The largest protected cruisers ever built, they dis-

placed 14,200 tons, nearly double that of *Edgar*, an increase almost entirely devoted to raising the engine power for a speed of 22kts. They had a very high freeboard and, unlike other British cruisers of this period, a full length forecastle deck (a slightly false impression as there was a well amidships) presenting a large unarmoured broadside apart from the casemates of the 6in guns. They were the first British ships fitted with Belleville boilers, having a total of forty-eight, which together with some problems with their four-cylinder triple expansion engines proved troublesome throughout their careers. They were expensive

ships both to build and operate and were of little use to the Royal Navy which required large numbers and not large size to provide defence against commerce raiders.

In appearance and armament layout the *Powerful* class, with four large funnels, a single 9.2in turret mounted gun fore and aft and two double-story and two single 6in gun casemates on each side was to become the standard arrangement in later British First Class cruisers until Watts replaced White as DNC in 1902. *Powerful* was followed by eight similar but smaller ships in which the speed, armament and protection were reduced to bring the displacement down to 11,000 tons. These ships, the *Diadem* class constructed during 1895–1903, were similar in layout to *Powerful* but the 9.2in guns were replaced by two single 6in guns mounted abreast on both forecastle and quarterdeck. Developments abroad and the introduction of KC armour led the Admiralty to reconsider its policy of constructing only protected cruisers and in the following *Cressy* class, six ships built between 1898 and 1902, a 6in belt was added to what was basically the *Diadem* design but with the single 9.2in guns of *Powerful* reinstated. These ships and the following *Drake* class, in which the displacement was increased from 12,000 tons to 14,000 tons in order to increase the speed from 21kts to 23kts, were primarily intended to counter French construction but were in part inspired by a group of highly successful Italian ships intended to operate with the battlefleet. These ships were the *Garibaldi* class of which ten were built between 1895 and 1905. Only three of these were for the Italian navy as four were sold to Argentina, one to Spain and two to Japan. Although displacing only 7000 tons they combined a speed of 20kts with 4.8in side armour

In the 1890s armoured cruisers grew to the point where they were not much smaller than battleships, and their great length and multiple funnels (six in some French ships) suggested speed and power. HMS Duke of Edinburgh *of 1903 was one of the first ships designed under the new Director of Naval Construction, Phillip Watts and with six 9.2in turrets was an improvement in gun-power over previous classes. However, the attempt to reduce the silhouette made the low casemate-mounted 6in battery ineffective in all but calm conditions. (CMP)*

and a heavy armament of one 10in gun in a single turret forward, two 8in guns in a twin turret aft and fourteen 6in guns disposed equally on each side. They were specifically intended to operate with battleships using their heavy guns as opportunity offered and their speed to escape should they find themselves in an awkward position.

Between 1899 and 1905 Britain built a further twenty-five armoured cruisers starting with the reduced *Monmouth* (9800 tons) and *Devonshire* (10,800 tons) classes, whose main function was trade protection, and ending with the 14,600-ton fleet cruisers of the *Minotaur* class. The speed of all these ships remained at 23kts and the main belt at 6in thickness (except *Monmouth* where the figures were 22kts and 4in), the principal alterations being in the change from casemate to entirely turret mounted guns, the increase of the armament from fourteen 6in in *Monmouth*, through various mixed arrangements, to four 9.2in and ten 7.5in in *Minotaur* and in a dramatic change in appearance from the complex upperworks of the White ships to the clean uncluttered designs of Watts.

Other countries in general followed the pattern set by Britain and France, although there was some divergence particularly in Russia where armoured cruiser construction was supplanted by medium and small ships at the end of the 1890s. The United States paralleled French developments very closely. During 1889–95 the Americans built two armoured cruisers (one of which, *Brooklyn*, resembled

contemporary French battleship designs, having the same armament layout and a marked tumblehome), and eight protected cruisers but then abandoned small and medium sized cruiser construction for ten years (with the exception of the 16kt colonial cruisers of the *Denver* class of 1900). Starting somewhat later than the Europeans they began modern armoured cruiser construction in 1899 and during the next five years laid down fourteen such ships. Japan added eight armoured cruisers to her fleet during 1899–1904, four built by Armstrongs, two by Italy, one in France and one in Germany. All these, apart from the Italian ships, were of fairly uniform design, averaging 9500 tons, armed with four 8in and twelve or fourteen 6in guns, protected by a 7in belt and with a speed of about 20kts. Unlike the major navies, Japan continued to add small and medium sized cruisers to her fleet throughout the 1890s and early 1900s.

German large cruiser development matched that of her battleships not only in pace but in the general appearance and layout of the ships themselves. In 1890 they laid down the *Kaiserin Augusta*, a 6000-ton protected cruiser armed fairly lightly with four 5.9in and eight 4.1in guns. She was the first ship to adopt the triple-screw machinery arrangement that was later to become standard in the German navy. She was followed by the five ships of the *Victoria Louise* class laid down in 1896 and completed in 1897–98. These 18.5kt vessels had an armament of two 8.2in guns in single turrets and eight 5.9in, equally divided between upper

The American cruiser Brooklyn *exhibited a rather French appearance, with extreme tumblehome and sponsored broadside turrets. The ship was the US flagship at the Battle of Santiago during the Spanish War and is seen here at the postwar fleet review in 1898. (CMP)*

deck turrets and main deck casemates. This design was expanded to produce Germany's first armoured cruiser, the 11,000-ton *Fürst Bismarck*, laid down in 1896 and completed in 1900. She had a full length waterline belt of KC armour with a maximum thickness of 8in, and an armament of four 9.4in guns in two twin turrets and twelve 5.9in guns. Compared with foreign ships she was rather slow at 18.5kts but in subsequent designs this was steadily increased from 20kts in the 9600-ton *Prinz Heinrich* to 23.5kts in the 12,700-ton *Scharnhorst* and *Gneisenau*. At the same time the armament was increased and refined, ending with eight 8.2in and six 5.9in guns in the last ships, while the protection was steadily increased in extent in each succeeding class.

As with the battleships the early vessels were not particularly outstanding but the later ships could easily stand comparison with vessels of equivalent size. It was not, however, with these ships that Germany was to make her mark but in development of the small cruiser. A few small cruisers had been built during the early years of the 1890s but were soon dropped from the construction programmes of most of the major navies in favour of larger vessels. Germany, however, evolved the small torpedo cruiser of the 1880s into a slightly larger and

The Germans took the lead in developing an effective scout for fleet duties and with the Gazelle class of 1897 produced the first modern light cruiser. Armed with only 10.5cm (4.1in) guns, whose faster rate of fire the Germans believed would make them a better anti-torpedo boat weapon than the 6in, they were fast and tough little ships. Ten vessels were built to this design, including Amazone pictured here as completed. (CMP)

more general purpose vessel – the light cruiser. The first of these, the 3000-ton *Gazelle* class of ten ships built during 1897–1904, had a speed of 20kts; they had a 2in protective deck and an armament of ten 4.1in guns and three torpedo tubes. These were fleet ships, particularly suited to the waters of the North Sea and the Baltic, and were intended to serve as scouts, in support of torpedo boats and in a defensive role against torpedo boats. They were also comparatively cheap and could be built in substantial numbers. They were subsequently developed and improved through a large series of classes which continued well into the dread-nought period. The basic design concept was eventually adopted in most countries and it was the ships of this type that ultimately pointed the way in future cruiser development. The big cruisers, so popular at this time, evolved first into the battlecruiser and then disappeared from the cruiser category completely as these, in turn, merged into the fast battleship type.

John Roberts

The Pre-Dreadnought Age: Typical Vessels 1889–1905

Ship or class	Nationality	Disp (load) (tons)	Dimensions (loa × breadth × draught) (feet–inches) (metres)	Armament	Armour (belt/turrets/ deck) (max, ins)	Speed (max, kts)	Launch dates	Numbers built
Battleships								
BRENNUS	French	11,190	361–10 × 67–0 × 27–2 110.7 × 20.4 × 8.3	3–13.4in, 10–6.4in	18/18/3	18	1891	1
BRANDENBURG	German	10,500	379–6 × 64–0 × 26–0 115.7 × 19.5 × 7.9	6–11in, 6–4.1in	16/5/2.5	16.5	1891–92	4
ROYAL SOVEREIGN	British	14,150	410–6 × 75–0 × 27–6 115.8 × 22.9 × 8.4	4–13.5in, 10–6in	18/–/3	16.5	1892–94	7
CHARLES MARTEL	French	11,693	379–0 × 71–0 × 27–6 115.5 × 21.6 × 8.4	2–12in, 2–10.8in, 8–5.5in	18/15/3.5	18	1893	1
INDIANA	American	10,288	351–0 × 69–4 × 24–0 107 × 21.1 × 7.3	4–13in, 8–8in, 4–6in	18/15/3	15	1893	3
MAJESTIC	British	14,560	421–0 × 75–0 × 27–0 128.3 × 22.9 × 8.2	4–12in, 12–6in	9/10/4	17	1894–96	9
CHARLEMAGNE	French	11,100	380–10 × 66–5 × 27–6 116.1 × 20.2 × 8.4	4–12in, 10–5.5in	14.5/15/3	18	1895–96	3
FUJI	Japanese	12,533	412–0 × 73–0 × 26–6 125.5 × 22.2 × 8.1	4–12in, 10–6in	14/6/2.5	18	1896	2
ILLINOIS	American	11,560	375–4 × 72–4 × 23–6 114.4 × 22.0 × 7.2	4–13in, 14–6in	16.5/14/3	16	1898	3
HENRI IV	French	8807	354–4 × 72–10 × 22–11 108.0 × 22.2 × 7.0	2–10.8in, 7–5.5in	11/12/2.4	17	1899	1
MIKASA	Japanese	15,140	432–0 × 76–0 × 27–0 131.7 × 23.2 × 8.3	4–12in, 14–6in	9/10/3	18	1900	1
RETVISAN	Russian	12,900	386–8 × 72–2 × 26–0 117.9 × 22.0 × 7.9	4–12in, 12–6in	9/9/3	18	1900	1

Ship or Class	Nationality	Disp (load) (tons)	Dimensions (loa × breadth × draught) (feet–inches) (metres)	Armament	Armour (belt/turrets/ deck) (max. ins)	Speed (max, kts)	Launch dates	Numbers built
BRAUNSCHWEIG	German	14,167	419–0 × 84–0 × 26–6 127.7 × 25.6 × 8.1	4–11in, 14–6.7in	9/6/3	18	1902–4	5
LIBERTÉ	French	14,450	439–0 × 79–7 × 27–6 133.8 × 24.3 × 8.4	4–12in, 10–7.6in	11/14/2.75	19	1904–7	4
CONNECTICUT	American	16,000	456–4 × 76–10 × 24–6 139.1 × 23.4 × 7.5	4–12in, 8–8in, 12–7in	11/12/3	18	1904	2
REGINA ELENA	Italian	12,550	474–5 × 73–6 × 26–0 144.6 × 22.4 × 7.9	2–12in, 12–8in	9.8/8/1.5	21	1904–7	4
LORD NELSON	British	16,000	443–6 × 79–6 × 26–0 135.2 × 24.2 × 7.9	4–12in, 10–9.2in	12/12/4	18	1906	2
First Class cruisers								
DUPUY DE LOME	French	6676	364–2 × 51–6 × 24–7 111.0 × 15.7 × 7.5	2–7.6in, 6–6.4in	4/4/1	19.5	1890	1
RURIK	Russian	11,690	435–0 × 67–0 × 27–3 132.6 × 20.4 × 8.3	4–8in, 16–6in, 6–4.7in	10/–/3.5	18.5	1892	1
BROOKLYN	American	9215	402–7 × 64–8 × 24–0 122.7 × 19.7 × 7.3	8–8in, 12–5in	3/5.5/6	20	1895	1
POWERFUL	British	14,200	538–0 × 71–0 × 27–0 164.0 × 21.6 × 8.2	2–9.2in, 12–6in	–/6/6	22	1895	2
VICTORIA LOUISE	German	6390	363–2 × 57–2 × 22–10 110.6 × 17.4 × 6.9	2–8.2in, 8–5.9in	–/4/4	18.5	1897–98	5
CHÂTEAURENAULT	French	7898	443–0 × 55–10 × 24–4 135.0 × 17.0 × 7.4	2–6.4in, 6–5.5in	–/1.5/3	24	1898	1
JEANNE D'ARC	French	11,092	477–0 × 63–8 × 26–7 145.4 × 19.4 × 8.1	2–7.6in, 14–5.5in	6/6/2.6	21.5	1899	1
CRESSY	British	12,000	472–0 × 69–6 × 26–0 143.9 × 21.2 × 7.9	2–9.2in, 12–6in	6/6/3	21	1899–1901	6
IDZUMO	Japanese	9700	434–0 × 68–10 × 24–6 132.3 × 20.9 × 7.4	4–8in, 14–6in	7/6/2.5	20.75	1899–1900	2
TENNESSEE	American	14,500	504–6 × 72–1 × 25–0 153.8 × 22.2 × 7.6	4–10in, 16–6in	5/9/4	22	1904–6	4
EDGAR QUINET	French	13,847	521–4 × 70–7 × 27–7 158.9 × 21.5 × 8.4	14–7.6in	6/8/2.5	23	1905–6	2
MINOTAUR	British	14,600	519–0 × 74–6 × 26–0 158.2 × 22.7 × 7.9	4–9.2in, 10–7.5in	6/8/1.5	23	1906–7	3
Cruisers					deck/gun shields			
APOLLO	British	3400	314–0 × 43–0 × 17–6 95.7 × 13.1 × 5.3	2–6in, 6–4.7in	2/4.5	20	1890–91	21
CINCINNATI	American	3183	305–10 × 42–0 × 18–0 93.2 × 12.8 × 5.5	1–6in, 10–5in	2.5/4	19	1892	2
DESCARTES	French	3960	316–0 × 42–7 × 21–4 96.3 × 13.0 × 6.5	4–6.4in, 10–3.9in	1.8/2	19.5	1894–95	2
ARROGANT	British	5750	342–0 × 57–6 × 20–0 104.2 × 17.5 × 6.1	4–6in, 6–4.7in	3/4.5	19	1896–97	4
GAZELLE	German	2916	344–10 × 40–1 × 18–2 105.0 × 12.2 × 5.5	10–4.1in	2/–	20	1898	10
BOGATYR	Russian	6645	439–8 × 54–6 × 20–7 134.0 × 16.6 × 6.3	12–6in	2.7/5	23	1901–3	4

8

Underwater Warfare and the Torpedo Boat

THE simplest way to sink a ship is to make a hole below the waterline large enough to destroy her buoyancy. In the nineteenth century for the first time it became possible to do this at a distance by explosive means. Initially this could only be achieved passively by the use of mines of various kinds, but the development of different patterns of torpedo made active underwater attack possible – and for the first time in naval history smaller vessels had the potential of destroying much bigger adversaries and getting away with it.[1]

Early underwater warfare

The word 'torpedo' originally covered more devices than the cylindrical object with propellers and rounded ends which is automatically associated with the term today. It was originally coined, apparently by Robert Fulton before 1814, to describe what would now be called a mine – an explosive device which was either free-floating, moored or lying on the seabed. It was also used to describe weapons towed on the end of a cable ('towing torpedo') or attached to the end of a long pole ('spar torpedo') – all of these devices developed by the inventive Mr Fulton – before it came into currency for the self-propelled device ('locomotive torpedo' or 'fish torpedo') developed by Robert Whitehead which was the ancestor of what we now call 'torpedoes'.

Before going into the history of the development of this weapon and the craft which came into existence to carry it into battle it would seem appropriate to consider its ancestry in the earlier history of underwater attack.

In the period of Classical Greece and Rome the fighting ship was a form of oared galley whose chief weapon was the ram – and therefore was dedicated to underwater attack. By the end of the Middle Ages, though the chief fighting ship in the Mediterranean was still a form of galley, the *underwater* ram had disappeared and had been replaced by a bow projection *above* the waterline – a 'beakhead'. This might be used to break opponents' oars or as a boarding bridge but it was not, in the true sense, a ram. The records of the navies of the time make it clear that the chief weapon of these vessels were at first bows and arrows and other projectile weapons used by 'marines' from aboard the galleys and, from some time in the fifteenth century, cannon mounted forward shooting over the bow.

The date of the change away from ramming was at some time in the Dark Ages – centuries before the appearance of guns. The most probable explanation for this would seem to be the change in ship construction which happened at some time between the end of the classical period and the beginning of the Middle Ages. That change meant the abandonment of the 'shell-first' form of 'edge-joined' construction in favour of 'skeleton-first' construction in which the planks are fitted to a pre-existing frame but not to each other.[2] The earlier method of construction meant that the blow from a ram could smash a hole in the side of a ship by shearing the pins which held a plank in place – and once this was done there was little chance of replacing the plank. Also the structural integrity of the whole hull would be affected. With the new structure it would be much more difficult to make a permanent hole. Even if a plank could be forced out of place by ramming (less easy with the stronger and closer frames needed by this structure) it would be much easier to spring back into position. Underwater attack was no longer an option in galley warfare. Steam power and metal hulls would produce a brief and futile revival of ramming as a tactic in the late nineteenth century, but by then the future of underwater attack lay with the use of explosive charges at a distance.

The idea of underwater attack took new forms in the sixteenth and seventeenth centuries. There were various projects from submarines – some of which proceeded as far as tentative demonstrations (the Dutchman Drebbel in the Thames for King James I, for example). The power of waterborne explosives was already known and demonstrated in stunningly effective form by the Italian engineer Gianibelli with his 'hellburners' – vessels turned into floating bombs which accounted for several hundred Spaniards at the siege of Antwerp (1585). Drebbel actually produced what were called 'water mynes' and other 'engines' for the unsuccessful English attempts to relieve La Rochelle in 1627–8 but these appear to have been floating bombs rather than devices for submerged attack.[3]

Underwater warfare with explosives began to be a practical proposition thanks to the efforts of three American pioneers. The first was David Bushnell who developed a submarine (*Turtle* 1776) and floating mines (1777) both of which were used in action against the British Navy. Both proved, up to a point, practical, but neither did much damage.[4]

---

1. Fireships could, of course, destroy bigger vessels in favourable circumstances – but only at the expense of their own destruction. Torpedoes – even spar torpedoes – were not suicide weapons, though torpedo attack could be very dangerous which is why the use of speed and/or stealth was so desirable, as were numbers and expendability.

2. For a well illustrated account of this change see Basil Greenhill and Sam Manning, *The Evolution of the Wooden Ship* (London 1988). It was Greenhill's earlier *Archaeology of the Boat* which inspired the present writer to make the connection between the change in construction and the disappearance of the ram – as far as he is aware this is the first time this idea has been put forward in print.

3. See the pretentious and inadequate, but still useful book by A Roland, *Underwater Warfare in the Age of Sail* (Bloomington, Indiana 1978) for a summary of these and other early attempts to produce underwater weapons.

4. *Turtle* actually made an attack on the line of battle ship *Eagle* in New York harbour. Its one-man pilot and power source, Sergeant Ezra Lee, did superbly well to make the attempt and survive it. However the sheer difficulty of attempting to move the boat whilst maintaining depth was really too much for any man, still more so the difficulties of attempting to force the screw of the primitive 'limpet mine' into the hull of *Eagle* – as anyone with practical experience of diving beneath a ship will realise. The suggestions that copper sheathing protected *Eagle* from this are neither necessary nor correct (it was not until three years later that she was given this sheathing) – see D Lyon, *et al*, *Navies of the American Revolution* (London 1975) for an earlier discussion of this point.

The battered hull of a Confederate 'David' seen after the end of the American Civil War shows how much like a submarine these semi-submersible spar torpedo boats looked. (US National Archives)

velopments in torpedoes and the craft that carried them – and the rest of this chapter is devoted to them.

The locomotive torpedo

The earliest torpedo boats had torpedoes attached to them – either on spars over the bows or, less frequently, towing from ropes. Either system necessitated a very close approach to the prospective victim. The spar torpedo by its nature enforced a head-on approach which would only stop when the charge was in contact with the target's side. In effect the torpedo boat had to ram its opponent and then back away (if still capable of such a move). The tamping effect of an explosion underwater against a hull would direct the main force of the explosion into the victim and upwards – so less fatal to the attacker than might appear at first sight. If surprise was on his side he might face no greater threat than rifles and other individual weapons from the deck of his target. The heavy guns of the time were traversed and aimed by human muscle-power and were both slow and imprecise to operate, whilst reloading took a great deal of time. A small, speedy and man-

Robert Fulton's contributions were made in the next series of wars, those of the French Revolution and Napoleon. An extremely inventive man and pioneer of steam propulsion, he developed Bushnell's *Turtle* design into his more workable version, *Nautilus*, which blew up ships moored as demonstration targets but was never seriously tested in action. His 'catamarans' – floating mines propelled by swimmers – were used by the British against invasion craft sheltering in harbour, but without much success. He seems to have produced the first spar torpedoes and towing torpedoes, and during 1814 a 'turtle boat', powered by hand-operated paddles and protected by minimal freeboard and thick timbers, was built to tow five such torpedoes into action. It was sent out against the British fleet but was destroyed in a pre-emptive attack. Arguably this was the first torpedo boat. Fulton carried his ideas for attempting to distance the effect of an underwater charge from an attacking vessel to the extent of proposing guns firing shells underwater. He produced various forms of sea mine including the first ever moored mine.[5] He even appears to have been the first to use the alternative name of that extraordinary fish, the electric ray or torpedo, to describe his mines and other explosive devices.

He does not appear, however, to have used electricity in these devices. This advance is claimed for a third inventive American, Samuel Colt, who is better known for developing the revolver. Colt developed electrically-fired 'observation mines' which could be used for coastal and harbour defence under the control of shore stations. In 1848 the Prussians were

using their own versions of such mines to protect Kiel against the Danish fleet. The Russians made further developments in the next decade and used electro-chemical 'horns' in mines which caused damage to two small British warships in the Baltic during the Crimean war.[6]

However it was in America that underwater attack came of age – during the Civil War of 1861–1865. Warships were sunk by contact mines and by controlled mines. The CSS *Virginia* (ex-*Merrimack*) made effective use of her ram at Hampton Roads, thus helping to start the misguided fashion for ramming as a major method of attack once again.[7] More to our present purpose, however, is the fact that the first successful spar torpedo attacks were made. The Confederate man-powered submarine *H L Hunley* sank the Federal screw sloop *Houstatonic* (17 February 1864) and the Northerner Lieutenant Cushing using a steam launch sank the Southern ironclad *Albermarle* (28 October 1864). Both these attacks led to the swamping of the attacking craft, in the case of the *Hunley* with fatal effect. Undeservedly less well known is the earlier attack of 15 October 1863 in which a Confederate torpedo boat (*David*) damaged the biggest Federal ironclad, *New Ironsides*. These successes are a convenient moment to abandon tracing the more general aspects of the history of underwater warfare to concentrate on the development of torpedo boats. Submarines would not begin to become practicable weapons systems until the very end of the nineteenth century; mines developed steadily but not spectacularly during the same time. The last third of the nineteenth century, however, witnessed spectacular and varied de-

5. See J S Cowie, *Mines, Minelayers and Minelaying* (London 1949), pp15–16 for both the 'turtle boat' and the moored mine.

6. Contact between the 'horns' and the hull of a ship would cause a glass container to break, mixing the contents with another chemical and producing an electrical impulse which would fire the detonator. These Russian mines are associated with the names of Jacobi and Nobel (the father of the founder of the Nobel Prizes) and the concept of the 'horns' would be further developed and refined by the German scientist Herz during the subsequent decade (see Cowie, *op cit*).

7. The sinking of *Re d'Italia* at the Battle of Lissa (1866) was actually more influential. For several decades ram bows were to be a feature of all major warships – but would prove to be a danger only to consorts in company. It would prove almost impossible to ram an alert and well-handled enemy, and the increasing range of guns and torpedoes during the last quarter of the nineteenth century made this method of attack even less sensible. It would be revived as a weapon of opportunity or last resort for escorts against surfaced submarines, but its use was discouraged because of the likelihood of severe damage to the ramming ship. In at least one case (the 30-knotter destroyer HMS *Fairy*) the damage caused in ramming a submarine (*UC 75* in 1918) caused both ships to sink (though it is only fair to add that *Fairy* was somewhat smaller than her adversary).

oeuvrable spar torpedo boat stood a reasonable chance of both making and of surviving a successful attack under these conditions. A towing torpedo could be used at slightly greater range and by a boat steaming past broadside to broadside. However it required more skill to operate and was less certain in its effect (particularly if the target used nets or other obstructions to surround her hull). With both types of weapon the favourite time to attack would be when the target was at anchor or otherwise stopped, so that there was no possibility of evading the blow by manoeuvre.

However it would obviously be better to have a torpedo which was capable of being used as a missile – which could be discharged at a distance and move under its own power to-

A contemporary impression (from the Illustrated London News) *of the appearance of the steel river launches adapted by the Russians as spar torpedo boats for use against the Turks in 1877. Like the Confederate 'Davids' it was hoped that the curved boiler-plate decks would deflect bullets and give the crew some necessary protection.* (All uncredited photographs from the author's collection)

wards the enemy. This 'locomotive torpedo' evolved from a rather different idea thanks to the genius of the English engineer Robert Whitehead working at Fiume[8] in the Austrian Empire. An Austrian officer, Captain Luppis, had invented a clockwork-propelled, floating bomb intended to be steered by lines from the shore.[9] He went to the engineer for practical help in making this device more viable. Instead of doing this Whitehead looked more deeply at the problem – and developed a submerged missile which was powered by compressed air. He saw that a submerged charge was more lethal than a surface one, and that over the range of a few hundred yards which was the maximum possible at the time, steering was not necessary – properly adjusted and aimed the weapon should go fairly straight. The main problem was keeping the right depth. The way this was done was Whitehead's particular 'secret', developed over several years of experimentation. By 1868 this hydrostatic device was reliable enough for Whitehead to offer his weapon to the navies of the world. The Royal Navy purchased a number of weapons and the 'secret' in

1870 after successful trials. The Austrians had already invested in the weapon. It is interesting that the French, who were later to make so much of their torpedo arm, did not initiate trials until 1873.[10] The Germans eventually

---

8. Now Rijeka in Croatia (late Yugoslavia).

9. Many inventors would continue to play with the idea of a guided torpedo, mostly for coastal defence from shore batteries. Large numbers of electrical torpedoes were experimented with, but it was not until the middle of the twentieth century that technology had reached the state when 'wire guided' and electrically operated torpedoes became practical weapons of war. By this time homing torpedoes were also in service. However there was one late nineteenth century guided torpedo which was successful. This was the elegantly simple Brennan torpedo in service in the 1880s with the British Royal Engineers. It was, in effect, wire guided – but not by electricity. Two wire reels in the body of this large weapon (just over 20ft long) were each geared to a propeller. Each wire was pulled in by a small steam winch in the shore station. As the wire came off the reel it rotated it and thereby powered the screw. Steering was done by varying the speed with which each winch operated. Range was about a mile.

10. Defeat in the Franco-Prussian War – which also entailed heavy reparations – does help to explain this delay.

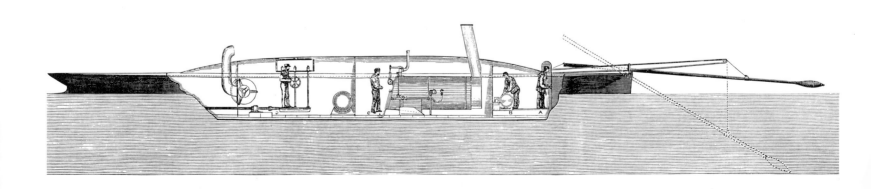

developed their own similar weapon, the Schwartzkopff,[11] but most other navies purchased what became generally known as 'Whiteheads'. The British were soon building their own under licence in the Royal Laboratory of Woolwich Arsenal and soon began the process of modification and steady improvement which has continued ever since.

The Americans briefly introduced a radically different type of torpedo – the flywheel-powered Howell torpedo – in 1889. It was simple and cheap and its flywheel gave it directional accuracy. However it was unsuited to small torpedo boats both because of the size and weight of the steam engine needed to get the flywheel up to speed and because of the appalling noise it made. The Whitehead torpedo had far greater development potential and by the end of the 1890s the US Navy abandoned the Howell in its favour.

This potential of the Whitehead can be illustrated by considering the development of the British versions. The first type was 16in (40.6cm) in diameter but by the mid 1870s was being replaced by the 14in (35.6cm) type. By the 1890s 18in (45.7cm) weapons were coming into service – and the shape of these weapons had changed from the original conical pointed-end version to the hydrodynamically more effective and capacious form with rounded head and tubular body tapering to the propellers which is still familiar. Meanwhile the strength of containers of compressed air and the speed and efficiency of engines had steadily increased – as had the power of explosives. Accuracy, range and speed (the two latter could be varied by a trade-off between one and the other) had increased, but not enough to compensate for the development in the range, power, rate of fire and ease of pointing of the new breech-loading quick-firing guns. Two developments of the end of the nineteenth century compensated for this. 'Air heaters', burning fuel in the compressed air to produce what was in effect an internal-combustion engine, permitted much greater range and speed. This would have been of little use had not the development of gyroscopic guidance given the necessary greater accuracy to take advantage of the increase in range.

Early torpedo craft

The British Torpedo Committee of 1873 identified four main types of craft which might use torpedoes of all kinds. Already existing types of major warship could (and did) add torpedoes to their armament – and with these we are not concerned, though the first use of a locomotive

EARLY TORPEDO CRAFT 1875–1890

Date is laying down; tonnage is load; scale is 1/1250

Zieten, *German torpedo vessel, 1875, 1152t*

Leitenant Ilin, *Russian torpedo gunboat, 1885, 714t*

Pietro Micca, *Italian torpedo cruiser, 1875, 598t*

Rattlesnake, *British torpedo gunboat, 1885, 550t*

Polyphemus, *British torpedo ram, 1878, 2640t*

Wattignies, *French torpedo cruiser, 1889, 1280t*

Bombe, *French torpedo gunboat, 1883, 400t*

Circe, *British torpedo gunboat, 1890, 810t*

torpedo in war was by the large steam frigate *Shah* in action against the Peruvian ironclad *Huascar*.[12] The larger sort of ship's boat, especially the steam-powered ones which were just coming into service at this time, made useful improvised torpedo craft as Cushing had already proved. Fast steam launches would make appropriate launching platforms, whilst specially designed torpedo ships were the fourth alternative. All three of these latter options were taken up and appeared in varying forms – the ship's boat developed into the purpose-built 'Second Class TB' which then was abandoned in favour of slower and sturdier picket boats. The steam launch became the torpedo boat, which grew in size, strength and power until it evolved into the ultimate purpose-built torpedo ship, the destroyer.

The Confederate '*Davids*' – copies of the original vessel of this name – were basically steam launches adapted to proceed nearly awash. They were given a 'turtle-backed' deck of boiler plate intended to deflect rifle fire. All

11. There was, apparently, a Mr Schwarzkopff, but one still suspects a certain degree of copying and a ponderous sense of humour at Whitehead's expense, as the German name translates into English as 'Blackhead'!

12. This was in 1877. The unarmoured *Shah* with a smaller and equally unarmoured consort had been unable to do much damage by gunfire to the armoured *Huascar*, which was behaving in a piratical manner after opting for the wrong side in a Peruvian revolution. The new weapon was fired at *Huascar*, which being somewhat faster evaded it until it ran out of compressed air. The Peruvian vessel later surrendered to its own government and was eventually captured by the Chileans (who have recently restored her as a museum ship). Stories about the incident abound, including the allegation that the torpedo was slid overboard from *Shah* off the wardroom table, which made a better launcher than the purpose-designed one.

that showed above this were the funnel and the spar torpedo. Because of the industrial weakness of the South they could not be given engines that would provide any great speed and since they were intended for harbour defence they required no real degree of seaworthiness. In these circumstances the decision to build small vessels with a minimal silhouette and a degree of protection made a good deal of sense. The element of stealth is a recurrent theme in the history of the torpedo boat, though speed is perhaps the dominant one.

The first purpose-built torpedo vessel was built for the US Navy as a response to these Southern vessels. This was the *Spuyten Duyvil* of 1864. She was much larger but shared the feature of a protective (in her case properly armoured) turtle-back deck and the ability to 'flood down' to a very low freeboard for attack. Her spar torpedo was run out underwater and was reloadable. She was a very interesting and ingenious design, but never saw serious action; her low maximum speed of 8kts would have

proved a handicap. However her combination of 'stealth attributes' and protected deck were useful features for her design function of attacking enemy ships in harbour.

Much the same purpose seems to have been envisaged for the Royal Navy's first torpedo vessel. *Vesuvius* completed in 1874 was armed with a bow torpedo tube for the newly adopted Whitehead torpedo (and several reloads), had very low freeboard, engines that were as near noiseless as they could be made and boilers that burnt coke to produce the minimum of smoke. She was initially intended to discharge what little smoke she made through vents along her sides, though she was given a funnel in service. The concomitant of this devotion to stealth was that she could make only 9.7kts. Clearly intended for night attack on French fleet bases – especially Cherbourg – she had in the event a long, peaceful, but useful life as an experimental vessel for the torpedo school.

Two years later the German Navy had a yacht-like torpedo vessel built on the Thames

A contemporary artist's impressions of the torpedo ram HMS Polyphemus *show her submarine-like form with the necessary minimum of superstructure and with machine-gun towers on the flying deck the only gun armament. A floral wreath is somewhat incongruously perched on the end of the ram, which formed a cap to the bow torpedo tube. The black holes of the submerged broadside tubes (the first of their kind, for which* Polyphemus *was the experimental ship) can also be seen.*

– the 16kt *Zieten* with bow and stern submerged tubes. In her, perhaps, can be seen one of the origins of the light cruiser, in whose evolution the German navy played an important part. The 'torpedo cruisers' built in Britain in the mid 1880s were part of the same story – that of cruisers rather than torpedo vessels.

The most extraordinary of all early torpedo vessels was the Royal Navy's *Polyphemus*. Begun in 1878 and completed in 1882 this powerful vessel could be considered as an updated and much faster *Spuyten Duyvil* equipped with Whiteheads. Her maximum speed of

18kts was very high for the day, she had a 3in armoured protective deck, and five submerged torpedo tubes with reloads (one tube in the bows and the others on the broadside). She was the 'lead ship' for submerged broadside tubes. In case these did not work and as a weapon of last resort she was also equipped with a spur ram. She was called a 'torpedo ram' and this title put the main elements in her armament in the right order: she was intended from the start primarily as a *torpedo* vessel. The fact that the rapid development of quick-firing guns soon made her more vulnerable does not detract from the interest and potential power of her original concept. Had she been used in action early in her career she might well have proved an extremely dangerous opponent to the battleships of her day, despite teething problems with both boilers and submerged tubes.[13]

Development of the torpedo boat

The story of the torpedo boat (TB) proper, which evolved from high-speed steam launches, is basically that of a very few firms which started by building those launches. These lightweight craft and their powerful but temperamental machinery were at the outer limits of the technology of the day. Few firms could cope with this technology, whilst only half a dozen or so in the world were capable of making successful innovations. Only four firms were consistently successful: in England, Thornycroft and Yarrow; in France (slightly later) Le Normand; and (later still) in Germany, Schichau. The American firm of Herreshoff and the English J Samuel White made more occasional contributions, whilst some other British (Laird), French (La Seyne) and German (Germaniawerft) yards were reasonably successful designers and builders of this type of vessel. More yards in these and other countries built TBs, but these were either to the specialists' designs or not very successful.

The original pioneers were John Isaac Thornycroft and Alfred Fernandez Yarrow, who began building light and fast steel river launches on the Thames in the 1860s. The history of both men's firms is more reminiscent of the early days of aviation than that of most shipbuilders and there are striking parallels between these rivals. They developed light and powerful machinery to power the light and strong hulls they built. Inventiveness and quality control acquired a new importance in their high-precision work. The steam launches they built were the fastest watercraft of their day, and it was only a matter of time before they were adapted for warlike use. In the 1877–78 war with Turkey, Russia actually converted a number of steam launches acquired from private owners to torpedo boats carrying spar or locomotive torpedoes – but the first purpose-built torpedo launches had appeared even earlier. It is generally accepted that the first real torpedo boat of this kind was Thornycroft's *Rasp* (or *Rap*) built for Norway in 1872.[14] Though originally intended to operate a towing torpedo (attached to her funnel), her design was soon altered to incorporate the spar torpedo, which was also to be the weapon of the majority of her immediate successors. During the 1870s most navies acquired a number of such craft – some 70ft or so (*c*21m) in length with very little beam, and a speed of around 16–17kts. Spar torpedoes were soon exchanged for 'Whiteheads', usually fired from tubes.[15]

Initial enthusiasm for the torpedo boat was great: in particular both France and Russia ordered large numbers of these high-speed craft. This is hardly surprising as both navies were extremely concerned with coastal defence against the threat of coastal *offence* posed by the ironclads and gunboats of the Royal Navy.[16] The actual limitations of the small, fragile and very short-ranged torpedo boats of the time were overlooked by politicians and strategists wanting a cheap answer to the expensive ironclad. Torpedo boats were also exciting commands for junior naval officers and the seductive power of the new weapon, and in particular the lure of unrealistic trial speeds, had an enormous and very public appeal. Record-breakers like the French *Forban* (the first vessel to make over 30kts – and this in 1896) became famous. Speed was the great selling point and the main builders competed fiercely to score such records. Specialist trials

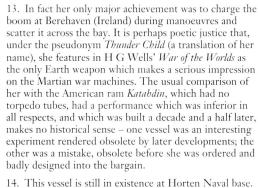

13. In fact her only major achievement was to charge the boom at Berehaven (Ireland) during manoeuvres and scatter it across the bay. It is perhaps poetic justice that, under the pseudonym *Thunder Child* (a translation of her name), she features in H G Wells' *War of the Worlds* as the only Earth weapon which makes a serious impression on the Martian war machines. The usual comparison of her with the American ram *Katahdin*, which had no torpedo tubes, had a performance which was inferior in all respects, and which was built a decade and a half later, makes no historical sense – one vessel was an interesting experiment rendered obsolete by later developments; the other was a mistake, obsolete before she was ordered and badly designed into the bargain.

14. This vessel is still in existence at Horten Naval base.

15. Thornycroft's *Lightning* (*TB 1*) – the Royal Navy's first conventional torpedo boat – was completed in 1877 with torpedo discharging frames. These were lowered into the water and the torpedoes then fired. As this was not possible at any speed they were replaced in 1879 by a bow torpedo tube.

16. I owe this point about the Royal Navy as a force oriented towards coastal offence at this period to conversations with Andrew Lambert. It is a concept that makes much sense both in the context of the unchallenged superiority in major warships of the RN at that period, and in the designs of the ships built at the time.

The Lightning, *the Royal Navy's* TB No 1 *and early Second Class torpedo boats at Portsmouth, probably in the early 1880s (the* Lightning *has the later bow torpedo tube in this picture).*

*Just after completion a Thornycroft-built 'Lightning'
(one of the boats numbered 2 to 12 by the Royal Navy
and built to a slightly modified design of TB No 1)
demonstrates the launching of torpedoes from 'frames' –
a most unsatisfactory means of launch from a fast boat
and rapidly replaced by tubes and 'dropping gear'.*

crews using hand-picked coal and a whole arsenal of tricks of the trade made every effort to
wring the last fraction of a knot out of their
charges during official trials under not particularly realistic conditions.[17] The design of
the boats themselves tended to be optimised to
meet this challenge, to the detriment of
qualities of sturdiness and military utility.

It was generally accepted that ordinary service crews found difficulty (particularly in the
smaller and less well-trained navies who
bought so many of these vessels) in obtaining
speeds within 5kts of the original trial speed,
even in the best conditions. Too often the light
machinery was over-strained in the trials. The
competition between builders was as understandable as that between the manufacturers of
warplanes today – orders from round the world
were at stake between a very few firms. It
would appear that the real money to be made
was from export orders – and these were
mostly swayed by the dictates of naval fashion
rather than by any rational consideration of a
particular navy's needs. In this context to be
known as the builder of the world's fastest
boats was the surest road to success. The result
was that most navies had flotillas consisting of
assortments of boats of different ages from different builders. Hardly any navies did not have

at least a few examples from all four of the
major torpedo boat builders.[18]

From very early on the two biggest torpedo
boat navies were France and Russia, the countries that in the diplomatic circumstances of
the last three decades of the nineteenth century
were most likely to find themselves at war with

the biggest navy of the time and therefore most
in need of a counterbalance to British preponderance in battleships. The French developed a
theory of warfare, propounded by the *jeune
école*, which involved using torpedo boats for
coastal defence and for attacking blockading
battleships so that the way could be cleared for
commerce-raiding cruisers to attack British
trade on the high seas. Both the French and

*An early French torpedo boat of the 'mobile defence'
intended for the defence of ports and built in large
numbers. The characteristic French 'whaleback' deck is
reminiscent of Confederate and Russian spar TBs.*
(CMP)

17. The 'measured mile' on the trials courses was
generally in shallow water – and in at least one case
(Maplin) the depth was such to cause a boosting effect on
the speed of a vessel of torpedo boat length.

18. The Royal Navy was virtually the only exception, the
only foreign-built torpedo boat purchased being the
Herreshoff-built Second Class boat *TB 63* – because of
her pioneer water-tube boiler. She was used for trials but
never for military service. A Schichau-built TBD did
serve in the Royal Navy, one of the four captured from
the Chinese at Taku by Roger Keyes in 1900.

*Typical of the many torpedo boats designed and built by
the German firm of Schichau, this particular boat, the
Italian 67S, was built under licence by Guppy at Naples
in 1881.* (CMP)

Russians let enthusiasm run away with them and overloaded their navies with flotillas of boats which were too small, fragile and unreliable to be of much practical use. Perhaps the most carefully developed and thought-out torpedo boat force was Germany's, with its strong emphasis on training and seaworthiness. The Danish torpedo boat force was also noted for its efficiency and the amount of care devoted to its organisation.

Whilst the torpedo boats of the 1870s were of little use for more than local defence of ports, there was a general growth in size, seaworthiness and sturdiness in the 1880s which made at least the larger boats (such as the French '*torpilleurs de haut mer*') true coastal defence craft. The appearance of the torpedo boat destroyer in the 1890s did not immediately remove this coastal defence role from the TB, and many craft of around 160ft in length and displacing about 200 tons continued to be built into and beyond the first decade of the twentieth century. Indeed the Italians continued to build much smaller TBs as well for local defence tasks, and went on doing so until motor torpedo boats appeared to take over that role (during the First World War). However the appearance of the bigger, faster, better armed, though essentially similar, destroyer

The torpedo depot ship HMS Vulcan *whilst serving with the Mediterranean Fleet. Her general cruiser-like appearance is only modified by the large number of boats including the Second Class TBs numbers* 39, 42, 43 *and* 44. (CMP)

immediately took away most of the glamour and a good deal of the real *raison d'etre* of the steam torpedo boat.

Second Class TBs and torpedo depot ships

The boats of sailing warships had always been part of their warlike equipment, allowing their crews to strike closer in to the enemy's coasts and harbours. The near-simultaneous developments of torpedoes and steam boats for carrying aboard ship were bound to be combined – as indeed they were in the first spar torpedo attack (Cushing's). The largest steam ship's boats (in the Royal Navy these were 57ft steam picket boats) turned out to be quite suitable for carrying a couple of the smallest type of locomotive torpedoes in 'dropping gear'.

However in the late 1870s and the early 1880s the emphasis was on purpose-built torpedo boats to be carried aboard large warships. These were the so-called 'Second Class torpedo boats'. They were small (usually some 60ft long) and fragile. Thornycroft seem to have pioneered the type, at least for the Royal Navy (a majority of whose early torpedo boats were of this description), but it was soon copied elsewhere. A major influence on this development was the partial success obtained by the Russians using improvised torpedo boats in their 1877 war with Turkey. As a result of the Crimean War peace treaty Russia had no major warships in the Black Sea, and instead con-

A small, shallow draught, spar torpedo boat built by Thornycroft for the Brazilian Navy for use on the river Amazon. Three of these (Alpha, Beta *and* Gamma) *were delivered in 1883. This picture was taken on the upper Thames near Chiswick just before the handing-over.*

verted a number of merchantmen to carry steam launches fitted out with spar and locomotive torpedoes. Later the French were to obtain success against Chinese warships in the

TB No 75, *one of the Yarrow-built versions of the British '125-footer' boats built in large numbers in the mid-1880s. This picture shows how wet these boats were forward thanks to the bow torpedo tube (the two sets of paired deck tubes can also be seen). The lectern-like structure just abaft of the after pair of these is a chart table. The inconspicuous bullet-proof 'conning tower' between the forward deck tubes and immediately in front of the funnel was cramped and had little visibility. These towers were hardly ever used and eventually dropped from later designs.* (CMP)

River Min (1884) using ship's boats as torpedo boats. In the short run there was great enthusiasm for Second Class boats, and most navies acquired some. The Italian ironclad *Duilio* even had what a later generation would call a 'hangar' built in the stern to accommodate a torpedo boat. However the fragility and unseaworthiness of these small steel craft told against them. In 1883 White's built the first of a number of wooden Second Class boats for the Royal Navy, which marked the beginning of a trend back towards using wooden ship's boats for this purpose. Their sturdiness and general utility were found to outweigh a comparative lack of speed (much less important than stealth and surprise for launching a successful torpedo attack in any case).

During the Russian War scare of 1878 the Royal Navy purchased a vessel building for commercial owners and had her converted as a 'torpedo depot ship' under the name of *Hecla*. Besides being a base for torpedo flotillas she was also intended to act as a 'torpedo boat carrier' for Second Class boats. She had a very successful career with the Mediterranean Fleet, and this success influenced the building ten years later of a specially designed vessel of this description on what was basically a cruiser hull. This was *Vulcan*, which was fitted with large and distinctive goose-neck cranes to hoist the six Second Class boats she carried outboard and comparatively powerfully armed with 4.7in guns. Unfortunately, initial problems with her boilers and structure tended to disguise what was basically a successful design. However the French thought enough of the concept to build their own equivalent in *Foudre*. These vessels were successful in their role as depot ships – but the concept of ships built primarily as carriers of small attack craft would have to wait for

One of the First Class of the larger French 'high seas' torpedo boats intended for coastal as opposed to merely local port defence, the Capitaine Cuny *built at St Nazaire in 1888 to a Le Normand design. Bow torpedo tubes were supplemented by a couple of revolving cannon.* (CMP)

the development of the aircraft for its vindication.

Catchers and destroyers

Countermeasures to attack by torpedo boat soon appeared. Some of these remain as permanent features of the coastline – the long 'moles' built to protect fleet anchorages such as Portland, Cherbourg and Dover. The development of the machine-gun, followed by that of quick-firing guns, gave larger ships a better chance of self-defence. They also offered the alternative of 'setting a thief to catch a thief' – arming a larger, faster version of the torpedo boat with quick-firers instead of torpedo tubes and using them as 'catchers' and 'destroyers' of their counterparts. The British '125-footer' boats of the early 1880s were originally mainly introduced as fleet escorts to protect the fleet against the Russian Baltic torpedo flotillas. In the event they were put into service in the al-

ternative torpedo-armed version. In a similar way most of the notable increases in size of torpedo boats were to a greater or lesser extent marked by the intention to use the new craft against its smaller equivalents (for example White's *Swift*, built as a private venture and purchased by the Royal Navy as *TB 81* in 1885). The Germans built 'division boats' as somewhat larger and more powerfully armed leaders of flotillas of torpedo boats, whilst the French *'torpilleurs de haut mer'* were in the same sort of category. Increases in size, speed and armament on what was still basically a bigger torpedo boat eventually produced the destroyer. In part this was an answer to developments in size and power by French TBs, in part simply a logical development in its own right, spurred on by British needs and the energy of 'Jackie' Fisher, who as Controller called (in 1892) for Thornycroft and Yarrow to design the prototypes – *Daring* and *Decoy* from the former and *Havock* and *Hornet* from the latter.

HMS Daring, *one of the pioneer quartet of destroyers, on trials. She and her sister* Decoy *were completed by Thornycroft somewhat later than the two Yarrow destroyers* Havock *and* Hornet, *but were actually ordered a day earlier and proved somewhat more satisfactory to the Royal Navy than the Yarrow pair.*

The appropriately named 'torpedo boat destroyer' (TBD) was an immediate success copied by other navies (though somewhat slowly and reluctantly by the French). This was as much because it could take over the torpedo boat's main task of torpedo attack (the prototypes were fitted with two tubes – a proposed alternative all-gun armament never saw the light of day) as because its obvious superiority in gun-power, speed and seaworthiness made it a useful fleet escort against its smaller rivals.

There had been an earlier attempt to produce just such a fleet escort, but by scaling down contemporary cruiser design to produce small fast vessels armed with quick-firing guns and torpedoes. These were called 'torpedo gunboats' (TGBs) or 'catchers'. The British started with *Rattlesnake* built between 1885 and 1887; later there were the *Sharpshooter* and then *Jason* classes, the last appearing at the same time as the first destroyers. These should have been useful ships, powerfully armed for their size and in many ways well suited to become fleet escorts. What caused them to be written off as failures was the fact that they were not fast enough to catch the TBs they

Early French destroyers were enlarged versions of their torpedo boat designs. Here is the Arbalete *(1903) of the* Arquebuse *class. Here again we can see the submarine-like hull with its curved whaleback deck – and the added planked 'flying deck' to give the crew some sort of dry footing in a seaway. The small bowsprit was useful in handling anchors. (CMP)*

were designed to counter. This was made considerably worse by bad problems with their boilers. Torpedo boats had used locomotive boilers to combine the necessary compactness, light weight and good steam-raising ability. These were really too small to power vessels as large as the TGBs and caused endless problems for them, problems which were highlighted by the success of Thornycroft's *Speedy* – the only one of the type fitted with water-tube boilers and built by a specialist torpedo boat builder. The French built some roughly similar vessels (the *Bombe*, *Lévrier* and *D'Iberville* classes) with not much greater success, and went on building them (*Dunois* class completed 1898–9) when they would have been far better advised to build destroyers. However it is possible that

these bigger and sturdier craft might have performed better in action than their more spectacular smaller contemporaries. Two brand-new Chilean TGBs (built by Laird) achieved success in torpedoing and sinking the battleship *Blanco Encalada* which was on the other side in the 1891 Chilean civil war, one of the very few times a locomotive torpedo was used in anger between the Russo-Turkish War of 1877–78 and Russia's war with Japan in 1904.

In this latter conflict the Japanese made much use of their destroyers, a type which had developed rapidly in the decade after their first appearance. The prototypes capable of 26kts were followed in the Royal Navy by a big order for '27-knotters', and then an even bigger series of orders for '30-knotters'. Once the Royal Navy had found what looked like both antidote and replacement for the torpedo boat it acted with speed and built up a force of over one hundred of the new type in well under a decade. To do so it spread its orders far beyond the original torpedo boat specialists. Now many other shipbuilding firms were involved in building these light and technically demanding craft. The few failures are less remarkable than the general success. Other navies followed suit, but none could match the speed or scale of this massive re-equipment. Nor at this stage did anything very different from the original British pattern of TBD appear in other navies, who more or less copied the British type, though the Germans tended to continue the emphasis on the 'torpedo boat' rather than the 'destroyer' element of their designs – and, in the *S 90*

Early destroyers were small vessels, and with coal fuel and oily reciprocating engines were not the cleanest of craft, as is evident from this picture of the 30-knotter HMS Bittern *of 1897 alongside. Just forward of the gangplank is a collapsible Berthon Boat of the type used in torpedo craft to save space and weight. Their canvas sides tended to deteriorate in service with unfortunate results.* (CMP)

class of 1899 introduced the raised forecastle instead of the low and wet turtleback which had been the fashion up to then. This greatly improved seakeeping and the ability to fight the forward guns.

By the beginning of the new century in the Royal Navy dissatisfaction with the excessive influence of high trial speed, and an increasing user-demand from the destroyer-men themselves was pointing to building larger, more seaworthy ships which could maintain a useful sea speed of some 25kts or 26kts. The German innovation of a raised forecastle was combined with an increase of some 100 tons and the same armament as earlier destroyers to produce the 'River' class. These epoch-making ships mark the break between the TBD and what we can now call the 'destroyer'. They also represent a true seagoing purpose-built torpedo vessel – what the TGBs should have been but were not. The torpedo boat formula had been enlarged and altered enough to produce an entirely new type of ship. With them the story of the modern destroyer begins and our period ends.

Conclusion: the spiral of development

In the last decades of the nineteenth century we can see a classic pattern of warship development being repeated. A new weapon permits the building of a new small and cheap type of craft. The practical demands of service at sea and the progressive development of weapons

19. The hull of the *Whitby*, *Rothesay* and *Leander* classes – also that of the Canadian *Saint Lawrent* class. In the latter case a very different apearance was a matter of deliberate policy in order to cope with Canadian susceptibilities.

Smaller torpedo boats built for foreign customers could be delivered by hoisting them aboard ship, but larger craft were usually delivered on their own bottoms – often under sail as their coal-carrying capacity was strictly limited. Here is Thornycroft's Habana *on the upper Thames in 1886 prior to her delivery to the Spanish navy. Once she arrived the temporary masts and sail rig would be removed. The voyages of delivery of such vessels were often sagas of seamanship and determination, without which the frail craft would never have succeeded in reaching their destinations.*

force a steady and inexorable increase in size, cost and complexity as the new type moves from being an experimental toy to an accepted weapon. As it does so it moves away from the area of action it originally filled, leaving a gap to be filled by a new type of small craft, usually taking advantage of a further technical development. The pattern of development goes round and round, but on an ascending path, not so much circular as spiral. In the early years of the twentieth century the new element was provided by the development of the internal combustion engine, and boatbuilding firms were already experimenting with torpedo carrying motor boats in 1905.

We only need look at the British Royal Navy to see how the growth factor operated:

Tonnage is load displacement (when known), the speed is that achieved on trials and the date the year of completion. The 1877 figures are for *Lightning*, 1885 the small group of '113-footers'; 1886 represents the 'Russian scare' group of 125ft long boats; the first set of 1894 figures are for the group of torpedo boats ordered in 1892, the second set that for the prototype destroyers; 1895 is for the first '27-knotters' and 1897 the '30-knotters'; 1900 is the prototype turbine destroyer, *Viper* – with which the speed given becomes both more attainable and more sustainable. With the 'River' class in 1904 the design speed takes another step towards realism, though it is arguable that it was not until after the Second World War with the British Type 12[19] frigate hull that true

	1877	1885	1886	1894	1894	1895	1897	1900	1904
Length (ft)	87	113	125	140	185	200	210	210	225
Tons	32.5	64	60	130	275	295	350	350	620
Knots	19	20	20.75	24	26	27	30	33	25.5

A classic photograph of an early destroyer at high speed on trials, but this is the first which could maintain the power for that speed without difficulty or bad vibration, because she was the first to be fitted with turbines. HMS Viper would be lost within the year by running aground, but had already made her mark in the history of marine propulsion. (CMP)

'sea speed' and 'trial speed' began to bear a reasonably close relationship to one another in flotilla craft.

The weapons carried also grew in number, variety and power. We have already seen how by the 1890s 18in torpedoes were replacing the later versions of the 14in. Meanwhile light automatic and semi-automatic guns developed in parallel with torpedo craft and were fitted both to those craft and to larger ships as a defence against them. In the late 1870s 'rifle calibre' (at that stage 0.45in or similar) machine-guns were in use. Rotary action Gatling and Hotchkiss guns and lever-operated ones like the Nordenfelt and the Gardner. These were superseded by the Maxim, which like its rivals appeared in a larger, shell-firing form of 37mm or 40mm calibre (the Vickers 'pom-pom'). By the beginning of the 1880s the first of the 'quick-firers' were coming into service – light cannon firing 3pdr, 6pdr or 12pdr projectiles. Most torpedo boats were armed with the lightest of these, early destroyers had a mixture of one 12pdr and several 6pdrs; 4in guns would come into service both as an anti-torpedo craft gun and to arm destroyers soon after that period ends.

Machinery developments were crucial in producing the high speeds required by torpedo craft. The steam reciprocating engine was pushed up to, even a little beyond, its limitations, creating problems of maintenance and vibration. In this context Parsons' development of the steam turbine as a practical marine powerplant during the 1890s was vital. Not only could it produce higher rotary speeds than the reciprocating engine, it produced them without heavy vibration (which took rapid toll on serviceability) and above all it maintained them with ease. It brought its own problems with propellers in absorbing the high speed and power, but really high speed was sustainable for much longer and with much greater ease than before. The pioneer turbine destroyer HMS *Viper* was unfortunately wrecked soon after completion in 1900, but not before she

A 'River' class destroyer, HMS Jed, at Malta. The classic destroyer appearance with raised forecastle is established. Note the 'sponsoned' 6pdr gun at the break of the forecastle, beneath the bridge.

had conclusively demonstrated the advantages of the new engine.

Steel construction was used from the start in building torpedo boats, years before the material was in general use for shipbuilding. The small size of the boats and the value of high speed meant that what was initially an expensive material could be afforded, as could the degree of quality control needed before the development of the electric hearth process made production of large quantities of steel of reasonably uniform quality both easier and cheaper. Other materials such as brass and aluminium[20] were tried without success. Many other experiments were tried. One British Second Class boat (Thornycroft's *No 98*) was water-jet powered by a centrifugal pump. The system worked, but the boat was much slower than her sisters. Torpedo boats were at the extreme edge of the technology of their day. They were spectacular, experimental, and probably would not have proved very effective

instruments of war if put to the test. Their development was particularly distorted by the pressures for unrealistic high speed and for small size. They are a particularly good example of the way technical developments can outstrip rational thought in weapons development – particularly when record-breaking speed is combined with spectacular and unprecedented destructive ability and the media take a hand. The torpedo boat introduced a giant-killing potential to naval warfare and it is that potential which makes its story important even though the steam torpedo boat was an under-developed, over-estimated and not very seaworthy weapons system. Out of it, after all, grew that well-balanced fighting ship, the destroyer.

David Lyon

20. Yarrow's aluminium boat for the French navy decayed from electrolytic action even faster than could have been expected as she was moored in the outfall from a sewer. Her effective life was less than a year.

Torpedo Craft: Typical Vessels 1860–1905

Ship or class [Type]	Nationality	Displacement (normal) (tons)	Dimensions (loa × breadth × depth in hold) (feet–inches) (metres)	Armament	Speed (max trials, kts)	Launch dates	Numbers built	Remarks
H L HUNLEY [Submersible]	Confederate States		40–0 × 3–6 × 4–0 / 12.2 × 1.1 × 1.2	1 spar torpedo (90lb charge)	2.5	1863	1	Made first successful submarine attack
DAVID [Semi-submersible]	Confederate States		54–0 × 5–6 × 5–0 / 16.5 × 1.7 × 1.5	1 spar torpedo (134lb charge)	?	1863–65	20+	Low freeboard torpedo boat
SPUYTEN DUYVIL [Spar torpedo vessel]	American	116	75–0 × 19–6 × 8–0 / 22.9 × 5.0 × 2.4	1 power worked spar torpedo; 12 charges	8	1864	1	Armoured; could be flooded down in action
RAP [Torpedo launch]	Norwegian	10	59–9 × 7–10 × 2–11 / 18.2 × 2.4 × 0.9	2 towed or 2 spar torpedoes; (1879) 2 Whiteheads	14.9	1873	1	Prototype Thornycroft torpedo launch
VESUVIUS [Torpedo vessel]	British	245	90–0pp × 22–0 × 8–6 / 27.4 × 6.7 × 2.6	1–16in submerged bow TT; plus reloads	9.7	1874	1	First British purpose-built torpedo vessel
ZIETEN [Torpedo cruiser]	German	1152	260–8 × 28–1 × 15–2 / 79.4 × 8.6 × 4.6	2–15in TT; 10 torpedoes	16	1876	1	Mainly used as tender for torpedo trials
LIGHTNING [Torpedo boat]	British	32	87–0 × 10–9 × 5–2 / 26.5 × 3.3 × 1.6	2 torpedo launching frames; (1879) 1–14in TT	19	1877	1	Prototype Thornycroft torpedo boat
'MINONORSKI' TYPE [Torpedo launch]	Russian	24.5	75–0 × 10–6 × 4–0 / 22.9 × 3.2 × 1.2	Spar torpedoes or 1–15in TT	17	1877–78	100+	Yarrow designed small TB built in large nos
HECLA [Torpedo depot ship]	British	6400	361–6 pp × 38–10 × 24–4 / 119.3 × 11.8 × 7.4	5–64pdr, 1–40pdr 6 Second Class TBs	13	1878	1	TB carrier and support ship
TB 74 [Second Class TB]	British	12	63–8 × 7–9 × 3–6 / 19.4 × 2.4 × 1.0	2–14in bow TT, 1 MG	16	1881–83	4	Yarrow design
POLYPHEMUS [Torpedo ram]	British	2640	240–0 pp × 40–0 × 20–6 / 73.2 × 12.2 × 6.3	5–14in submerged TT; 18 torpedoes; 6 MGs	18	1881	1	Curved 3in armoured deck
BOMBE [Torpedo gunboat]	French	369	194–3 pp × 19–7 × 10–5 / 59.2 × 6.0 × 3.2	4–3pdr, 3–1pdr revolvers; 2–14in deck TT	18	1885–6	8	Early form of anti-TB vessel
TB 25 [First Class TB]	British	60	128–3 × 12–6 × 6–0 / 39.1 × 3.8 × 1.8	4–14in deck TT (2 × 2); 2 twin MGs	20.75	1885	1	Thornycroft prototype 125-footer
TB 81 [First Class TB]	British	137	153–9 × 17–6 × 9–6 / 46.9 × 5.3 × 2.9	2–14in TT (1 fixed bow, 2 deck); 4–3pdr	23.75	1885	1	White private venture Swift, called a TBD
BALNY [First Class TB]	French	58	138–102l × 10–11 × 3–9 / 40.7 × 3.3 × 1.2	2–14in bow TT; 2–37mm revolvers	19	1886	9	Normand 'torpilleurs de haute mer'
D 1 [Division boat]	German	295	184–0 × 21–8 × 11–2 / 56.1 × 6.6 × 3.4	3–14in TT; 4 torpedoes; 6 MGs	20.5	1886	2	Schichau flotilla leaders
ALMIRANTE LYNCH [Torpedo gunboat]	Chilean	713	230–0 pp × 27–6 × 8–4 / 70.1 × 8.4 × 2.5	5–14in TT (1 bow, 4 deck) 3–3in, 4–3pdr	20	1890	2	Torpedoed Blanco Encalada in 1891
HAVOCK [TBD]	British	275	185–0 × 18–6 × 7–3 / 56.4 × 5.6 × 2.2	3–18in TT (1 bow, 2 deck) 1–12pdr, 3–6pdr	26	·1893	2	Yarrow design; first TBD completed
FORBAN [First Class TB]	French	121	144–6 wl × 15–3 × 4–5 / 44.0 × 4.6 × 1.4	2–14in deck TT; 2–37mm	31	1895	1	Normand design; first vessel to exceed 30kts
S 90 [First Class TB]	German	388	206–10 × 22–11 × 9–4 / 63.0 × 7.0 × 2.2	3–18in deck TT; 3–50mm	26.5	1898–1901	12	Introduced raised forecastle deck
VIPER [TBD]	British	344	210–4pp × 21–0 × 7–0 / 64.1 × 6.4 × 2.1	2–18in deck TT; 1–12pdr, 5–6pdr	33.75	1899	1	Prototype turbine-powered destroyer
ERNE [Destroyer]	British	550	233–6 × 23–6 × 9–9 / 71.2 × 7.2 × 3.0	2–18in deck TT; 1–12pdr, 5–6pdr	25.5	1903	3	First group of 'River' type destroyers

Notes:
Length is overall, except pp = between perpendiculars; wl = at waterline.

Armament abbreviations: TT = torpedo tube(s); MG = machine-gun.

9

Early Submarines

THE idea of a submersible – or submarine as it is more usually called these days – is not new; it is not even a nineteenth century innovation. Ancient illustrated manuscripts show Alexander the Great descending in a form of submarine. William Bourne, an Elizabethan seaman, wrote quite practical principles of constructing a submarine with ballast tanks controlled by jack screws. Cornelius Drebbel actually built a twelve-oared boat in which – according to folklore – he is supposed to have taken the cautious and fearful King James I on a short trip beneath the surface of the Thames. However, the first man to consider seriously the submarine as a weapon of war was Leonardo da Vinci (1452–1519). His plans or sketches of a submarine were not published until long after his death, for he feared for the use that might be made of the idea, and he wrote of 'the evil nature of men who would practise assassinations at the bottom of the seas by breaking the ships in their lowest parts and sinking them together with the crews who are in them.'

The earliest pioneers

One of the famous names in early submarine history is that of David Bushnell, an American who graduated from Yale University in 1775. During his time at the University he became interested in the problems of sub-surface navigation and the whole concept of a submarine craft. It was about this time that the American War of Independence broke out and Bushnell applied his ideas to a method of attacking the British fleet that was blockading the American coast. He designed and built a vessel to do just that, *Turtle*. The idea was that it would carry one man out to the blockading fleet where he would submerge his craft and fix a charge of 150lbs of gunpowder against the hull of a ship, and after starting a clockwork mechanism to ignite the charge he would retire to a safe distance before it exploded. Operating the craft was much similar to the one-man band: the tiller of the rudder was long enough to reach

under the arm, water was admitted through a cock into a tank to control the buoyancy while the feet pedalled to turn a small screw at the bow of the craft. There was a compass to keep the craft on the right course.

Sergeant Ezra Pond is credited with the first attack against an enemy ship by a submarine when in September 1776 he sallied out in Bushnell's *Turtle* against HMS *Eagle* in New York harbour. There is no record of his efforts even being noticed aboard *Eagle*; neither the Captain's nor the Master's Log, which are held in the Public Record Office in London, make any mention of the affair. Nevertheless, the occasion is a notable one. Bushnell will always be remembered as the inventor of the first submarine vessel to attempt an underwater attack on an enemy. If just one of his three attempts had been successful, who can tell just how differently the evolution of this form of warship would have been.

Another American, Robert Fulton, now enters the story. He was born in 1765 in what is now the town of Fulton in Pennsylvania. In 1797 he was persuaded to live in France, where he came to prominence with plans for various dams and canals which were sold to the French

A general arrangement of Fulton's Nautilus *of 1800. The ingenious folding sail was for surface use, to give the crewman some respite from the laborious hand-cranked method of propulsion.*

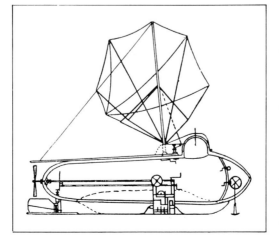

government. Also in 1797 he experimented with elementary mines in the River Seine, while at the end of the year he offered to the French navy the services of a submersible, *Nautilus*, with which he would attack the British fleet. Obviously he had great hopes for this submarine vessel, for his proposed contract with the French contained details of payments he would receive for every success.

Nautilus was laid down in the winter of 1800 and completed in the spring of the following year. She was just over 21ft long and 7ft in diameter, the hull being constructed to permit a diving depth of 25ft. Like a modern submarine there was a small conning tower – at the forward end of the vessel. As with Bushnell's *Turtle*, motive power when dived had to be by pedals turning a small screw. Unusually, there was a mast and sail for use on the surface. After some trials which impressed his backers, during which the boat covered some 700yds in just seven minutes (about 2kts), he proposed to put *Nautilus* to a practical test attacking an English frigate lying off the port of Brest. It is understood that this was prevented by the Prefect of the port fearing reprisals for such an unusual act of war.

Fulton became disillusioned with the French and went to England in 1804. There, only ten days before Nelson's famous victory at Trafalgar, Fulton gave an effective demonstration of the potential of undersea warfare by exploding a charge beneath the hull of the 200-ton brig *Dorothea* in Walmer Roads off the Kent coast. Despite the patronage of the Prime Minister, Mr William Pitt, Fulton did not receive any encouragement from the Admiralty for his achievement. Indeed, the First Sea Lord, the redoubtable Admiral the Earl of St Vincent, was resolutely against the development of such a weapon. It was on this occasion that he made the remark that was to become the keystone of the British Admiralty's thinking on submarine warfare for almost a hundred years: 'Pitt was the greatest fool that ever existed to encourage a mode of warfare which those that command the sea did not want, and

which, if successful, would deprive them of it.' Looking at events of 1916–17 and again in 1940–42 few in Britain would disagree.

Another early submarine designer was the Russian Yefim Nikonov who, with the patronage of the Czar, proposed a 'secret vessel' with which 'in calm weather it would be possible to destroy ships with projectiles'. A prototype was launched in 1720 and others were planned, but after some accidents on trials and with the death of the Czar the project was dropped.

Success in war

The true development of the submarine needed the impetus of two other technological advances: a satisfactory engine to propel the boat underwater, and a weapon which would not only justify the use of a submarine against an enemy but which could give the crew a chance to survive their attack. The importance of the latter is shown by the efforts of the Confederate Navy during the American Civil War. In the Southern states a hand propelled submarine was built for the navy which was fitted with a spar torpedo attached to the bow. Basically this means that an explosive charge of 134lbs of gunpowder was fixed to the end of a long pole and secured to the bow of the submarine, the weapon being fired by impact when the target was rammed.

In an allusion to the biblical Goliath story, these vessels were known as 'Davids', and the first such craft to be built was 54ft long and was steam driven. For an attack water ballast was taken onboard and the craft then proceeded in an 'awash' condition, looking rather like a large baulk of timber with a funnel. In one of the first trials a passing steamer caused a heavy wash to break over the vessel and swamp it; only one officer and one rating were saved. An actual attack was carried out on *New Ironsides*, a Union ironclad (see Chapter 4), in October 1863 off the port of Charleston. The watch onboard sighted a strange object approaching and hailed it, there was a volley of musketry and then there was an explosion as the charge detonated on impact. There was some flooding and other minor damage; one Union sailor broke his leg. The Confederate vessel was swamped, three of the crew managed to escape and swim ashore, but eventually the 'David' was recovered.

One lesson was learnt: the funnel was too visible. The next craft to be built was capable of full submersion and consequently could only be driven by muscle power. The lesson of what happened when the charge exploded was overlooked. When on 17 February 1864 the submarine (named *H L Hunley*, after its designer) attacked the Union 200-ton screw sloop *Housatonic*, the resulting explosion sank the unalerted sloop. It also sank the submarine. This was not a very satisfactory way of making an attack, especially from the submariner's viewpoint. Nevertheless the attack is historic as being the first genuine submarine success in war.

The Bavarian engineer Wilhelm Bauer built a number of practical submersibles. The first was Le Plongeur Marin *(also called* Brandtaucher *in German) of 1850, which incorporated some ingenious ideas. It had a treadmill to power the screw and a weight that could be moved fore and aft controlled the diving angle. This cutaway model shows the basic features of the craft.* (Deutsches Museum, Munich)

Wilhelm Bauer

At this stage it is appropriate to go back a few years and return to Europe and look at developments there. In 1850 there was a war between Prussia and Denmark during which the Danes, though largely unsuccessful on land, tried to blockade the Prussian coast. The Prussians then engaged the services of Wilhelm Bauer, a Bavarian by birth and a one-time corporal of artillery, who had ideas of how to act secretly against the Danish fleet. The result was a submarine laid down in Kiel called *Le Plongeur Marin (Sea Diver)*. The boat was 26½ ft long and propelled by means of a large internal handwheel which through a gear turned a small screw at the stern of the vessel. To submerge the boat water was let into the double bottoms while a pump was provided to eject it when it was time to surface. For the first time provision was made for correcting longitudinal trim, or inclination, which was done by moving a heavy weight forward or aft as required. A pair of large leather 'gloves' enabled the crew to detach a torpedo from the submarine, though one was not fitted. The first trials were reasonably successful but on 1 February 1851 while submerging in Kiel harbour the sheet iron in the stern gave way and the boat began to sink deeper and deeper as flooding increased. Then the iron weight slipped and the boat nosed dived to the bottom and came to rest in about 50ft of water. At all events Bauer now proved he was a courageous man for he ordered more water to be admitted to the boat, although his crew were not easily persuaded to obey the order. Gradually the pressure inside built up and then forced open the hatches. Bauer and his crew shot to the surface like corks from a bottle. The craft was eventually salved but not until 1887.

Bauer's next submarine, *Le Diable Marin*, was built in St Petersburg in 1856 and was 56ft long. He is reputed to have made 134 successful dives in trials for the Russian navy. In this version the weight for correcting longitudinal errors in trim was replaced for the first time by horizontal rudders, a feature that is still to be found in even the most modern submarines. Bauer must have been a good showman for on the occasion of the coronation of the Czar he is reputed to have taken several musicians underwater in *Sea Devil*. When the guns of the fortress of Cronstadt began to fire a salute the band struck up the national anthem, the tune being clearly heard on the nearby ships.

The boat was lost when Bauer was ordered to take it under one of the Russian battleships lying at anchor. Either through jealousy or ineptitude Bauer was not told that the depth of water under the ship was less than he imagined and *Sea Devil* became stuck. He was eventually able to get the boat safely to the surface but it took several weeks to repair the damage. *Sea Devil* was irretrievably lost soon afterwards. Bauer was then invited to build an even larger boat by the Russians, but he was disillusioned by life in Russia and by the attitude of the Russian officers to his work and he went to France. Penniless, his health poor, his hopes shattered, he never did build another submarine.

Garrett and Nordenfelt

Two other Europeans were destined to take over where Bauer had left off: the Reverend George William Garrett from Liverpool and the Swede, Mr Thorsten Nordenfelt. They started off working out their ideas unknown to one another, but came together as a result of their early work.

After a brilliant academic career Garrett was ordained in 1873 and the new curate went to work in a parish where his father was the vicar, but was soon off on a Grand Tour learning navigation while studying the Russian navy and the Czar's expansionist ambitions. During the Russo-Turkish war of 1877 Garrett's attention was drawn to an attack by a Russian torpedo boat armed with a spar torpedo against a ship of the Turkish Danube flotilla. The attack failed because the Turkish ship was well defended by steel chain nets hung around it. Two weeks later a similar attack by Russian torpedo boats was again foiled by the same defence. How much better, thought Garrett, if the attacks had somehow been made underwater and would have reached under the net defences.

On his return to England Garrett founded a company, with a capital of only £10,000, supported by five local businessmen and his father. This gave him sufficient money to build an experimental submarine. The Garrett prototype, named by him as *Resurgam* ('I will rise again') was 14ft long and 5ft in diameter, displacing 4½ tons when dived. For trimming he reverted to an old device, first suggested in the sixteenth century, of altering the volume of the submarine by means of a piston connected with the sea. This had the effect of changing the submerged weight of the submarine and hence its buoyancy. Power was by means of a hand crank and the one-man crew, Garrett himself, would have been kept fully occupied turning the screw, steering and regulating the depth by means of the piston. Like Bauer before him he fitted larger leather gloves which he used to test the possibility of attaching a charge to an enemy vessel.

The first experiments were encouraging and in 1879 Garrett decided to build a larger vessel powered by steam. *Resurgam II* was cigar shaped and weighed about 30 tons. The engine was steam driven and similar in principle to that then used on London's underground railway. Water was heated in a large steam boiler at a pressure of 150psi. When the submarine was to be dived, the fire door to the furnace and a smoke escape valve in the funnel were shut. When the throttle was opened steam was supplied to the return connecting-rod cylinder engine, while as the pressure reduced latent heat supplied further steam from water in storage tanks. The submarine could thus run independently of the outside atmosphere for as long as steam was available, giving a theoretical

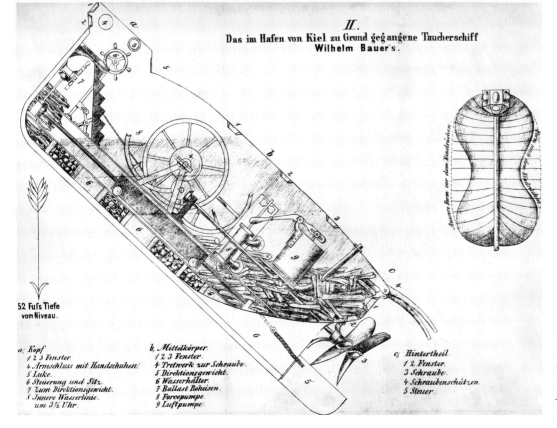

II.
Das im Hafen von Kiel zu Grund gegangene Taucherschiff
Wilhelm Bauer's.

52 Fufs Tiefe
vom Niveau.

a, Kopf.
1 2 3 Fenster.
4 Armschluss mit Handschuhen.
5 Luke.
6 Steuerung und Sitz.
7 Zum Direktionsgewicht.
8 Innere Wasserlinie.
   um 3½ Uhr.

b, Mittelkörper.
1 2 3 Fenster.
4 Tretwerk zur Schraube.
5 Direktionsgewicht.
6 Wasserhalter.
7 Ballast Roheisen.
8 Forcepumpe.
9 Luftpumpe.

c, Hintertheil.
1 2 Fenster.
3 Schraube.
4 Schraubenschützen.
5 Steuer.

One of the lessons Bauer learned the hard way concerned increasing water pressure. Le Plongeur's hull was breached on one dive and ended up 50ft down on the bottom of Kiel harbour. This fascinating drawing shows the predicament of the boat, the shaded area representing the internal flooding (figure 8 at the top is the waterline after 3½ hours). Bauer was able to persuade his two companions to wait until the pressure built up sufficiently for them to escape in a bubble of air, expelled like a cork from a bottle. Bauer went on to design further submarines for the Russians. (Deutsches Museum, Munich)

Much of the credit for early advances in submarine development must go to individual inventors rather than governments or navies. One such unlikely pioneer was an English clergyman, the Rev George Garrett, who built two boats called Resurgam *(this shows the second ready for launching). The boat was propelled by steam, even underwater, where a reservoir provided power even after the furnace had been shut down. The disadvantage was that the boiler took up most of the interior space in the boat.* (CMP)

range of up to 12 miles at 3kts. Also fitted to the boat were horizontal rudders amidships to aid in depth-keeping – not the best place for these hydroplanes, as they came to be known, to be fitted, but nevertheless a great improvement on Bauer's movable weight.

Surviving records do not indicate whether or not *Resurgam* ever ran fully submerged. More likely that she steamed most of the time in a low buoyancy condition, or awash, rather like the first Confederate boat. On one particularly humiliating day Captain Jackson, who was giving professional advice to Garrett, lost his bearings in Liverpool Bay and Garrett had to open the hatch to hail a passing ship and ask for his position.

Garrett wished to show his idea to Nordenfelt at Portsmouth, and resolved to have *Resurgam* towed there, against advice which suggested that it would be better to take the boat south by rail. However, a small steam yacht, *Elfin*, was engaged for the tow and the two vessels set off from Rhyl on 22 February 1880 and headed west along the coast in pitch darkness and rising seas. The crew were taken off *Resurgam*, which was just as well for during the forenoon of the 26th the tow parted and the submarine foundered. She has never been seen again, despite several attempts in recent years to find her using the latest minehunting equipment.

Nordenfelt was a successful arms manufacturer. Garrett had proved himself to be a successful engineer. In these circumstances, and despite the loss of *Resurgam*, the two decided to join forces. Between them the two men then produced a number of submarines over the years between 1882 and 1891. Yet they were not a military success.

Nordenfelt I was laid down in Stockholm in 1882 but not launched until 1885. It had an elliptical shaped hull 64ft long and with a max-

imum diameter of 9ft. Once again there was a steam powerplant and the boat was designed for a crew of three. To help with submergence there were two vertical propellers and diving rudders at the bows but not at the stern. The sea trials of this extraordinary vessel attracted the attention of the major European naval powers and both Japan and Mexico. On their completion none of the thirty-nine spectators was impressed. However, the submarine did manage to pass under the observers' boat, but the longest period dived was only five minutes. Recording the events of the day *The Times* of London said: 'It is certain that the Nordenfelt boat will effect no revolution. . . .' In 1886 the Greek navy bought the boat which eventually reached Piraeas, but then never went to sea again.

Alarmed by the fact that the Greeks possessed a submarine, and no doubt more so by the ambitions of the Czar, the Turks decided that they too ought to have submarines and approached the Nordenfelt-Garrett consortium. Two more boats were built, this time in what may be regarded as the peaceful site of Chertsey on the River Thames. Having been

Thorsten Nordenfelt, the Swedish inventor of the Nordenfelt machine-gun, took up submarine development with the assistance of Garrett. His first boat was built in Sweden and sold to Greece in 1886; this was armed with the new Whitehead torpedo (for the first time in a submarine) but was barely operational. Two larger boats built in Britain were sold to Turkey in the same year and Nordenfelt's submarine endeavours concluded with an even bigger 160-ton boat that was lost while on passage to demonstrate its performance to the Russians. This is the first boat, still in Sweden, about September 1885. (Submarine Museum)

built they were shipped to Constantinople in sections for reassembly there. Only one was ever completed. Half as long again as the original *Nordenfelt I* and with a steam engine reputedly capable of giving 10kts surface speed and 5kts dived she had many faults and few, if any, virtues. Being so long there was an almost total lack of longitudinal stability with water surging back and forth every time the boat took on an angle, however small. She was fitted with one torpedo tube. It is reported that she did fire this once with disastrous consequences, for the boat immediately stood on her stern and slipped to the bottom. Not surprisingly the Turkish navy were unable to find a crew for the vessel after her trials, completed by Garrett and an English crew, and she remained on the dockside for many years. She was still there surrounded by grass and weeds when the German U-boats came to Constantinople in 1915. Garrett himself, however, had achieved one more distinction, having been commissioned as a Commander in the Turkish navy.

Despite these failures the two men designed another submarine, this time destined for the Russian navy. It was built at Barrow, in what was later to become the premier submarine building yard for the Royal Navy. *Nordenfelt IV* was 125ft long and displaced 245 tons when submerged. Once again the latent heat steam engine was used to provide propulsive power, while the eight tons of coal she carried was intended to give a range of 1000 miles. Ill-fortune continued to dog the work of Garrett and Nordenfelt for on launching this new submarine it was found that the boat settled badly by the stern, drawing 9ft aft and only half that forward. Adding extra ballast to correct the error robbed the boat of speed. Garrett had a heart attack which laid him up for six months. In November 1888 the *Nordenfelt IV* set off

for the Russian base at Cronstadt in the seaward approaches to St Petersburg. Although escorted by a yawl, navigation proved to be the weakness of both crews and the submarine went aground on an ebb tide off the coast of Jutland. She was not refloated for two weeks, after which the Russians refused to pay for the wreck and it was left to an insurance company to settle some of the bill.

At this stage the two men parted. Nordenfelt tried two more boats by himself for the German navy but they were no more successful than the others, and he returned to making weapons. Garrett failed to get back into the Church and emigrated to America where he briefly served with the US Army Engineers during the war with Spain. He died, destitute, in New York in 1902.

Neither Bauer's *Le Diable Marin* nor *Nordenfelt IV* were the only submarines built for the Russians at this time, for the Russians took an interest in submarines which has persisted to this day. A Russian, General Shilder, is reputed to have built the first submersible with an iron hull in that country in 1834, while both Nikolai Spiridonov, a naval officer, and General Gern had designs during the Crimean War for a submersible craft to improve the defences of Sevastopol and Revel. General Gern went on to construct a number of craft up to 1864. Another Russian designer, Ivan Aleksandrovski completed a submarine in 1866 which was 115ft long and propelled by a 70hp compressed air engine.

The Russian-Turkish war of 1877, which had set Garrett on the path of submarine construction, also saw the start of Drzewiecki's career as a submarine designer which extended into the twentieth century. He designed and built five different submarine types as well as developing a torpedo mounting and other

items of equipment for use in submarines. The French actually awarded Drzewiecki a prize of 5000 francs for the design of a torpedo launching cradle, an item which was the feature in many French submarines until after the First World War, though they turned down his submarine designs.

Mention has already been made of the requirement of a suitable propulsion system for use when submerged and of a weapon independent of the submarine itself. Garrett's steam engine was not the real answer. However, a Lieutenant Isaac Peral can claim to have made strides in that direction when he designed and built the first submarine to be fitted with an electric motor. Neither the Spanish government nor navy were particularly interested and it was to be left to the French to develop the idea further. Another invention which influenced submarine development was the self-propelled torpedo perfected by Robert Whitehead at his factory in Fiume, now part of Croatia but then within the Austro-Hungarian Empire. The prototype was developed in 1866 but for many years this weapon was only suitable for above-water discharge, but nevertheless, when it did come to be fitted in a submarine it meant that they could presume to avoid the fate of the Confederate *Hunley* with its spar torpedo.

John Philip Holland

From Europe the story returns to America and follows the fortunes of one of the foremost submarine inventors of the period – John Philip Holland. Holland was born in Ireland, overlooking the sea in County Clare, in 1841. At the age of seventeen he took the initial vows of the teaching order of the Irish Christian Brothers, so that once again, like Garrett, a man who was destined for the Church subsequently became well known in the world of submarine development. Life was not easy in Ireland, and with the Civil War over America offered better opportunities, so in common

John Philip Holland's early essays in submarine engineering were funded by the Irish Nationalist Fenian organisation in the United States in the hope that it might be a weapon usable against the British. As a result his second boat was known as the Fenian Ram. *This was the boat on which most of the principles of submarine design were worked out by Holland, and this original drawing demonstrates the relative sophistication of the concept. (Submarine Museum)*

The first Spanish submarine was a steam-driven vessel called Ictineo *built by Narcisco Monturiol at Barcelona in 1859–60. However, a more practical proposition was Isaac Peral's boat of 1888 which was powered by electric motors, submerged using ballast tanks and had a torpedo tube. As shown here, the boat was preserved as a memorial. (Submarine Museum)*

with millions of others Holland and his family emigrated. Holland himself was just thirty-one years of age at the time and because of his ill health he received permission to quit the religious teaching order.

By 1876 Holland had become enthusiastic about submarine development and built a 30in long working model of a submarine. This was demonstrated to the Fenian Society in Boston who, fired by the hate of the Irish for the English, thought that such a machine could be a wonderful way of advancing their cause. Holland was asked to build a full sized submarine. It turned out to be lozenge shape, 14½ft long and only 2½ft high with a small turret-like fixture on top and weighing 2½ tons. Funded by the Fenians the boat cost $4,000 and was completed in 1878. There are several reports of the boat's launch on 22 May of that year: how it was hauled onto a waggon at the factory where it was built and drawn to the water's edge by eight pairs of stallions; of a remark by a spectator referring to it as 'a coffin'; and of the launch itself – for, as soon as the craft entered the water it disappeared from sight to the bottom of the river. Luckily Holland had prudently attached wires to it before the accident so that salvage was comparatively easy, and having checked his arithmetic and made some adjust-

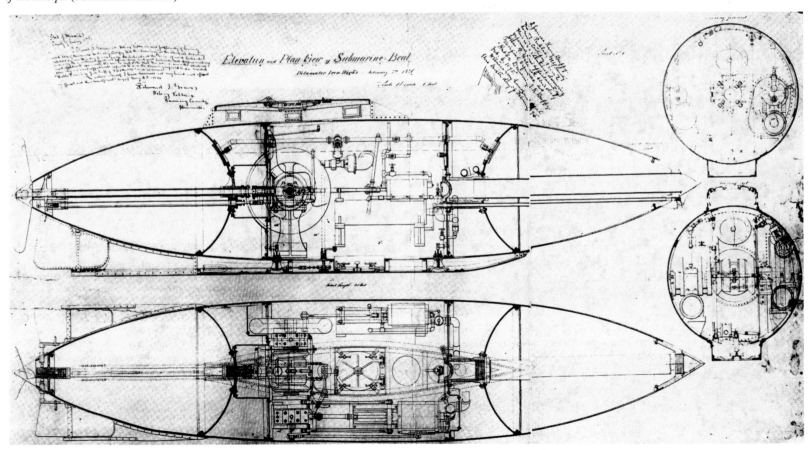

ments to the trim the boat was finally floating free and level in the river. There was then another snag when the petrol engine refused to start.

At this stage, with bankruptcy staring him in the face and with his Irish supporters becoming suspicious, the genius and moral courage of the man really showed itself. He converted the petrol engine to run on steam, and taking his supply from an escorting launch he soon had the submarine chugging along at a steady 3kts. Space onboard was constricted, that available being under 4ft long, and with his head in the turret-like structure – perhaps the fore-runner of a conning tower – there was barely 2ft of headroom, space indeed only for Holland himself. The next stage was to dive the boat, and this he did successfully enough to impress his backers.

Other boats followed over the years, each larger than the last. One, hijacked after a dispute between Holland and his backers, foundered in choppy seas while being towed away. Another was stolen and left in a lumber yard as the thieves decided that they could not operate it with any certainty of safety. It was discovered again many years later and put on display in New York. Another boat had an even more disastrous launch than the first, for it hit a log pile, was holed and went straight to the bottom. Penniless but undeterred, Holland was saved when strained relations with both Great Britain and France in 1893 caused Congress to pass an appropriation for $200,000 for a submarine.

Despite allocating the money the submarine was not ordered until 1895. It was to have been 85ft in length, displaced 149 tons and been armed with two torpedo tubes. Although launched as *Plunger* in 1897 she was never completed thanks to endless changes in design and a steam boiler which took up too much space and made the vessel much larger than Holland had wished. Yet, it does show the tremendous strides that Holland had taken in less than two decades since launching his first in 1878.

To replace this submarine Holland began work on another, his sixth, and the submarine began to take shape in the winter of 1896, before work stopped on *Plunger*. Appropriately for Holland it was launched on St Patrick's day 1897. Two years later, after numerous alterations and more trials the boat was purchased by the US government and on 12 April 1900 Lieutenant Harry Caldwell became the commanding officer of the USS *Holland*, the first submarine captain in the US Navy.

Less well known than Holland was his contemporary Simon Lake, an American who had experimented with underwater vessels from an early age, and lost out to Holland in the competition to provide the first submarine for the US Navy. Despite several quite successful designs it was not until after the period covered by this book that he succeeded in selling one of his designs to the US Navy. A feature of some of his boats was the addition of wheels for travel across the ocean bed, while the provision of a diving chamber allowed a diver to leave and re-enter the hull. Lake's vision of a submarine's value was in cutting underwater cables and destroying defensive minefields rather than as an attacker of enemy shipping. One of his early designs, *Protector*, launched in November 1902 was eventually sold to the Russians.

Practical progress in France

In France Admiral Simeon Bourgois had designed a submarine, *Plongeur*, which had been built in 1863. Like her American contemporaries she was armed only with a spar torpedo but nevertheless marked a great step forward in that she was propelled by a compressed air engine. Like Garrett's boats she was unstable longitudinally and had difficulty in keeping a correct depth, and in consequence development never went beyond the trials stage.

The first significant submersible for the

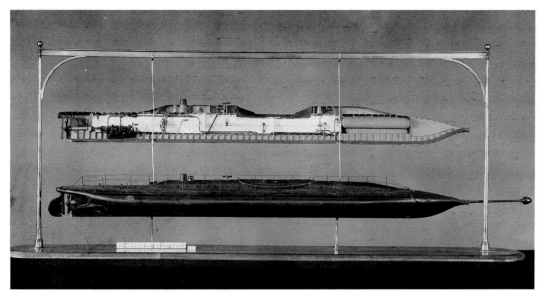

A cutaway and external model of the French submarine Plongeur *of 1863, a vessel powered by compressed air. It was a workable design, but lacked an adequate method of depth control, despite small horizontal rudders aft. She was confined to depths of about 40ft and since the only conceivable weapon was a spar torpedo, any offensive action may well have implied a suicide mission.* (CMP)

French was designed by Dupuy de Lôme, but he died before the project could be started and it was left to his friend Gustave Zédé to carry on his work. *Gymnote*, as this boat was named, took two years to build and was completed in 1888. The most notable aspect of this 59ft long vessel was her electric battery; no less than 564 cells were used to drive a 55hp motor, giving a full speed of 6kts. The first trials were run on 4 September 1888. The French press enthused, perhaps with more patriotism than reason. With no superstructure and only a small reserve of buoyancy surface running was dangerous, while dived she had many of the faults of *Plongeur*. During the next few years she had to be rebuilt twice to try and improve the performance.

In 1890 plans were finalised for Zédé to build another, bigger, boat. But he was a sick man and before building could start he too was dead. Posthumously he was honoured by the new submarine being named after him. The hull was 159ft in length and 10½ft in diameter, while a 208hp electric motor was fitted to propel her through the water. Provision was made to carry three torpedoes. Initially no hydroplanes were fitted and for this reason it was almost impossible to keep the craft at a set depth when dived; later three sets of planes were fitted, which went some way to cure the problem. But such a large boat, at a time when

development was still relatively primitive, was not a success. Again the only motive power was the electric motor and when the batteries had run down there was no way they could be recharged at sea; even so she proved her worth by completing a passage of 41 miles from Toulon to Marseille. Nevertheless there were severe tactical limitations on the use of the submarine, although perhaps not as much as might be thought for at that time submarines were regarded as fit only for harbour defence. Another innovation was the fitting of a periscope, probably the first in any submarine, and also a small conning tower.

Following on from *Gustave Zédé*, a third boat was built in 1899 called *Morse*, of 118ft and a surface displacement of 143 tons ostensibly combining the best points of the earlier boats. But it was the next submarine built by the French at Cherbourg that was to be the big step forward. *Narval* was built to a design by Maxime Laubeuf as the result of an open competition between twenty-nine designs sponsored by the French Admiralty. Basically Laubeuf had designed a torpedo boat which could submerge for attacks or to avoid detec-

tion, but which also had the qualities and seaworthiness of a contemporary torpedo boat. Of double hulled construction, the submarine was fitted with two separate propulsion systems, one each for surface and dived running. A steam boiler which fed a steam reciprocating engine was used on the surface while electric motors provided the power when dived. *Narval* herself came into service in June 1900 and proved a complete success. Although the submarines of this type could recharge their batteries while still at sea there was the disadvantage that they took at least fifteen minutes to shut down the boiler and be ready to dive. Nevertheless the French, with some justification, considered that steam was safer than a petrol engine.

Across the Channel in London the Admiralty were concerned to note the developments so close to home. In December 1898 *Gustave Zédé* had carried out a successful mock attack on a battleship which had onboard at the time the Minister of Marine, such success being achieved despite the exercise limitations which laid down that the submarine was not allowed to dive until after the exercise had started, only eight minutes before firing. As she had no periscope her commander had to broach several times to enable him to gain target information through a small porthole fitted to the conning tower. With the arrival of the more efficient *Narval* the Admiralty were uneasy. Indeed, in the opening years of the twentieth century the French built large numbers of submarines of both the *Narval* and less effective *Morse* types, seventy-six having been completed before the outbreak of war in 1914.

France was undoubtedly the first navy to have an effective submarine force. As early as 1896 an official requirement was established for a 200-ton boat with a radius of 100nm on the surface and 10nm underwater. Of twenty-nine designs, Maxime Laubeuf's was chosen. This became the Narval, *an innovative craft with double hull and steam/electric propulsion that exceeded the specification handsomely.* (CMP)

The small size of Holland boats is apparent from this close-up of HM Submarine No 1 *alongside the depot ship* Hazard, *a converted torpedo gunboat.* (CMP)

The Admiralty takes the plunge

In the summer of 1900 Mr Isaac Rice of the Electric Boat Company, which had acquired *Holland*'s patents, visited England hoping to obtain orders for his company to build submarines for other European nations. He was introduced to the Admiralty by Lord Rothschild and after a few negotiations it was agreed that Messrs Vickers Son & Maxim Ltd at Barrow would build five submarines for the Royal Navy on behalf of the American company. Negotiations were concluded so quickly that in November the Admiralty were forced to approach the Treasury for the money to pay for the submarines which had already been contracted.

This was a radical change of policy for the Admiralty who had been so firmly set against submarines for so long. In the Naval Estimates for the following Financial Year, 1901/2, it was excused by stating that the boats were to be

built so as to allow destroyer commanding officers the opportunity of working against them! Even then, the Controller of the Navy who was responsible for warship building was Admiral Sir Arthur Wilson who had won a VC, sword in hand, fighting the Dervishes on land, not sea, in the Sudan. This vitriolic gentleman was known to have expressed the view that all submariners should be treated as pirates if captured and hanged.

A firm order was placed with the shipyard in December 1900 and Captain Reginald Bacon, RN, a torpedo specialist, was sent to Barrow to oversee the construction. Lieutenant F Arnold-Foster, another torpedo specialist, followed, destined to become Britain's first submarine commanding officer. At Barrow the work of building the submarines was carried out in great secrecy; Arnold-Foster recalls that on arrival in the yard he was anxious for a first sight of his new command but no one seemed to know anything about a submarine being built. Eventually the boat was found in a large shed prominently marked 'Yacht Shed', while parts were made and delivered as 'Pontoon Number One'.

Submarine Number One, or *Holland 1* as she became known, was launched without ceremony on 2 October 1901 and began her sea trials on 15 January the following year. These were completed in April though not without the usual excitement that might be expected in the construction of such a radical new type of craft. Early in February she ran into the dockyard wall damaging her bow. Two days later the flange over the opening for the torpedo tube failed – the boat had been completed in such haste that she was made ready for trials without the tube which would be fitted 'later'. Water rushed in causing the bow to sink steeply, much to the alarm of the dockyard workers inside, though fortunately all was corrected without casualty. The other four boats followed at regular intervals and were towed to Portsmouth for the worth of a submarine to be evaluated.

It would appear that the Admiralty, once they had taken the rather distasteful step of ordering submarines, wanted as little to do with the project as possible and Captain Bacon and his team were given an extraordinary degree of autonomy. Even the American liaison

A 1 *was little more than a lengthened Holland but notable as the first all-British submarine. Innovations included a proper conning tower to reduce the chance of being swamped while running on the surface. Unfortunately the boat had a tragically short career, being accidentally rammed and sunk in March 1904, less than a year after entering service.* (CMP)

boat. There was little freeboard and virtually no conning tower so that surface navigation was both difficult and hazardous. The diving time was a matter of a few minutes depending on the amount of buoyancy given when running on the surface, but was in any case markedly more satisfactory than the 15 to 20 minutes of the French *Narval*, already mentioned.

One novel item of equipment that came to be fitted, but only through the work of Captain Bacon, was a periscope. There was no provision for this in the original American design, and it was expected that the commanding officer would take bearings through a glass port fitted to the cupola over the hatch as the submarine broke surface – as *Gustave Zédé* had been forced to do. Unlike the modern periscope it was stowed horizontally along the hull and was raised about a ball socket joint. Once raised it was trained round by means of a geared handwheel. For the user it had the dis-

officer was sent back to the States as soon as *Holland 1* was accepted. Bacon soon realised that these submarines could never be anything more than experimental craft, despite their initially encouraging performance. With the co-operation of the Vickers design staff the plans for a new class of submarine – the 'A' class – was produced even before the last of the *Holland*s had left Barrow and the Admiralty were persuaded to include an initial order for four of these boats in the 1902/3 Programme and a further nine the following year. It was the beginning of a regular and progressive annual building programme which was to continue up to the start of the war in 1914.

These first submarines for the Royal Navy were single hulled of spindle form, that is the main ballast tanks which were filled with water to make the submarine dive were internal to the pressure hull, while the hull itself was circular in section with the centre of all sections in a straight line. At the forward end was a single 18in torpedo tube. There were no internal water-tight bulkheads in the hull, which was 64ft long. There was no provision for crew comfort and the cluttered interior was devoted solely to the working of the boat. A 60-cell battery provided power for the electric motor which when dived gave a nominal range of 25nm at the claimed maximum speed of 7kts. There was a single rudder and a single set of hydroplanes aft to control the angle of the

Russia showed an early interest in submarines – indeed, in underwater warfare generally – the first workable prototype being Alexandrovski's boat of 1865. A series of midget submarines was built to Drzewiecki's designs during the Turkish war of 1877–78, but the first effective submersible warship in Russian service was the Delfin *(seen here), launched in 1903.*

advantage that whilst objects ahead were seen correctly, those astern were inverted, and those on the beams were on their sides. Primitive though this may sound there were officers who claimed that they thereby could gain an instant idea of relative bearing.

While the British, French and Americans had all been including the submarine as a unit of their fleets the Russians too had not been idle. They too had a submarine fleet, mainly through the influence of an engineer, Bubnov, and with other boats built in St Petersburg to a

Simon Lake design and with three others ordered from the Germania yard at Kiel. By the end of the period under review the Russians had spent many years acquiring knowledge of submarine construction from numerous designers – they had even transported some small craft by rail to the Far East to be available for action against the Japanese during the war of 1904–5 – yet they did not possess any submarines which could be used effectively in war. The Japanese had countered the Russian progress by using a Holland design similar to that

in use in the Royal and United States Navies, but the boats were not completed before the peace of 1905.

Thus by 1906 the submarine was firmly accepted as a unit of many navies, but had yet to be tested in war. The boats were still relatively primitive in conception but becoming more efficient as the years produced progressively better craft. In the years to come more and more navies would add the submarine to their navy list.

Michael Wilson

Early Submarines: Typical Boats 1860–1905

Submarine [type]	Nationality	First of class launched	Length (feet) (metres)	Displacement (surface/dived) (tons)	Torpedo tubes	Armament	Speed (surface/dived) (kts)	Surface endurance (nm/kts)	Dived endurance (nm/kts)
DIABLE MARIN [Bauer type]	Russian	1855	52 17.0	Not known	None	None	Hand cranked		
H L HUNLEY	Confederate States	1864	40 12.2	Not known	1 spar torpedo (90lb charge)	None	2.5 hand cranked		
Aleksandrovsky Design	Russian	1864	110 36.0	355/	2 mines	None	1½ (compressed air engine)		
Holland's 1st [Private venture]	American	1878	14½ 4.8	2¼/	None	None	Not known (petrol engine)		
RESURGAM II [Garrett type – private venture]	British	1879	45 14.8	30/	None	None	About 3 (steam driven)	12/3	
FENIAN RAM [Holland's 2nd – private venture]	American	1881	31 10.2	19/	None	1–9in pneumatic gun	3–5		
NORDENFELT I	Bought by Greece	1885	64 21.0	60/	1–14in	1 MG	9/4 (steam driven)		
NORDENFELT IV	Russian	1887	120 39.4	160/243	2–14in	2 MG	14/5 (steam driven)		
Holland's 6th (Became USS HOLLAND in 1900)	American	1897	54 17.7	63/74	1–18in	1 dynamite gun (design)	8/5		
MORSE	French	1899	120 39.4	143/149	1–45cm	None	7¼/5½	90/4½	
NARVAL	French	1899	111½ 36.6	117/202	None (4 torpedoes in drop collars)	None	9¾/5¼	345/9	58/3
ADDER (SS 3)	American	1901	64 21.0	107/123	1–18in	None	8/7 (claimed)		
HOLLAND I	British	1901	64 21.0	113/122	1–18in	None	7½/6	235/	20/5
SOM [Holland type]	Russian	1904	65½ 21.5	105/122	1–15in	1 MG	8½/6	585/	42/
OSETR [Lake type]	Russian	1905	72 23.6	153/187	3–15in	None	8½/4½	385/	35/
[NUMBER] I	Japanese	1905	67 22.0	105/130	1–18in	None	9/7	185/8	

10

Naval Armaments and Armour

THE increase in destructive power of naval weapons during the years between 1840 and 1905 certainly exceeded that in any previous century. By far the greater part of this increase occurred in the last forty-five years and was directly associated with corresponding improvements in armour protection. The roots of this competition between gun and armour are to be found in the 1840–1860 period but the main feature in these years was the increasing use of smooth bore shells against wooden hulled ships. Spherical shells could be fired by any medium or large smooth bore gun, but the greatest effect was from what were known as 'shell' guns of larger bore and somewhat lower muzzle velocity than the 'solid shot' gun of equivalent weight. The destructive power of such shell guns had been shown by the work of the French General Paixhans, particularly in trials against the old two-decker *Pacificateur* in 1824, but their introduction to service in large numbers was slow. Further demonstrations of the power of shells against wooden ships occurred in the actions at Eckernförde in 1849 (during the Danish–Prussian War) and at Sinope in November 1853, and after this last their effect was widely appreciated. Even so the three-decker *Bretagne*, the largest French warship of the day, completed in 1856, only had thirty-six 22cm shell guns out of a total armament of 130, forming half the number on the two lower gundecks. In Britain *Victoria*, completed in 1861, had sixty-two 8in shell guns forming the whole armament of the two lower gundecks, out of 121.

It must be noted that the outfit for 8in and similar guns was largely hollow, or sometimes solid, shot and it was seldom if ever more than 40 shells per gun and usually less.

The 8in gun had an actual bore of 8.05in (204.47mm), nominal weight 65cwt (330kg), length 9ft (2.74m) and fired a 51lb (23.1kg) shell or 56lb (25.4kg) hollow shot. The solid shot was *c*68lb (30.8kg). For the corresponding French 22cm No 1 (1849) figures were: 223.3mm (8.8in), 3617kg (71.2cwt), 2.786m

(9.14ft), and shell 27.65kg (61lb). Larger shell guns were limited in service use, though the British 10in of 85cwt (4318kg) firing an 84lb (38.1kg) shell, formed at one time the main armament of the largest screw frigates, and the US Navy mounted a few 11in of 7 tons with 135lb (61.2kg) shell. As a shot gun this armed the famous *Monitor* and was widely used in the American Civil War.

The standard British shot gun remained the 32pdr, though in France the former *canon de 36* of 1786 with 39.8lb (18.04kg) shot was replaced by the *canon de 30* of 1840-1849 with 33.4lb (15.14kg) shot. This is not to say that the manufacture of British guns was restricted, as in 1840 the Navy declared 10,000 guns and carronades obsolete, and introduced new 32pdrs and 8in (noted above). Over fourteen years 14,000 new guns were made.

The British 68pdr/95cwt, noted below, was seldom mounted in numbers greater than one or two per ship in pivot or rear-chock carriages, but the big *Mersey* class frigates had up to twelve, the paddle frigate *Terrible* seven and the armoured floating batteries fourteen or sixteen. The French equivalent was the *canon de 50* of 1849 which was of 194mm (7.64in) bore and weighed 4630kg (91.1cwt). It fired a 25.15kg (55.4lb) shot.

All the guns so far noted were made of cast iron, but some very large pieces of wrought iron construction were built and tested. The best known of these was the 36in (91.4cm) Mallet mortar, first tried in October 1857. Part of this was actually cast iron, and it was never intended for use afloat. The US screw sloop *Princeton* completed in 1844, originally had two 12in wrought iron smooth bore guns, one bought in England and the other made in the US. The previous history of neither gun was reassuring, and the US one eventually burst with disastrous results killing six, including the Secretaries of State and the Navy.

Development of naval armament was rapid and extensive in this period, though it followed different paths in the various navies. This was the result of a number of factors: to advances in

metallurgy, so that steel of reliability could replace wrought and cast iron; to developments in precision engineering, particularly as applied to heavy items such as major calibre guns and their mountings; and also to the introduction of satisfactory rifling systems and breech mechanisms. Advances in the chemistry of propellant explosives led from black powder to the slower burning brown powder, and then to 'smokeless' propellants of gelatinized nitrocellulose with or without nitro-glycerin.

Naval guns

British rifled ordnance

In 1860 the British 68pdr 95cwt (4826kg) cast iron smooth bore was of 8.12in (206.2mm) bore and fired a cast iron round shot of *c*66¼lb (30kg) at a muzzle velocity of *c*1580f/s (feet per second) or 482m/s (metres per second). Against this the first generation of armour like the 4½in (114mm) wrought iron in *Warrior* was a good protection at 200yds (183m). Rifling of the bore offered a heavier shell from a gun of given size, greater range due to reduced air-resistance from an elongated projectile and increased accuracy. The principles had been known and neglected for three or four centuries. Though never officially introduced the British made some use of the Lancaster muzzle-loading rifle during the Crimean War. These had an elliptical helical bore and fired a projectile of elliptical cross-section, but were not a success as the shells were liable to jam and burst the gun, or to break up in the bore.

It was hoped that the 7in (177.8mm) Armstrong rifled breech-loader might serve as the standard naval heavy gun and as the army siege gun. It was never designed specifically as an armour-piercing gun, for which role its muzzle velocity of 1175f/s (358m/s) with 110lb (50kg) projectile was quite inadequate. It was intended to use a steel barrel, supported by

The first British operational rifled breech-loader was the 110pdr (7in) Armstrong, seen here on a pivoting slide mounting aboard the ironclad Black Prince *in the 1860s. Problems with the breech mechanism caused the replacement of the gun with RML types. (NMM)*

shrunk-on wrought iron coils, but nearly all had to have wrought iron barrels made from coils. The projectiles were lead coated, the diameter over the coating being larger than the bore, and the seventy-six small rifling grooves of uniform twist, cut into the lead. The breech block with a coned face was inserted radially, and also served as the vent-piece as it was called. It was kept in position by an axial hollow breech screw through which the gun was loaded once the vent-piece was withdrawn. This system was not satisfactory though it might have been so with better materials and precision engineering. The gun would not stand an increased muzzle velocity and as an armour-piercer it was no better than, if not inferior to, the 68pdr.

The best armour-piercers of this time were the experimental Whitworth guns, due to good quality projectiles of relatively large weight/cross-section ratio and to the gun being strong enough to stand the charges needed for ade-

Comparison of the built-up construction of British 9in RML guns of the 1860s: (top) Armstrong construction, with a number of thin wrought iron coils; (bottom) the more economical Woolwich construction, using fewer, larger coils.

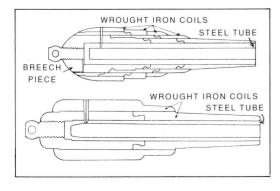

quate velocity. Later guns were built with a mild steel barrel reinforced by mild steel hoops forced on cold, but in November 1862 a wrought iron 6.4/7in (162.6/177.8mm) ML (muzzle-loader) sent a 151lb (68.5kg) flat-ended unfused steel shell with 5lb (2.27kg) burster through a very good quality 5in (127mm) wrought iron plate at 800yds (730m), the shell bursting in the backing. Muzzle velocity was *c*1370f/s (418m/s). Unfortunately the rifling system of a spiral hexagonal bore with rounded corners and a projectile of similar shape was not very satisfactory and later heavy Whitworth naval guns were only used by Brazil.

In 1863 to 1865 extensive trials were held to determine the best type of rifled gun for the future, and meanwhile a limited number of smooth bores, built up with wrought iron coils, were introduced as a temporary measure. These were a 9in (228.6mm) first in *Prince Consort* completed in February 1864, and a few 10.5in (266.7mm), first in *Royal Sovereign* completed in August. As a result of the above trials rifled muzzle-loaders were adopted with steel tubes reinforced by hoops and tubes machined from coiled wrought iron. A rifling system based on a modified French groove, known as the Woolwich groove was adopted. In this there were six to nine grooves with increasing twist in heavy guns, and bronze studs on the projectile which engaged in the grooves. This system was cheap and made loading in ML guns relatively easy, but it did not give good centring of the projectile which led to inaccuracy, and the rush of powder gas through the clearance between projectile body and bore caused severe scoring of the latter when used with heavy charges. Such guns could be justi-

fied for a few years, but their continuation through the 1870s was deplorable. The 9in (228.6mm) was first in *Prince Albert*, completed in February 1866, followed by 10in (254mm) in *Hercules* (November 1868) and the 25-ton 12in (304.8mm), limited to turret ships, in *Monarch* (June 1869). Firing Palliser chilled iron shot at 1000yds (914m), these guns could pierce about 9in, 11in and 12in of unbacked wrought iron, though with improved powder, these figures were improved by about 10 per cent.

Other major navies in the 1860s

Meanwhile the French navy had introduced a few cast iron rifled muzzle-loaders, the 164.7mm (6.48in) M1855, with two lugs cast on the projectile and later zinc lugs. This was not very satisfactory and the gun was superseded by the 164.7mm M1858 and M1860 RMLs. These were cast iron with a layer of puddled steel hoops over the breech, and had three rifling grooves with zinc studs on the projectile. They were introduced in *Gloire*, completed in August 1860, but as armour-piercing guns they were of little use, the MV (muzzle velocity) with 99lb (44.9kg) projectile being only 1055f/s (322m/s), and they were limited to twenty rounds of this heavy shot per gun. The M1860 BL (breech-loader) introduced in the rearmed *Gloire* in 1861 was similar, but had the advantage of being breech-loading. An interrupted screw block was used with obturation by a steel diaphragm. The next French guns, M1864 and 1864–66, resembled M1860 BL but had more hooping. Performance was inferior to the British RMLs. The 240mm (9.45in) was introduced in 1866 but the 274.4mm (10.8in) not until July 1870 in *Océan*, and its performance was well down on that of the British 10in.

A French breech-block of the interrupted screw type.

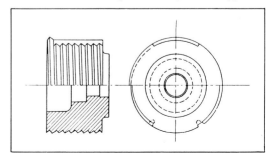

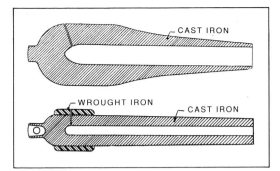

A comparison between the basic shape of American Dahlgren smooth bores (top) and Parrott RMLs. Both types existed in various calibres but each series showed a family resemblance to those illustrated here.

Although Germany was not then a major naval power, by the end of 1868 a Krupp 235.4mm (9.27in) had proved distinctly better than an Elswick 9in RML, ballistically the same as the standard British. The Krupp gun was of hooped all steel construction with a horizontal wedge breech block, and obturation by a steel Broadwell ring. Rifling was polygroove with a lead coated projectile of either Gruson chilled iron or Krupp steel. Guns of this type were in *König Wilhelm* (February 1869) and a similar 9in was introduced to the Russian navy, the same year.

The United States was the only navy engaged at this time in a major war, and both the North and South depended on rapidly built or improvised ships. The North was by far the stronger side but their industrial facilities were not commensurate, and their heaviest guns were cast iron smooth bores. A few 20in (508mm) were made in 1864 but never mounted afloat, where the largest was the 15in (381mm) Dahlgren first mounted in *Passaic* (November 1862), and in a longer pattern in *Saugus* (April 1864). These guns were cast with a water-cooled core as was the Rodman version used on land. With large grain black powder developed by Rodman, one of the latter guns was tried in England. Muzzle energy was higher than that of the 10in RML, but fell off even at short ranges. American RMLs of the Parrott (North) or Brooke (South) type were limited to 8in (203.2mm) and smaller in ships.

The 1870s: the last muzzle-loaders

The next British heavy RML, the 12in (304.8mm) 35-ton, was first in *Devastation*, completed in April 1873, and could pierce *c*14in (35.6cm) unbacked wrought iron at

Loading arrangements for the 80-ton 16in RML guns in HMS *Inflexible.*

1000yds firing pebble powder charges. The 12in 38-ton followed in *Thunderer* (May 1877), but of the two guns made, one was destroyed accidentally by firing when double loaded, and the other expended in tests.

Other 38-ton guns, bored to 12.5in (317.5mm), were first in *Dreadnought* (February 1879), though Elswick had mounted a very similar 12.5in in two Chinese gunboats in 1877. With larger grain P² powder, *c*15.5in (39cm) of unbacked wrought iron could be pierced at 1000yds, and with this gun copper gas checks were fitted to the base of the shot which expanded against the bore on firing and reduced leakage of powder gases. The above were limited to turret ships in Britain, while in central battery ships an 11in (279.4mm) was introduced in *Alexandra* (January 1877) and an Elswick version of the 12in 25-ton in the ex-Turkish *Belleisle*, (July 1878).

Meanwhile in France the 274.4mm M1870, built with a cast iron body and partial steel tube and hoops, and with polygroove rifling and copper driving band, was in *Friedland* and *Richelieu* in 1876 and although this was slightly inferior to the 12in 35-ton RML at 1000yds,

The forward 11in Dahlgren pivot gun aboard the US sloop Kearsarge *after her victory over the Confederate raider* Alabama. *(CMP)*

the all-steel 274.4mm M1875 in *Redoubtable* (December 1878) was better than the 12.5in, though the shot was only 476lb (216kg) as against 818lb (371kg).

The USA had lost interest in naval developments, but although Germany was still a minor naval power, Krupps continued to progress, and the 30.5cm (12.01in) MRKL/22, first in the gunboat *Wespe* (November 1876), had a muzzle velocity of 1591f/s (485m/s) with 716.5lb (325kg) projectile, compared with 1415f/s (431m/s) for the 12.5in. Copper driving bands replaced lead coating and prismatic powder with regular hexagonal grains was used.

The British RML was not quite dead, however, as it had a deceptive simplicity, though loading difficulties increased sharply in larger guns; furthermore, the plant at Woolwich Arsenal, which had an unfortunate near-monopoly on British naval guns, was not suited to longer BLs. An experimental 80-ton gun of

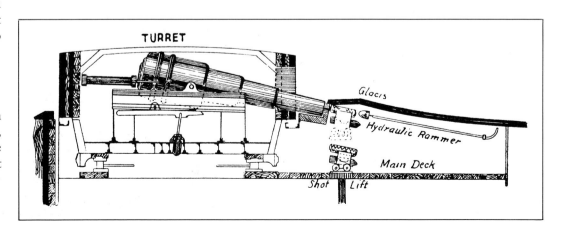

the usual Woolwich type and rifling, with the addition of a gas check, was completed in September 1875. After many troubles it was found necessary to change the rifling to polygroove with rotation of the shot by copper gas check and eventually four 16in (406.4mm) RML were mounted in *Inflexible* (not completed until October 1881). Meanwhile Elswick were building eight 17.72in (450mm) RML for the Italian navy, the first four destined for *Duilio*, completed in January 1880. The four for *Dandolo* were bought by Britain in 1878 for the coast defences of Malta and Gibraltar and another four made for Italy. These guns were built with a jointed steel 'A' tube and a large number of relatively small wrought iron coils. Rifling was polygroove with rotation by copper gas check. The Italians used a very large grain Fossano powder, occasionally liable to pressure irregularities, and in March 1880 a gun in *Duilio* failed due to a fracture in the 'A' tube forward of the chamber, the outer coils pulling apart just in rear of the trunnions. As a result full charges were reduced in the Italian navy and more drastically in British coast defence guns. Both these guns were chambered like BLs, and bore length rose to 20.5 calibres in the 17.72in. The 16in could pierce 22½in (57cm) of wrought iron at 1000yds which meant that little of a ship could be protected. These very large guns were difficult to load and very slow firing, and really demanded a larger ship to mount them than governments were willing to afford.

The last heavy RMLs of moderate size were an Elswick 11in (279.4mm) of 35 tons and 23.2 calibre bore mounted in seven gunboats for China built in 1879–1881, and the Mk II version of the 12.5in 38-ton first mounted in *Agamemnon* (completed March 1883). This was chambered and firing a prismatic powder charge muzzle velocity was raised to 1575f/s (480m/s) and 17.5in (44.5cm) of wrought iron could be pierced at 1000yds.

Guns and armour in the 1880s

The 1880s, which saw the re-introduction of BL guns to the British navy, was a period of many ordnance improvements. Prismatic brown powder was introduced by the Rottweil company in Germany in 1882, in England in 1884 and the improved SBC – slow burning cocoa – in 1887. The percentage break-down of black powder was typically 75 potassium nitrate, 15 charcoal, 10 sulphur, and of brown 79 potassium nitrate, 18 partially carbonised rye-straw, and 3 sulphur. Brown powder required great care in manufacture, but was slower

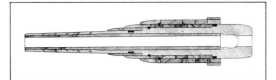

The Krupp 26cm (10.2in) mantle-ring gun of 1875.

burning than black. Very large charges were required, that in the 16.25in (412.8mm) noted below weighing 960lb (435.4kg), the heaviest service charge ever used afloat. Bore lengths needed to be c30 calibres and it was learnt by bitter experience that guns should be hooped to the muzzle. Construction was improved with short hoops often of wrought iron, being replaced by longer hoops and tubes of steel. The shrink assembly of these caused great trouble originally, and long delays by Woolwich in completing heavy guns were notorious, though they still provided the majority of British heavy guns instead of Elswick or the smaller Whitworth plant.

Armour plates were also much improved. In compound armour, steel of c0.5/0.6 per cent carbon was either poured onto white hot wrought iron in Cammell plates or steel and wrought iron plates were joined by pouring steel between them in Brown plates. The resulting steel faced wrought iron was used for some of the turret armour in *Inflexible*, and for belt armour in *Colossus* (completed October 1885, though the *Riachuelo* completed for Brazil in February 1884 had priority). About one-third of the total thickness was steel. Meanwhile mild steel armour from Schneider provided the protection for *Duilio* and *Dandolo*. Steel armour was gradually improved and by 1890 was slightly better than compound. Chilled iron projectiles were not suited for attacking steel or compound plates, though still carried for economic reasons. Against such projectiles 10in (25cm) compound or steel was equivalent to 15in or 16in (38cm or 41cm) wrought iron. A reliable steel AP (armour-piercing) projectile was first achieved by the French firms of Holtzer, Firminy and St Chamond. These were made from forged high carbon, chromium steel, and Holtzer shot became part of the standard outfit for the more powerful British heavy guns. Against such projectiles 10in (25cm) compound or steel was equivalent to 12.5in (32cm) wrought iron.

After much experimental work the 12in (304.8mm) Mk II of 25 calibres was adopted and first mounted in *Colossus* (October 1885). This was of thoroughly unsatisfactory construction of mixed steel and wrought iron, and after a gun failed in *Collingwood* in May 1886

when firing a three-quarter charge, the whole lot were withdrawn. The all-steel replacements (Mks III, IV, V and Vw) were first in *Edinburgh* (July 1887), and the much more powerful 13.5in (343mm) of 30 calibres in *Rodney* (June 1888). Construction of these built-up steel guns was very slow and there were variations in design details covered by four marks and seven sub-marks. Piercing of wrought iron at 1000yds was 20.6in (52cm) for the 12in and 28in (71cm) for the 13.5in. Interrupted screw breech blocks were used with De Bange obturation, based on an asbestos/tallow pad and the mushroom head of the vent axial. There were no carriers so that when open the breech block was separated from the gun.

Meanwhile Elswick had produced five versions of a 17in (431.8mm) 26- or 27-calibre gun for Italy, originally of steel and wrought iron construction and later all steel. The first gun was in the pontoon *Valente* (1884) and later patterns in *Italia* (October 1885), *Lepanto* (August 1887) and the *Lauria* class (February 1888). An improved version with single piece instead of jointed 'A' tube, and of 16.25in (412.8mm) 30-calibre bore was introduced to the British navy, and first mounted in *Benbow* (June 1888). In all twelve guns were made and there were nearly as many different constructions. They were not very satisfactory being too large for existing ships, while some were liable to droop and the first guns in *Benbow* suffered from too shallow rifling grooves. Guns with deeper grooves were first in *Victoria* (March 1890). At 1000yds 32in (81cm) of wrought iron could be pierced.

The French had at least as much trouble in producing their heavy guns and they were of inferior performance to British guns of similar calibre. The most powerful were the 370mm (14.57in)/28.5-calibre M1875–79, of which the Creusot version was in *Amiral Baudin* (December 1888) and the St Chamond in *Formidable* two months later. They were of built-up steel construction, heavier but of similar performance to the British 13.5in. They were later removed to coast defence and in 1914–1918 to railway mountings.

Krupps continued to develop their steel built-up guns with wedge breech mechanism including a 35.5cm (13.98in)/25-calibre in the Danish *Tordenskjold* (1883), and four very heavy 40cm (15.75in)/35-calibre for Italian coast defence twin turrets at La Spezia and Taranto. The two latter guns were mounted for a time in 1889 in the gunboats *Castore* and *Polluce*. The shell was heavier than in the 16.25in, but muzzle velocity was lower. The trial gun was returned to Krupps, rebored to

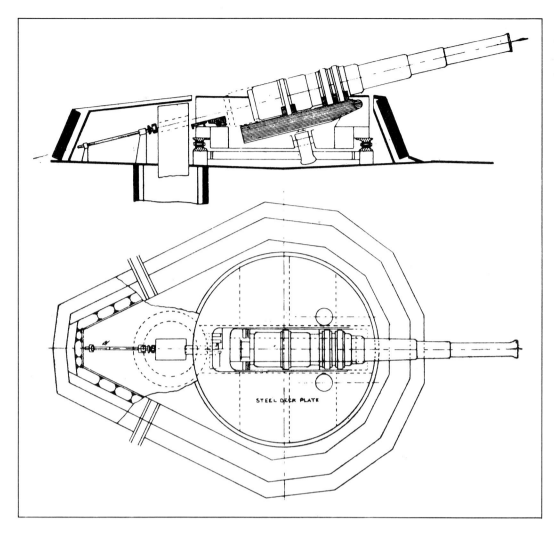

STEEL DECK PLATE

The barbette for BL guns designed by George Rendel of Armstrong's Elswick works. It was adopted in the 'Admiral' class in the 1880s, usually for twin 13.5in guns but in single 16.25in mountings in Benbow.

provement, but in 1890 Harvey in the USA introduced a plate with the face carburised and hardened. With an unalloyed steel the hardened face was about 1in deep, and the plate 15–20 per cent better than the above nickel-steel. The belt in the *Majestic* class, completed from December 1895, was of Harvey steel. Further improvements of up to 20 per cent were made if the steel was alloyed with nickel, but heat treatment was more difficult and in Britain the improvements were not thought worth the cost. However in 1895 Krupps introduced KC (Krupp cemented, *ie* carburised) armour using nickel-chromium steel with more complex heat treatment resulting in a deeper hardened face and tougher back. After a few years this was universally adopted, the first British ships with KC belts being the *Canopus* class completed from December 1899. Early Krupp and Harvey plates were far from consistent, but KC was perhaps 25 per cent better than Harvey nickel and 10in KC was equivalent to 23in wrought iron against the previous type of steel shot.

It was found that the addition of a mild steel cap over the point of the projectile improved performance against hard-faced armour so that 10in KC was equivalent to about 20in wrought iron. Capped alloy steel AP shells with 2–3 per cent black powder bursters were adopted in 1897 in the USA and Russia and were universal by 1905, Britain being the last major navy to adopt caps though they had been tried years before.

In Britain the 35.4-calibre 12in Mk VIII, first in *Majestic* (December 1895), was followed by the 40-calibre Mk IX in *Implacable* (September 1901) and by the 45-calibre Mk X in *Dreadnought* (December 1906). The Royal Navy had finally assumed responsibility for its own guns in 1891, and Woolwich though it remained a major supplier was joined by Elswick and Vickers. All three of the above marks were wire-wound, Mk VIII being a Woolwich design and the other two Vickers. The breech blocks were all supported by carriers hinged to the gun. Stepped screw Welin blocks were in Mks IX and X. Muzzle velocities increased from c2400f/s (732m/s) to 2725f/s (831m/s) with nominal perforation of KC with APC at 5000yds at normal impact, 11.5in, 13in, 14in (29cm, 33cm, 36cm) for the three marks.

French guns were of various built-up designs

42cm (16.54in) and was still on their proving ground in 1945.

A remarkable US weapon of this time was the Zalinsky Dynamite Gun, a 15in (381mm) smooth bore powered by compressed air, and firing a 980lb (445kg) shell with 500lb (228kg) dynamite or other high explosive burster which would not stand the discharge of a normal gun. Trials began in 1889 and a range of over 1700yds (1550m) was attained and up to three times as far with sub-calibre shells. Three were mounted in *Vesuvius* (June 1890), and trials continued, but poor accuracy was never overcome, though one was later in the Brazilian *Niteroi*.

The pre-dreadnought era 1890–1905

Great progress in guns was made between 1890 and 1905. A usable nitro-cellulose gelatinized propellant was developed in France from 1886, and the first heavy naval guns built for it, the 340mm and 305mm M1887, were in service in 1894. Britain was a year later with cordite Mk I in the 12in Mk VIII. Unfortunately this propellant which contained 58 per cent nitro-

glycerin, produced very hot and erosive gases, and in 1902 cordite MD with 30 per cent nitro-glycerin was introduced with doubling of the life in the above 12in. The USA and Russia favoured nitro-cellulose and Germany and Italy nitro-glycerin additions. These propellants, often known as 'smokeless', produced far less smoke than gunpowder and much smaller charges were needed. They were difficult to ignite, but traces of sulphur compounds and some other impurities in the nitro-cellulose could cause spontaneous explosions, and the French navy in particular suffered from this.

Bore lengths of 35 to 45 calibres and usually 40 to 45 were needed so that gun construction became more difficult, except that long steel forgings became more reliable, and the British introduced wire-winding after prolonged experimental work. This greatly simplified construction of heavy guns and objections on grounds of droop and lack of rigidity were often invalid.

There were also great advances in armour plate. Schneider added about 4 per cent nickel to their steel plate with perhaps 5 per cent im-

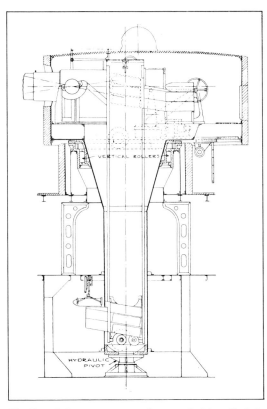

The French Canet type turret for a single 24cm (9.4in) gun. Similar mountings were used for a range of guns in the 1890s.

with a large number of short hoops in some. Shells were lighter and muzzle velocity higher than in British contemporaries. The 340mm (13.39in) M1887 of 41.5-calibre, first in *Jemmapes* (1894), was the only service naval gun of the period over 305mm (12.01in) but was apparently not very successful and in 1914–1918 they were converted to 400mm (15.75in) railway howitzers. The 305mm/45-calibre M1887 and M1893 were introduced in *Bouvines* (December 1894) and in *Bouvet* and *Masséna* (June 1898), the 40-calibre M1893–96 in *Charlemagne* and *Gaulois* in 1899, and the more powerful 40-calibre M1893–96M in *République* and *Patrie* (December 1906).

Of other navies, Russia introduced a 12in/40-calibre of Canet type in the *Sissoi* 1896, the USA, rapidly growing again as a major naval power, a 12in/40-calibre of built-up design in *Arkansas* (later *Ozark*) in October 1902, and a 45-calibre Mk 5, equivalent to the 12in Mk X, in *Louisiana* (June 1906). In Japan wire-wound 12in/45-calibre weapons of Elswick and Vickers design were in *Kashima* and *Katori* respectively (May 1906), and again equivalent to the Mk X.

A 6in BL gun on a Vavasseur centre pivot mounting, the first modern mounting for medium calibre breechloading weapons, introduced in the early 1880s.

Germany, also rapidly increasing the navy, took a different path. The built-up Krupp guns had an improved horizontal wedge breech mechanism and extended the use of brass cartridge cases to the main armament of battleships, though the calibre was smaller than usual. The 23.8cm (9.37in) SKL/40 was first in *Kaiser Friedrich III* (October 1898) and the 28.3cm (11.14in) SKL/40 in *Braunschweig* (October 1904). Neither, particularly the 23.8cm, were especially powerful for their size.

Medium calibre guns

The foregoing has considered the main armament of battleships, but smaller guns for their secondary armament and for cruisers, sloops and smaller vessels, generally followed heavy guns with simplified construction. The important innovation of QF guns is noted below. In Britain the early Armstrong BLs included 40pdrs and 20pdrs (4.75in, 3.75in – 120.7mm, 95.3mm), of which the latter long out-lasted the larger guns. British RMLs included 8in, 7in/6½ tons and /90cwt, 6.3in/64cwt (64pdr), and various 3in (203.2mm, 177.8mm, 160mm, and 76.2mm, respectively). There was also the 64pdr/71cwt Palliser (6.29in, 159.8mm), converted from a cast iron 8in smooth bore by means of a wrought iron tube. Of BL guns neither the 10in (254mm) or 8in (203.2mm) were much favoured, and the standard calibres were 9.2in (233.7mm), 6in (152.4mm), 5in (127mm) and 4in (101.6mm). Other navies whose guns were supplied by Elswick usually preferred 10in and 8in to 9.2in.

The medium calibre QF (quick-firing) gun was introduced by Elswick and the essentials were brass cartridge case including a primer, a quick-acting breech mechanism and a mounting suitable for rapid aimed fire. The breech block in Elswick guns was a coned screw, but cylindrical blocks or Krupp wedges were usual in other patterns. In tests in 1887 an Elswick

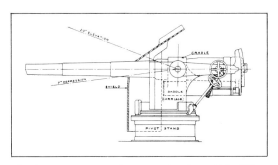

An Armstrong centre pivot mounting for a 4.7in QF gun, 1887.

4.7in (actually 4.724in or 120mm) fired 10 rounds in 47½ seconds, almost eight times faster than the 5in BL. In the Royal Navy the 4.7in/40-calibre was first in *Sharpshooter* (August 1889), and the 6in/40-calibre QF in *Royal Sovereign* (May 1892), though mounted in the Italian *Piemonte* with the 4.7in, in August 1889, while the 4.7in/32-calibre and 6in/32-calibre were available two–three years earlier. In the British navy these guns fired separate ammunition as did the 4in/40-calibre QF of 1895, but in other navies shell and cartridge case up to 4.7in were often fitted together in fixed ammunition, and there were instances up to 15cm (actually 14.91cm, 5.87in) in some Krupp guns. Provided breech mechanism and mounting met QF needs, the brass case was not thought essential in Britain and the 6in/45-calibre Mk VII in *Cressy* (May 1901) was a BL gun, and in 1905 this along with 9.2in and 7.5in (190.5mm) was the standard medium gun.

These developments were fairly typical of other navies. In France the favoured calibres were 240mm, 194mm, 164.7mm, 138.6mm and 100mm (9.45in, 7.64in, 6.48in, 5.46in, 3.94in). The 240mm was seldom used latterly, and QF versions of the three smaller guns were in ships completed in 1894–95. A 194mm QF was only in *Jeanne d'Arc*, completed 1902. Germany mounted 23.8cm, 20.93cm, 17.26cm,

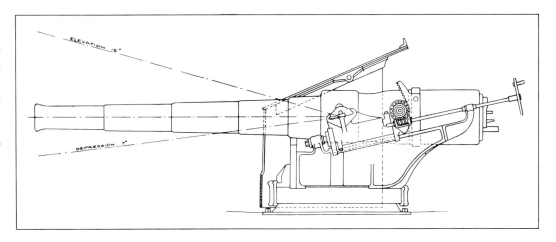

Large guns in the ironclad era were initially mounted on iron pivoting slide mountings, as with this 9in RML in the British Minotaur *in the 1860s. (CMP)*

14.91cm and 10.5cm (9.37in, 8.24in, 6.795in, 5.87in, 4.134in). A 10.5cm QF was in service in 1891 and a 14.91cm in 1896, while all subsequent larger guns were also QF. In other navies a 12cm Krupp QF was in use in 1889.

Anti-torpedo boat armament

The introduction of the torpedo boat stimulated the development of small quick-firing guns, firing fixed ammunition both for defence and also for the armament of these boats, as well as for sweeping the upper deck of a battleship from bulwarks or tops in very close action. The most popular initially was the 37mm (1.457in) Hotchkiss revolver with five barrels revolved by a hand crank and firing in turn. The cast iron shell weighed *c*450 grams (1lb) and 70 rounds could be fired per minute, reduced to 14 in aimed fire. It was first tried at Gavre in France in 1873, but was never adopted by Britain where the 1in Nordenfelt was preferred. There were two or four barrels fixed horizontally with lever operated breech mechanism and firing a 7¼oz (205 gram) solid steel shot. With four barrels 216 rounds per minute could be fired but 40 in aimed fire.

These were soon found to be inadequate, and in 1886 57mm (2.244in) 6pdr single barrel guns by Hotchkiss or Nordenfelt were introduced in Britain. The former, which had a vertical sliding breech block, was preferred and was supplemented by a 47mm (1.85in) 3pdr Hotchkiss where a lighter gun was required. The French navy used the latter calibre with

some 65mm (2.56in) 9pdr from 1891, while the Germans introduced a 5cm (1.97in) 4pdr for torpedo craft in 1893, but as defence against torpedo craft the 8.8cm (3.46in) SKL/30QF in 1890 followed by the SKL/35 in 1903. In Britain the 12pdr/12cwt of 3in (76.2mm) bore was introduced in 1894 followed by the 12pdr/18cwt in 1905, though the Elswick and Vickers versions called 14pdr, were in *Swiftsure* and *Triumph* taken over from Chile, a year before. These British guns differed from most 3in in firing separate QF ammunition.

Gun mountings

Gun mountings varied even more than naval guns, as shown by the six ships of the *Canopus*

class, all with 12in Mk VIII guns, having three quite distinct patterns of mounting. In heavy ships the principal types of mounting were broadside (firing through ports in the hull or central battery), and turret or barbette on the upper deck with greater arcs of fire. As long as sails with heavy masts and rigging were considered necessary in steam ships, broadside mountings were favoured as it was difficult to accommodate turrets, though this was tried with limited success in the British *Monarch* (June 1869) and in a few other ships. Some French central battery ships had barbettes or half barbettes at the upper deck edge, but often unarmoured for reasons of top-weight.

The earliest British and French armoured ships still had wooden mountings, but pivoting iron slides and carriages with friction or later hydraulic controlled recoil were soon introduced. In Britain broadside mountings were hand worked, and only four ships had 11in or 12in/25-ton RMLs, 10in being otherwise the heaviest; but with hydraulic training the French managed to mount 340mm/18-calibre and /21-calibre guns in the central battery ships *Dévastation* (1882) and *Courbet* (1886), though conditions must have been cramped. Originally turrets, whether of the Coles types supported on a roller path, or of the Ericson with a central pivot, were usually limited to ships of relatively low freeboard, while barbettes which had a fixed armour ring round the revolving part of the mounting and the guns exposed when firing were in those of higher

A typical anti-torpedo boat gun and crew, a British 12pdr/12cwt aboard the pre-dreadnought Hindustan. *(By courtesy of John Roberts)*

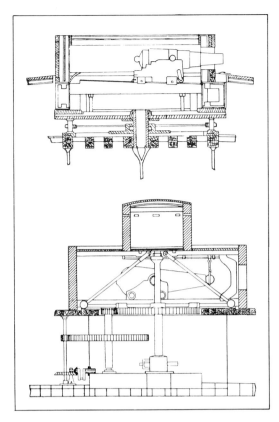

A comparison between the Coles (top) and Ericsson turrets. The former revolved on a below-deck roller path which reduced the profile and made it less vulnerable to shell damage; the latter used a centre pivot and needed to be jacked up before it could rotate.

freeboard. In most ships there was little protection below the barbette, and one of the main virtues of *Royal Sovereign* (May 1892) was that the barbette armour was taken down to the protective deck. The next step in *Majestic* (December 1895) was to add a revolving shield or gunhouse, later known as a turret, to the barbette. In both *Royal Sovereign* and *Majestic* the main loading position was still at fixed angles of training and elevation, and loading at any angle of train was not introduced until *Caesar* and *Illustrious*, the last two *Majestic*s, though the *Re Umberto*, armed by Elswick, had this feature in 1893. Loading at any elevation was in *Vengeance* (1902), the last of the *Canopus* class, and was in all ships from the *King Edward VII* class of 1905, but the advantages were less than had been thought. A controversial feature of British mountings was the large diameter of the barbettes, and it was not until the 12in/45-calibre in *Dreadnought* of 1906 that a satisfactory figure of 27ft (8.23m) internal diameter was reached.

The early turrets were trained by hand, but *Monarch* had steam training – not of the best apparently, as at the bombardment of Alexandria when thirteen years old, aiming was ac-

complished by keeping the turrets in slow rotation and firing when the sights came on. Hydraulic training was in *Inflexible* and was retained for all heavy turrets and the revolving part of barbettes.

Elevation and loading were originally by hand but hydraulic power was used from the fore turret in *Thunderer* (1877) onwards. The fore and aft 11in RML in *Temeraire* 1877 were in unique hydraulic disappearing mountings, protected by barbettes. These seem to have worked well, but were too large and heavy to be repeated.

When the USA started to increase its navy again, the Ericsson turret was long obsolete and US Navy battleships mounted turrets, and from the *Alabama* (October 1900), shielded barbettes on the British model. They were, however, electrically powered from *Kearsarge* (February 1900) onwards with recoil and run-out controlled by springs and hydraulic cylinders instead of the latter only. A peculiar feature in the *Kearsarge* class and also the *Rhode Island* class completed from 1906 was an 8in (203.2mm) twin turret fixed to the roof of the heavy calibre turret and training as a single unit. This was generally considered an unsatisfactory arrangement.

Although barbettes were generally similar, French turrets differed from British. The first as in *Cerbère* (1868) resembled the Coles type but had an armoured cylinder below, which carried the roller path. This arrangement was of British origin, due to Napier. The final type of French turret in this period was in first-line battleships from *Brennus* (1896) onwards. Details varied but there was a compact turret rigidly connected to a tube in the form of a truncated cone, which was supported just above the inner bottom by a hydraulic pivot or later by spring loaded rollers. Lateral support was provided by powerful spring rollers higher up, and a fixed armoured tube provided protection. The earlier installations were hydraulically powered but electrically in *Jauréguiberry*

A French barbette mounting as designed by Dupuy de Lôme and adopted by the Océan, *completed in 1870.*

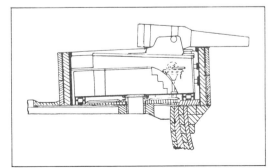

(1897), and from the *Charlemagne* class (1899) onwards, though limited to training and hoists as elevation and loading at any angle of train but a fixed angle of depression were by hand. Turrets in later Russian ships were of this general type.

Maximum elevation was usually from 10 to 15 degrees, the later British figure being 13½. Exceptions included the upper deck barbettes or half-barbettes in French central battery ships which allowed 21 to 25 degrees, apparently so that they could engage high sited coastal batteries, 25 degrees in the Italian *Regina Margherita* (1904), which had Elswick type 12in guns and mountings, and 30 degrees in *Braunschweig*. The 28.3cm (11.14in) Krupp mountings in this ship were hydraulically powered (except for hand loading), were supported on ball instead of roller races and had pusher hoists delivering shells and brass cartridges alternately.

Rates of fire were markedly increased in later British heavy guns and mountings. The 12in Mk X in *Dreadnought* could fire every 30 seconds compared with 72 seconds for the 12in Mk VIII in *Caesar*, 90 seconds for the main loading position in *Majestic*, 130 seconds for the later 13.5in barbette mountings and about 180 seconds for the earlier, including 12in and 16.25in. This last was slower than the 12.5in RML, but the figure for the 16in RML in *Inflexible* was about 4 minutes. Ships in other navies were usually slower firing, the slowest probably being the 450mm RML in *Duilio* at 7½ to 9½ minutes.

Most of the progress in mountings for smaller guns belongs to the latter part of the period. From 7.5in (190.5mm) upwards, turret mountings (using the word in its later sense) were widely used, and some navies favoured turrets for guns as small as c6in. In general these resembled simpler versions of heavy mountings. Before the introduction of QF guns, Vavasseur broadside or centre pivot mountings in which the gun recoiled up inclined slides were used in most navies, particularly the British where they were employed for nearly all 4in, 5in and 6in BL guns. They were also used for 9.2in guns up to and including the *Edgar* class, and even for the single 10in in *Victoria* and *Sans Pareil*; QF mountings and those for later BL guns were either of centre pivot (CP) or pedestal (P) type. In the former there was a roller or ball track centre pivot pin, over which the gun carriage fitted, and in the latter a pedestal with a ball race inside a top hollow in which the pivot of the gun carriage located, or else the race was at the top of the pedestal with a hollow pivot over it. The former type of P mounting was

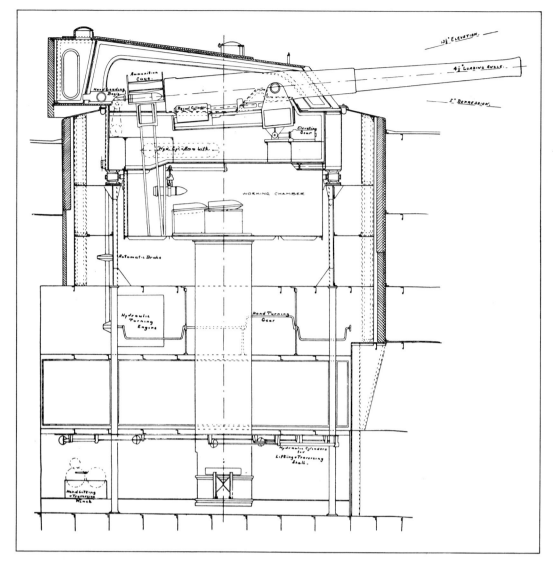

A typical pre-dreadnought barbette mounting (in the British Formidable) *for two 12in guns. The mounting was covered with an armoured hood and came to be known loosely as a turret.*

a committee of gunnery officers in the Mediterranean Fleet, the British requested Whitehead to bring two torpedoes to England and in August 1870 two 16in and two 14in were brought. Trials were satisfactory and the Admiralty paid £15,000 for 'the secret' and right of manufacture, and in 1872 production of the 16in began in the Royal Laboratory Department at Woolwich; France, Germany and China quickly followed.

The 16in Pattern B as made at Woolwich was 14ft (4.27m) long, weighed 600lb (272kg) and had a charge of 106lb (48kg) wet gun-cotton (17 per cent water). Air pressure was 800psi (56kg/cm²), with power from a two-cylinder Vee compound oscillating engine with single propeller. Ranges were between 250yds (230m) at 9½kts and 800yds (730m) at 7kts. The later Pattern A differed in having a three-cylinder Brotherhood engine and two contra-rotating propellers. Ranges were from 300yds (270m) at 12¼kts to 1200yds (1100m) at 9kts. In 1877 production of the 16in was replaced by that of the 14in Mk I and gradual improvements led to the Mk VIII in 1889. Charges were smaller than in the 16in, but performance was much improved, reaching 1000yds (910m) at 22kts in the Mk VIII with weight 706lb (320kg), charge 78.4lb (35.6kg) wet gun-cotton (22½ per cent water), and air pressure 1350psi (95kg/cm²). Later 14in with nickel-steel air vessels had pressures of 2000psi (140kg/cm²) with substantially improved performance, but these were overtaken by the introduction of the 18in (actually 450mm – 17.72in) torpedo. The first, a Whitehead Fiume, appeared in 1889 and with a 198lb wet gun-cotton charge could cover 870yds (800m) at 28.4kts. Air pressure was as in the 14in Mk VIII and weight 1236lb (561kg). At Woolwich manufacture of torpedoes was transferred to the Royal Gun Factory Department and Whitehead opened a factory at Weymouth in 1890, but did not get the quantity of Admiralty orders expected and relied mainly on exports.

Improvements in torpedoes included the addition of gyroscopes to control steering in azimuth from 1895, of net-cutters known as 'pioneers' by 1900 and in the next few years nickel-steel air vessels, noted above, and a new four-cylinder Brotherhood engine. Experiments with heaters were also in progress, but no heater torpedoes were yet in service. The original intention was to stop freezing which

favoured by Elswick and the latter by Vickers.

Early anti-torpedo craft guns were often in non-recoil mountings where the forces were absorbed by elastic deformation of the supporting structure. The first 6pdrs (57mm) in the British navy were in mountings of this type, but simplified P mountings with recoil gear were later favoured. Training and elevation were often by shoulder-piece.

Torpedoes

During the American Civil War spar torpedoes were used with limited success. In this weapon a black powder charge at the end of the spar was carried by a launch and exploded below the waterline in contact with the target. The drawbacks of this are obvious, and an Austrian Captain Giovanni Luppis conceived the idea of a spar-torpedo boat or small fireship with remote control by two ropes from the tiller. He

asked Robert Whitehead, the manager of an engine factory at Fiume, to work out the idea and a model was built, but Whitehead decided that this particular idea was not viable. However in 1866 after two years, he produced the first automobile torpedo which ran submerged. Whitehead never left a description, but it was blunt nosed with four fins for almost the whole length, was driven by compressed air at 370psi (26kg/cm²) and could cover 200yds (180m) at 6½kts. Depth, controlled by hydrostatic valve acting directly on the elevation controls, was very erratic and azimuth control was by trim tabs set by trial and error. Within two years Whitehead introduced 'the secret', a combination of hydrostat and damping pendulum, which remained virtually unchanged to 1945, and a 14in (356mm) and 16in (406mm) torpedo were demonstrated to the Austrian navy in 1868. Range was *c*700yds (640m) at 7kts. Adoption was recommended but the Austrian government refused exclusive purchase.

However in October 1869 on a report from

occurred with high pressure air, and the great increase in performance was largely unexpected. The latest torpedoes in 1906, RGF Mk VI and Fiume Mk III, were 16ft 7.4in (5.065m) long and had air pressure of 2100psi (148kg/cm²). The charge was 200lb (90.7kg) wet guncotton with ranges of 1000yds (910m) at 35kts, 2000yds (1830m) at 28.75kts, and 4000yds (3660m) at 21kts.

The torpedoes in most other navies were generally similar to the foregoing. The German firm of Schwartzkopf made excellent phosphor bronze torpedoes, fifty of which were ordered by Britain in 1885 as Woolwich and Fiume could not supply. The price was, however, 36 per cent up on Fiume.

All torpedoes so far noted were driven by compressed air, but many inventors tried other methods. Of these the only one to enter regular service afloat was the Howell in the US Navy from 1889 for almost a decade. In its final 18in form a 132lb (60kg) flywheel transmitting to twin propellers was spun to 12,000rpm before launch by a small steam turbine on the torpedo tube. It could range 800yds (730m) at 30kts and 400yds (365m) more at decreasing speed. It had the advantage of leaving no track.

Among others were the Lay torpedo of the late 1870s driven by compressed carbon dioxide, and controlled electrically by wire from ship or shore. The weapon ran awash, and was never a success though two were bought by Peru, a few by Russia for harbour defence and it was tried in Britain. Ericsson designed an electric torpedo about 1873 with the power cable unreeled from the weapon, and the Sims-Edison, supported by a float, was similar, and in 1889 one carried a 400lb (180kg) warhead over two miles. The Nordenfelt electric torpedo of about 1888 was 29in (737mm) diameter, battery propelled and guided electrically by wire paid out from the torpedo. It appears to have been supported by floats.

There were several rocket torpedoes in the 1870s and early 1880s, and one credited to Ericsson is said to have covered100yds (90m) at 61kts. The Berdan, sometimes called Borden, consisted of a floating torpedo, propelled by a

rocket fired at a turbine driving the propellers, and towing another small weapon. When the torpedo struck nets protecting the ship target, the slackening of the towline caused the small weapon to take a programmed dive under the nets and hopefully hit under the keel. Trials before the Turkish navy were not a success.

The Brennan torpedo was purchased under scandalously expensive terms by the British and was used exclusively by the Royal Engineers for the defence of important ports for about twenty years from the late 1880s. It was driven by pulling two piano wires out of the weapon by powerful steam winches on shore, the wires being unreeled from two drums in the torpedo directly driving contra-rotating propellers. Depth control was similar to Whitehead's and steering by varying the relative tension in the two wires. The torpedo was 21in (533mm) in diameter, had a 200lb (91kg) charge and range of 3000yds (2740m) at 20kts.

Mines

Unlike guns and torpedoes, the development of which continued in peace and war, mines were often neglected outside actual conflicts. In both the major naval wars of the period, the American Civil War of 1861–1865 and the Russo-Japanese of 1904–1905, mines were of very considerable importance. In the first of these, mines were used by the Confederates in attempts to stop the greatly superior Union navy in southern coastal waters and rivers. It should be noted that at this time and for some years afterwards, mines were known as 'torpedoes', and Whiteheads and similar as 'locomotive torpedoes'.

Of the Confederate moored mines, one of the best was a well caulked wooden keg with coned ends and five fuzes similar to the Jacobi type used by the Russians in the Crimean War.

An illustration from a contemporary magazine showing aspects of late nineteenth century underwater warfare. No 1 shows a steam pinnace with spar torpedoes attacking an ironclad. No 2 is an 'electrical pinnace' employed on a primitive form of minesweeping (an electrically detonated countermine is being used to clear a path through a minefield). No 3 is the reverse: a launch laying a field of electrical observation mines to protect a harbour entrance. No 4 depicts the original shape of the Whitehead torpedo.

In this a lead tube projecting from the mine had an inner glass tube containing sulphuric acid and embedded in a mixture of potassium chlorate and sugar. When the lead tube was bent by a ship striking the mine, the glass tube fractured and the resultant violent chemical reaction fired the main gunpowder charge.

Another pattern, the Singer or Fretwell mine, was a sheet iron truncated cone with a separate cast iron weight on top attached to a short chain connected at the other end to a friction tube, and firing when the weight was knocked off by impact with a ship. This particular mine suffered from corrosion problems.

The Brooks mine intended for rivers consisted of a case with c100lb (45kg) gunpowder charge on the end of a spar anchored at the other end to a heavy weight by a universal joint. Sometimes a wire was run to a nearby ground mine with a heavy charge and friction tube fired by a pull on the wire. The Brooks mine was very difficult to sweep and the ground mine served as an anti-sweeping device.

Some use was also made of ground mines fired electrically from the shore, and in some cases with gunpowder charges of 1000lb (450kg). There were several other types of Confederate mine, and among the ships sunk were the monitors Tecumseh, Patapsco and Milwaukee. In spite of these successes mines were not a priority weapon in the subsequent US Navy.

The same was true in Britain. An observation mine, fired electrically from a shore station when the enemy ship was adjudged to be in the right position, was developed by the Royal Engineers for harbour defence, and from the 1880s was carried by ships for protecting temporary bases. It was a powerful mine for its day with 602lb (273kg) wet gun-cotton (20 per cent water) charge. Electro-contact mines of similar date, where the firing battery was switched in from shore when the mines were to be made live, had much smaller charges of 91lb (41kg). Although there was experimental work on independent (ie not shore controlled) mines, it was not until 1906 that the Naval Spherical Mine entered service. It had a charge of 300lb (136kg) wet gun-cotton (22½ per cent water), but a notoriously unsatisfactory and unsafe pendulum inertia pistol.

At the time of the Russo-Japanese War, the Japanese used a spherical mine with 72lb (33kg) or possibly larger picric acid charge, and an internal battery powered firing circuit completed by movement of a pendulum. This blew up the Russian flagship Petropavlovsk and damaged several major ships, while an unmoored drifting version sank Navarin at Tsushima.

Russian mines were of truncated conical or later spherical shape, with Herz horns. These, invented in 1868, were a development of the Jacobi type noted above, but the glass tube contained battery electrolyte which activated an internal battery when the tube was broken, and fired the mine for which it was far the best method so far developed. Charges in Russian mines were 66lb (30kg) in M1877, 72lb (33kg) in M1888 and c125lb (57kg) in M1893 and M1898. All were gun-cotton. Hatsuse and Yashima were sunk on the same day, reducing the Japanese battleship numbers by a third.

Of other mines the most important was the German C/77. This was originally a controlled mine with 88lb (40kg) charge, and the first independent version was C/77 CA of 1884. This had Herz horns and hydrostatic depth taking, and was followed by the larger 1889 model with 154lb (70kg) charge. These mines had riveted pear shaped cases, but in the improved C/05 and C/06 the cases were welded with charges up to 187lb (85kg) wet gun-cotton. It was a mine of this type which sank Audacious in 1914. A special version with extra large buoyancy chamber was made for Kiaochau (Tsingtau) where currents were very strong.

Mine mooring and depth taking is a complicated subject in detail, but briefly with hydrostatic systems, mine and sinker went to the bottom together, where a soluble plug or other timing device released the mine which rose to the desired depth below the surface when the hydrostat operated a brake on the mooring wire drum. Most mines of the 1880s and later had plummet depth taking. In this British invention the mine floated on the surface while the sinker descended with a plummet and wire of length equal to the desired depth of the mine. On the plummet striking the bottom, a pawl and ratchet locked the mooring wire drum in the sinker which dragged the mine down to the desired depth.

John Campbell

Naval Guns: Typical Weapons 1860–1905

Gun	Bore inches (millimetres)	Length bore calibre	Weight of gun incl breech mechanism tons (tonnes)	Shell weight pounds (kilos)	Muzzle velocity feet (metres) per second	First in service
Great Britain						
7in RBL	7 (177.8)	14.2	4.1 (4.17)	110 (49.9)	1175 (358)	Warrior 1861
9in RML	9 (228.6)	13.9	12 (12.2)	250 (113.4)	1336 (407)	Prince Albert 1866
10in RML	10 (254)	14.5	18 (18.3)	400 (181.4)	1298 (396)	Hercules 1868
12in/25-ton RML	12 (304.8)	12	25 (25.4)	600 (272)	1180 (360)	Monarch 1869
12.5in RML Mk I	12.5 (317.5)	15.8	38 (28.6)	818 (371)	1415 (413)	Dreadnought 1879
16in RML	16 (406.4)	18	81 (82.3)	1700 (771)	1604 (489)	Inflexible 1881
12in Mks III–V	12 (304.8)	25.25	45 (45.7)	714 (324)	1914 (583)	Edinburgh 1887

Gun	Bore inches (millimetres)	Length bore calibre	Weight of gun incl breech mechanism tons (tonnes)	Shell weight pounds (kilos)	Muzzle velocity feet (metres) per second	First in service
16.25in	16.25 (412.8)	30	110.6 (112.4)	1800 (816.5)	2087 (636)	Benbow 1888
13.5in Mks I–IV	13.5 (342.9)	30	67 (68.1)	1250 (567)	2016 (614)	Rodney 1888
12in Mk VIII	12 (304.8)	35.43	46.1 (46.8)	850 (385.5)	2417 (737)	Majestic 1895
12in Mk IX	12 (304.8)	40	50.8 (51.6)	850 (385.5)	2567 (782)	Implacable 1901
12in Mk X	12 (304.8)	45	57.7 (58.6)	850 (385.5)	2725 (831)	Dreadnought 1906
6in Mk VII	6 (152.4)	44.9	7.4 (7.5)	100 (45.4)	2536 (773)	Cressy 1901
6in QF Mks I, II	6 (152.4)	40	6.6 (6.7)	100 (45.4)	1882 (574)	Royal Sovereign 1892
4.7in QF Mks I–IV	4.724 (120)	40	2.05 (2.08)	45 (20.4)	1786 (544)	Sharpshooter 1889
12pdr/12cwt Mk I	3 (76.2)	40	0.62 (0.63)	12.5 (5.67)	2259 (689)	Havock 1894
France 16cm M1860 BL	6.484 (164.7)	16.7	3.6 (3.66)	99 (45)	1055 (322)	Gloire 1861
27cm M1875 No 1	10.8 (274.4)	19.7	27.6 (28.0)	476 (16)	1640 (500)	Redoutable 1878
37cm M1875–79	14.57 (370)	28.5	71.4 (72.5)	1235 (560)	1969 (600)	Amiral Baudin 1888
34cm M1887	13.39 (340)	41.5	60.6 (61.6)	926 (420)	2559 (780)	Jemmapes 1894
30.5cm M1893	12.01 (305)	44.3	44.2 (44.9)	750 (340)	2559 (780)	Masséna 1898
30.5cm M1893–96	12.01 (305)	40	47.3 (48)	750 (340)	2674 (815)	Charlemagne 1899
30.5cm M1893–96M	12.01 (305)	40	47.3 (48)	750 (340)	2838 (865)	République 1906
Italy 45cm RML	17.72 (450)	20.49	102.25 (103.9)	2002 (908)	1673 (510)	Duilio 1880
Germany 24cm K2 RKL/20	9.27 (235.4)	16.6	14.9 (15.1)	306 (139)	1476 (450)	König Wilhelm 1869
8.8cm SKL/35	3.46 (88)	31.9	0.805 (0.818)	15.4 (7)	2526 (770)	Friedrich Carl 1903
28cm SKL/40	11.4 (283)	36.8	44.6 (45.3)	529 (240)	2690 (820)	Braunschweig 1904
USA 15in SB	15 (381)	8.7	18.6 (18.9)	440 (200)	1200 (366)	Passaic 1862

Notes:

The muzzle velocities for British RML guns are those for the original service charges. Improved charges gave the following: 12.5in Mk I 1442f/s (440m/s), 12in/25-ton 1292f/s (394m/s), 10in 1379f/s (420m/s), 9in 1440f/s (439m/s). On the other hand that for the 16in with brown powder was reduced to 1540f/s (469m/s), and for the 7in RBL to 1125f/s (343m/s) in 1863.

In *King Edward VII* (1905), muzzle velocities for the 12in Mk IX and 6in VII were increased to 2612 and 2770f/s (796, 844m/s). The muzzle velocities given for 6in and 4.7in QF are for the original gun powder charges. With cordite they were 2230 and 2125f/s (680, 648m/s).

The projectile for the French 34cm M1887 was later increased to 1080lb (490kg) with muzzle velocity 2428f/s (740m/s).

11

Warship Machinery

THIS chapter will deal with marine engineering developments as applied to naval ships. In many respects early mercantile and naval practice differed very little and the reader is directed to *The Advent of Steam* volume in this series for a more comprehensive general history of marine powerplant and auxiliaries. In some respects, however, naval applications imposed severe restrictions on machinery design resulting in some very novel arrangements indeed.

Throughout the nineteenth century naval propulsive plant was powered by steam which in turn was normally produced by the combustion of coal. Efficient power generation concerned navies just as much as it did merchant ship operators but for slightly different reasons. Whilst shipowners desired to keep coal consumption down to reduce cost, space aboard fighting ships was very much at a premium due to the larger number of personnel carried, the need for adequate armament and the stores needed to supply both of these in terms of food and ammunition. Coal for the boilers was a luxury and any device which improved operational efficiency, and so reduced coal consumption, was embraced just as enthusiastically by naval administrations as it was by the merchant shipowner.

Combustion of coal produced smoke, particularly when burned inefficiently, and whilst to the isolated merchant ship crossing an ocean such smoke was an inconvenience for passengers or seamen handling sails, for naval craft it could be much more serious. Effective communication has always been important for vessels about to engage in action but flag signals could often be obscured by smoke, thus preventing all vessels from executing desired manoeuvres at the correct time. This problem was very evident with the British Baltic Fleet when engaged in actions during the Crimean War, all ships apart from the flagship, HMS *Duke of Wellington*, burning British north country coal. The flagship steamed much better on its Welsh coal and the Admiralty ordered trials to be carried out. These proved

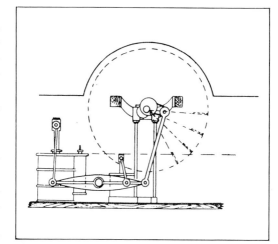

Typical layout of a side lever engine for powering early paddle warships.

that the latter was superior to any other available in Britain, thus Welsh 'steam' coal became the standard fuel for the British fleet.

Paddle steamers 1832–1850

Like their mercantile counterparts, early steam naval vessels were driven by paddle wheels and their machinery was the same as that used for merchant craft. That situation remained during the paddle era from the 1820s until the 1845 trials between HMS *Rattler* and HMS *Alecto*, and the 1849 trials between HMS *Niger* and HMS *Basilisk*, proved the superiority of screw propulsion. Early Admiralty steamers were generally used as mail packets by the post office but during the 1830s the first steam fighting vessels were constructed.

Many of the early vessels, including HMS *Dee* of 1832 and her near-sisters *Rhadamanthus*, *Salamander*, *Phoenix* and *Medea*, were propelled by side lever engines, a form of machinery much favoured for merchant craft. Although effective this plant was large and heavy, making it less than ideal for fighting ships and many engine builders sought designs which would save weight and space.

Maudslay, Sons & Field of Lambeth had a fine reputation for the construction of reliable

marine engines and that concern's work was held in high esteem by the Admiralty. Maudslay's side lever engines were second to none and Brunel selected the company to build the machinery for his first Atlantic liner, *Great Western*. However, Joshua Field and Joseph Maudslay, son of the founder, Henry Maudslay, devised an engine which overcame many of the restrictions of the side lever type. Their twin-cylinder design of 1839 quickly became known as a Siamese engine after the famous Siamese twins, Chang and Eng, then being exhibited in Britain.

Each engine unit consisted of a pair of cylinders, the piston rods of which connected to a crosshead which in turn drove the paddle shaft crank via a connecting rod. The crosshead was provided with extensions which worked in guides and it also operated condenser air pumps and feed pumps. Ships were provided with two such engine units for each shaft, the engine units usually being capable of operating in isolation from each other. The Siamese engine arrangement occupied less space than an equivalent side lever engine and it also allowed for the use of a longer piston stroke. Between the introduction of the design and 1846 nine sets of engines were constructed for Admiralty frigates, including *Retribution* and *Devastation*. It is generally accepted that HMS *Terrible* of 1845 was the finest British paddle wheel frigate and she was propelled by a set of Siamese engines which could develop in excess of 2000ihp (indicated horse power) from the 72in diameter by 96in stroke cylinders.

At about the same time that Maudslay and Field were developing their Siamese engine John Seaward was working on his design for a paddle engine. The first engine of the type was installed in HMS *Gorgon* during 1837 and because of this the name Gorgon was applied to all engines to that design. There were two cylinders for each installation, positioned vertically below the paddle shaft to the cranks of which the piston rods were attached by means of connecting rods. Just as with the side lever engine, a parallel motion mechanism ensured

A model of Maudslay's 'Siamese' engines for the paddle sloop Devastation *of 1841. (ScM)*

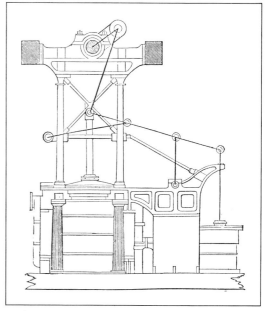

Seaward's vertical direct-acting engines of the 'Gorgon' type.

The prime disadvantage was the fact that the cylinder oscillated thus steam supply and exhaust had to take place through hollow trunnions which acted as cylinder pivots. Leakage presented constant problems particularly as steam pressure increased.

The engine builders Miller & Ravenhill and the company set up by John Penn produced oscillating engines which found favour with the Admiralty and these concerns supplied some of

Oscillating cylinder paddle engines.

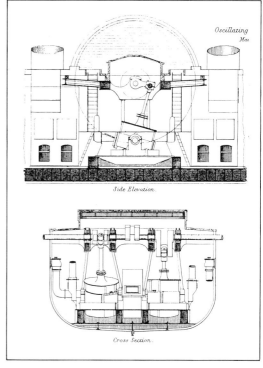

that the piston moved vertically and a system of levers also operated pumps from the piston crosshead. Jet condenser and pump cylinders occupied the same base plate as the main steam cylinders. Seaward supplied his Gorgon type engines for installation in several warships, including HMS *Sidon* of 1846. Although a Gorgon engine weighed less than a side lever engine of equivalent power, the short connecting rod which had to be used was considered to be a disadvantage and the design was not used as extensively as the side lever type or the Siamese engine.

During the 1840s several other engine builders devised paddle engines as alternatives to the side lever type and a number were tried by the Admiralty with varying degrees of success. Oscillating engines found favour because they did not require separate connecting rods, the piston rod being attached directly to the crank. That arrangement allowed for a long stroke and avoided the problems involved with connecting rod forces as well as the need for crosshead guides or parallel motion mechanisms. It was also light, compact and relatively simple compared with other paddle engines.

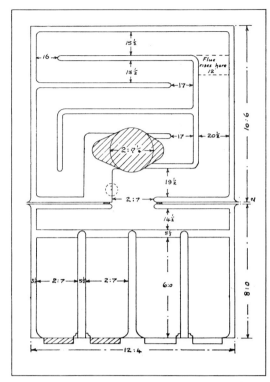

Arrangement of the flue-type boiler as constructed for HMS Comet *in 1828 by Maudslay's.*

the final paddle engines placed in British warships. During 1848 Miller & Ravenhill built the 1033ihp engines for HMS *Basilisk*, whilst Penn's engines for HMS *Valorous* of 1851 could develop 1145ihp.

Despite these develoments the paddle driven warship remained vulnerable to damage from gunfire which could render the propulsion plant useless. It had also not escaped the Admiralty that paddle boxes occupied space which could be better used for armament. Comparative trials between screw and paddle driven vessels added weight to the tactical arguments for adoption of the screw and elimination of the paddle wheel.

Early boilers were of the flue type and operated at pressure no higher than 5psi (5lb per square inch). Very little of the power developed by an engine actually resulted from the action of steam at boiler pressure acting on a piston; most of the work resulted from the fact that exhaust steam on the opposite side of the piston was at a very low pressure due to condensation. Condensing of steam was brought about by means of a jet of sea water sprayed into the condenser, hence the term jet condenser, but such action meant that sea water would find its way into the boiler as the warm contents of the condenser were used as feed water for the boiler. Salt scale impaired boiler performance and caused corrosion of the iron used for construction; actually, oxygen in the

feed water also resulted in corrosion but this effect was not discovered until later in the nineteenth century. These problems meant that early boilers had a very limited life.

The surface condensers, which kept condensing steam and cooling sea water apart, were tried in HMS *Megaera* and HMS *Penelope* during the 1830s but problems of tube blockage due to grease in the steam from lubrication of the engine cylinder, caused abandonment of the experiment. It was not until the 1860s that the concept was revived when the simple idea of passing sea water through the tubes (rather than the condensing steam) minimised the risk of blockage.

Flue type boilers constructed from flat wrought iron plates were standard for early steamers because they were relatively inexpensive but corrosion was a problem. Use of copper for boiler construction had its advantages although the cost was greater than for iron – in 1836 the copper boilers for HMS *Volcano* cost £5000, compared with £1500 for similar boilers of iron, although the copper boilers would have lasted about nine years, three times longer than those of iron. With the demand for higher steam pressures and improved efficiency it was recognised that flue boilers were unsatisfactory, which promoted development of the tubular boiler. As with paddle engines, the practice of the Royal Navy closely followed that of the commercial service, the first vessel to be fitted with a tubular boiler being the paddle frigate HMS *Penelope* when she was reboilered in 1843. Such boilers retained their

essential box shape but combustion gases passed through tubes on way to the funnel rather than through large section flues.

Screw propulsion, 1845 onwards

The real divergence of naval practice from that of the merchant fleet came about with adoption of screw propulsion. As the screw propeller was necessarily below the water it seemed reasonable that the machinery should also be placed below the waterline in order to provide a degree of protection from enemy fire. It was this requirement for low height which imposed restrictions on marine machinery builders, resulting in designs which were essentially for military use only.

Placing cylinders horizontally overcame height limitations but that solution itself caused difficulties with respect to connecting rod arrangement. A number of designs were produced but in 1858 an Admiralty Committee considered that only three types were suitable for screw propulsion of warships. All were directly connected to the propeller shaft and, like the paddle engines, all were essentially self-contained with their individual condensers and pumps on a common base plate.

In all designs steam cylinders were located on one side of the ship and condensers on the other but the limited width offered by ships of the period did not allow for a long connecting rod to be employed between crosshead and crank. A number of engine builders offered designs with short connecting rods but problems

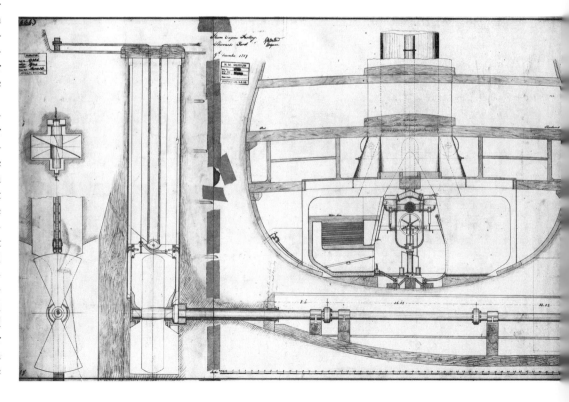

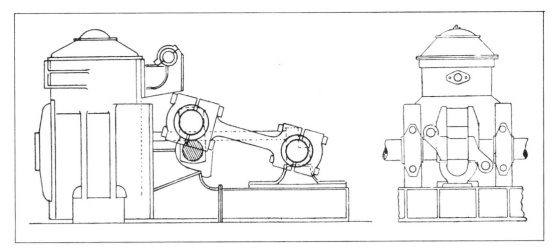

The horizontal return connecting rod type of engine.

were experienced due to the forces resulting from such short length connecting rods. However, all early horizontal screw engines for fighting ships were of this type, one of the earliest being the two-cylinder unit supplied by Maudslay, Sons & Field for the Third Rate battleship HMS *Ajax* in 1845. This wooden vessel, launched in 1809, was one of a number of similar ships converted to screw propulsion as the advantages of the screw steam ship became obvious to many at the Admiralty.

Maudslays eventually produced a return connecting rod type of engine which had two piston rods passing to a crosshead situated on the opposite side of the crankshaft. The connecting rod then 'returned' towards the cylinders in order to connect with the crank. This design allowed for a long connecting rod but it did take up a considerable amount of space and

was relatively complex, additional components also being required. One of the largest engines of this type constructed by Maudslay, Sons & Field was the two-cylinder unit for the broadside ironclad HMS *Agincourt* in 1865. With a steam pressure of 30psi the two 101in diameter by 54in stroke cylinders could develop some 6660ihp.

The 1858 committee on engines for the Royal Navy considered that, in terms of small engines, the single piston rod design with short crankshaft as produced by Humphrys, Tennant & Dykes was ideal. Relatively high powers could be obtained from such an engine if cylinders were of large diameter; however, the stroke had to be short in order to avoid problems associated with the short connecting rod. Humphrey's two-cylinder, 2121ihp engine provided for the turret ship HMS *Prince Albert*

in 1864 had pistons of 72in diameter and 36in stroke, the connecting rods being only 63in long. Double acting condenser air extraction pumps, bilge pumps and boiler feed pumps were driven directly from rods connected to the pistons.

Penn's solution to the horizontal engine design problem was to provide a long connecting rod attached to the piston. A circular trunk fitted to the piston allowed for movement of the connecting rod, that trunk being like a hollow piston rod which projected through the covers at both ends of the cylinder. It was necessary to increase cylinder diameter slightly in order to compensate for the reduction in effective piston area due to the trunk but that was no particular problem. The large cylinder head glands through which the trunk passed were more likely to leak than the small diameter gland of a conventional piston rod engine. One of the earliest engines of the type was provided for HMS *Arrogant* in 1848 and Penn's trunk engines became very popular for naval craft until the adoption of vertical cylinders. Selection of the Penn trunk engine for HMS *Warrior* was a compliment to the builder and the design as the Royal Navy could not afford failure in its first ironclad. Survival of the ship and its ultimate restoration not only allows the ingenuity of Penn's design to be appreciated but it also gives an insight into the cramped working conditions of the early naval marine engineers.

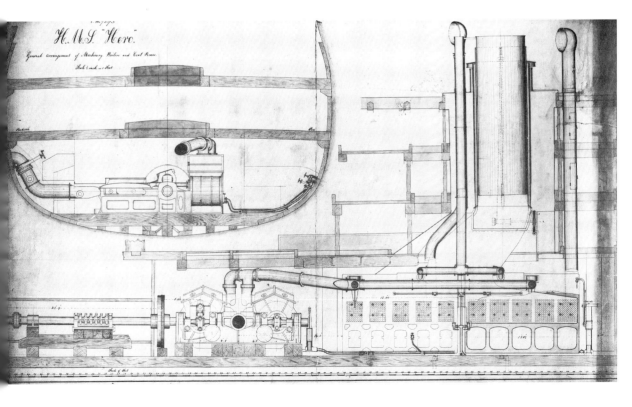

A typical machinery arrangement in a screw line of battleship (HMS Hero of 1858). The two-cylinder Maudslay return connecting rod engines developed 2662ihp on trials for 11.7kts. Steam was supplied by rectangular firetube boilers, and the screw was fitted with hoisting gear, so as not to impede the ship when under sail. (NMM)

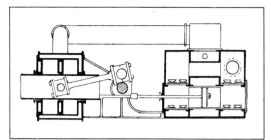

Penn's trunk engine with jet condenser.

Other builders also made engines of the three types mentioned and whilst details of construction varied, the general principle did not. Similar situations existed with overseas navies, particularly the French where competition with the potential British enemy was especially keen. Return crank and trunk piston engines found favour amongst its naval designers.

Compound engines and twin screws, 1860–1875

The designs mentioned above were of the simple type in which steam was expanded only in a single cylinder before being directed to exhaust. Experiments had been conducted with respect to compounding but an increase in boiler pressure was considered necessary. Commercial steamship owners began to embrace this newer technology towards the mid-1860s but in naval circles there appears to have been a certain understandable reluctance to follow. Compounding reduced coal consumption and that was an advantage to the shipowner who operated on long routes and to areas where local coal supplies could not be obtained, but there was a price to be paid in terms of more complex machinery and in operating boilers at higher pressure. On the relatively short trans-Atlantic route compounding did not find favour until the 1870s and during the 1860s the Admiralty had no good reason to believe that all new tonnage should be provided with compound engines.

Although a number of troopships had been fitted with compounds and produced some very good results, there was little enthusiasm for the new technology despite a successful trial in 1865. When the wooden sailing frigates *Arethusa*, *Octavia* and *Constance* were converted to screw ships, the engines for the first two were of simple expansion type but the Randolf & Elder engine for HMS *Constance* was a six-

cylinder vee-form compound. Trial results gave *Arethusa* and *Octavia* coal consumption figures of 3.64 and 3.17lbs per ihp per hour respectively but *Constance* required only 2.51. However, the compound engines were complicated, difficult to handle and unreliable, so the idea did not gain immediate favour.

Fortunately some people still believed in the advantages of the compound system and five *Amazon* class wooden corvettes were provided with compound engines by different manufacturers, during 1868–69. The specification called for engines of 2100ihp with boilers working at 60psi. Maudslays provided a four-

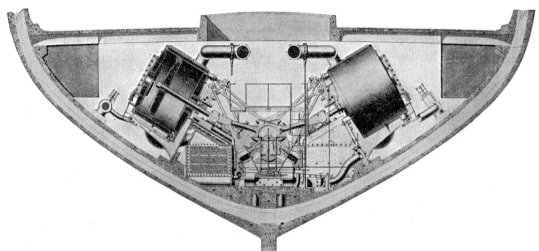

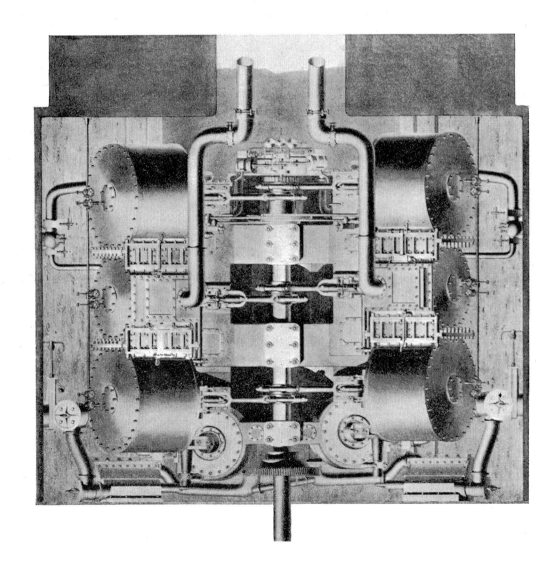

The six-cylinder compound engines by Randolph & Elder fitted to the screw frigate HMS *Constance of 1863.*

A model of the boiler room of HMS Thunderer, *a sister of* Devastation *and one of the last Royal Navy ships to have the old-style rectangular boilers. This model was made to demonstrate the effects of an explosion during her July 1876 trials, but shows the form of the boiler very well.* (ScM)

cylinder return crank engine for HMS *Sirius*, pairs of HP (high pressure) and LP (low pressure) cylinders being in tandem. Elders supplied a two-cylinder engine for HMS *Tenedos*, HP and LP cylinders being positioned side by side. HMS *Spartan*'s engine, to a rather complex design by A E Allen, proved to be the most unsatisfactory but the Rennie engine for HMS *Briton* was very economical and pointed the way to future development. Over a six-hour trial period coal consumption amounted to 1.98lbs/ihp/hour, the best figure obtained from any naval steam engine to that date.

From the early 1870s compound engines became the norm for new naval construction as it was quickly realised that the increased space required for the engine was more than offset by the reduction in bunker space. Problems associated with compound machinery had been eliminated by this time, the navy taking advantage of experience gained in commercial practice. Increased boiler pressure required for the efficient operation of compound engines could not be obtained from the rectangular type tubular boiler as flat surfaces could not readily support the forces involved. Development of the elliptical, and subsequently cylindrical, boiler followed closely merchant ship practice except that boilers for naval vessels had to be located completely below the waterline. The rectangular boiler remained popular until the 1870s, those provided for HMS *Thunderer*, launched in 1872 and completed in 1876, being the last of the type fitted in a British capital ship. Development of better steels and the use of ideas such as the corrugated furnace allowed designers to plan boilers capable of withstanding higher pressure, thus enabling the triple expansion engine to be subsequently introduced.

Although each introduction improved on earlier ideas, most changes were gradual since the Admiralty could not allow machinery considerations to compromise a vessel's fighting qualities. Space for machinery was always at a premium and each advance, although it might reduce coal consumption, tended to increase overall engine dimensions. In order to improve operating efficiency steam jacketing of cylinders was employed with many engines, including those for paddle driven steamers. Fresh water provision was more of a problem on

naval ships than on commercial steamers simply because of the larger crew carried, and some ships were fitted with piping to pass the condensate from the cylinder jackets to fresh water storage tanks. With the advent of higher pressure boilers it became necessary to use fresh water for feed purposes, so the jet condenser had to be abandoned and the surface condenser reintroduced.

By itself the surface condenser was little use as few ships had sufficient fresh water storage capacity for a voyage of even reasonable duration. A requirement existed for the production of potable fresh water on board ship and if condensate from cylinder jackets could be used as fresh water there was no reason why fresh water could not be made on board using evaporation and distillation plants. During the late 1870s and early 1880s several designs were produced and the navy quickly adopted the idea as it not only enabled boiler feed water to be produced but it also allowed for the making of drinking water. This latter point became in-

creasingly important as it allowed Royal Navy steamships to operate further from home waters and friendly ports where supplies could be obtained.

HMS *Devastation* of 1871 marked a major change in terms of machinery in the Royal Navy as she was the first mastless capital ship; for the first time steam power was all that was available. Her surface condensing, horizontal, simple expansion engines by John Penn were of conventional form but there were two sets – *Devastation* was a twin-screw ship. Twin screws provided for better manoeuvrability but they also allowed some safeguard against possible machinery breakdown. Twin screws had been fitted to a number of vessels during the 1860s but *Devastation* and her sister *Thunderer* had no sails to rely on and with them the age of steam can be considered as having truly arrived. Although single-screw fighting ships were still built for a few more years, propulsion for large warships from then onwards was by means of multiple screws.

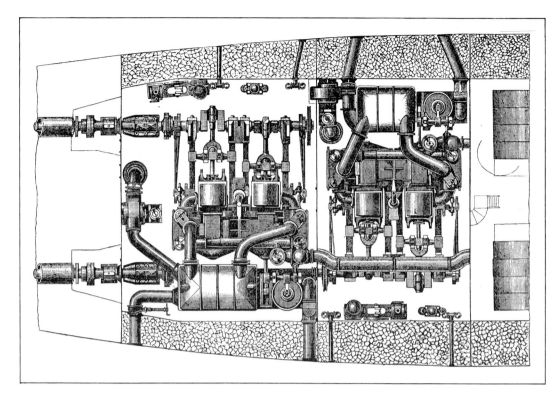

Vertical triple expansion engines, 1876–1905

Increased speed and larger ships demanded higher powers but horizontal engines had to be placed one in front of the other, resulting in longer engine rooms. This hampered the effectiveness of the ship as a fighting unit to some extent and the only solution was to position engines side by side as was usual in merchant ship practice. This meant that engine cylinders had to be positioned vertically, but although height restrictions still applied there was no longer any need to keep machinery completely below the waterline as better arrangements of armour had been devised.

The first large vessel to be provided with vertical compound engines was the battleship HMS *Inflexible* of 1876. Her design incorporated a huge central cofferdam which offered protection for boilers and machinery whilst armour plating and cork-lined chambers added

Arrangement of a three-cylinder triple expansion engine.

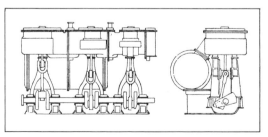

to the protective screen. *Inflexible*'s boilers were of the oval type, both single- and double-ended, and they operated at 60psi pressure. Each engine had a single 70in diameter HP cylinder and two 90in diameter LP cylinders, the stroke being 48in; total power potential was 8483ihp.

If the propulsion machinery of *Inflexible* was impressive, her auxiliary plant was more so as it comprised no less than eighty auxiliary engines. These were used for the usual pumping purposes but steam power also operated the steering gear, the capstan, ventilation fans and boat hoisting gear. In addition, power was applied to the armament area with steam and hydraulic machinery being employed for working gun turrets, hoisting shot and loading guns. *Inflexible* can be said to have perfected steam as a weapon of war. Steam also generated electricity and naval applications of this new power form followed closely that of merchant ship practice in that its earliest use was for lighting. In 1881 *Inflexible* had an 80-volt dynamo installed for powering searchlights. Soon electricity provided lighting in engine rooms and other working spaces, these being priority areas in a fighting ship.

Once the change to vertical engines had taken place, rapid strides were made in the development of engines along the lines of merchant ship propulsion, the only difference being that naval engines had shorter piston strokes in order to restrict engine height. The steamer *Aberdeen* proved the value of triple ex-

pansion engines during 1881 but it took some time for the advantages to be translated into practice as far as the Admiralty – and a number of passenger liner companies – were concerned. The apparent reluctance is more imaginary than real as it takes time for ideas to be translated into new ships, whether it be for naval or commercial use, and the engine builders also had to develop their own forms of triple expansion engine. Although the idea of expanding steam in three successive stages was not subject to a patent, the way in which those cylinders were arranged could be, and most engine builders were unwilling to pay royalties when they could design their own engines.

HMS *Sans Pareil* of 1885 had two three-cylinder triple expansion engines developing a total of 14,483ihp from steam at 135psi, cylinder diameters being 43in, 62in, 96in and stroke 51in. Steel was extensively used for engine and boiler construction and there was a further increase in the provision of auxiliary power as no less than ninety-two auxiliary engines were installed. Cylindrical boilers, of a form subsequently known as 'the Scotch boiler', were provided in order to withstand the high pressure.

Forced draught and water-tube boilers, 1880–1905

To produce more steam from a given size of boiler was possible if more coal could be burned, but the combustion of more coal required additional oxygen which could be obtained if air was supplied to the boiler under pressure. Thus the concept of forced draught was born. Several schemes were devised and the idea was introduced to naval ships in 1877 when Thornycroft built the torpedo boat HMS *Lightning*. In 1882, not much later than it had been applied to big commercial steamers, forced draught was specified for large warships. Quickly the navy standardised on the closed stokehold form of forced draught, whereas merchant ships tended to favour the closed ashpit system.

High outputs from the smaller naval boilers tended to cause problems particularly with respect to tube leakage. Redesign of combustion chambers and the use of ferrules for protecting the ends of tubes reduced the problems but the latter increased total cost. Despite problems, boiler pressure and rates of forced

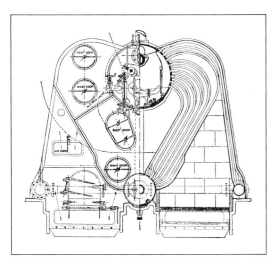

Thornycroft small-tube boiler of the type used in the early TBD Daring.

draught increased throughout the 1880s and there was no going back to the old system of open stokeholds. Doubts existed about the reliability of boilers for modern warships and in 1892 a design committee was appointed to consider the matter. Reporting later that year the committee emphasised the economy gained by the use of triple expansion engines and high pressure boilers, indicating an improvement at full power of 21 per cent compared with a compound engined ship employing steam at 60psi. Whilst recommending design improvements to overcome boiler problems, including a slight reduction in the rate of forced draught, the committee hinted that the day of the cylindrical boiler for naval purposes was drawing to a close and advised the testing of water-tube boilers without delay.

Water-tube boilers of assorted design had been tried in Royal Navy steamers for many years, an extensive series of trials being given to the type devised by Captain Cochrane between 1865 and 1870, but the first successful installation was that by Thornycroft in torpedo boat *No 100* during 1885. Several other torpedo boat installations followed and people began to consider the advantage of water-tube boilers for larger vessels. Naval requirements with respect to boilers differed somewhat from merchant steamers, not least being in respect of size and weight. A water-tube boiler for the same steaming capacity could be much smaller than a cylindrical boiler; in addition it contained less water and hence was appreciably lighter, thus reducing the overall machinery weight. Higher pressures were also possible, allowing for increased power from smaller engines, but the water-tube boiler also offered increased flexibility with respect to steaming. During times of peace warships tended to

steam at low speeds for the majority of the time and trials indicated that water-tube boilers could deal more economically with such conditions. A large number of relatively small units in different boiler rooms allowed for the shutting down of boilers not needed, but in an emergency the water-tube boiler could reach steaming pressure much more quickly than its cylindrical counterpart.

During 1894 a decision was made to fit the very large cruisers HMS *Powerful* and HMS *Terrible* with forty-eight Belleville water-tube boilers following successful trials in the re-boilered gunboat HMS *Sharpshooter*. This French designed boiler had a very good record in the Gallic merchant and naval fleets, having been originally designed during the 1850s. The boilers of *Powerful* and her sister worked at a pressure of 260psi, allowing the two triple expansion engines of each ship to develop 25,648ihp. Other Belleville boiler installations followed, but they proved to be somewhat troublesome in service and overall performance fell short of that promised in early trials. However, there were few alternatives available during the early 1890s, but other designers soon set to work when they realised the rewards to be had from large naval orders.

In 1900 the Admiralty appointed a committee to investigate water-tube boilers and an interim report submitted in 1901 suggested that

The Belleville boiler, one of the earliest practical water-tube installations. It was employed in French warships from 1879.

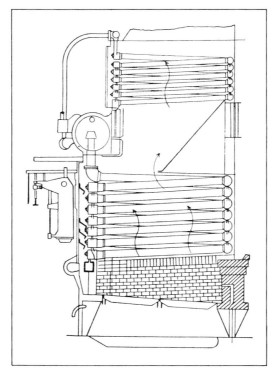

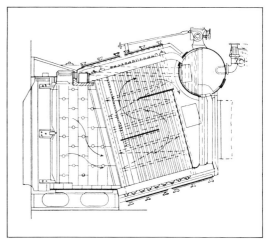

The Babcock & Wilcox boiler that largely superseded the Belleville in Royal Navy service.

the Belleville boiler be abandoned except for ships already too advanced in construction. It was further suggested that Yarrow or Babcock boilers be used for all future capital ships. Yarrow and Babcock boilers provided steam for the British fleet until the advent of gas turbine propulsion.

Coal-firing of boilers had many disadvantages but there was no real alternative until the commercial exploitation of oilfields came about during the latter half of the nineteenth century. In 1888 Admiral Fisher stated that the use of oil fuel would increase the Royal Navy's efficiency by 50 per cent and although there were sceptics some experimentation did take place. The destroyer HMS *Surly* was fitted out for oil fuel trials in 1898, and more detailed investigation took place between 1902 and 1905 when an in-depth research programme was carried out at Haslar, ultimately leading to the conversion of the fleet to oil-firing a number of years later. Fisher's arguments in favour of oil fuel included increased performance and endurance, easier stowage and transportation to the boilers, ease of refuelling, less manpower required, better response to the demand for steam, and improved availability of supplies overseas. That Fisher was proved correct is a matter of history beyond the scope of this brief chapter, but the substitution of imported oil for domestically produced coal had important strategic implications. Other navies were similarly involved in experimenting with oil fuel: in 1898 the Russians built a capital ship with half of the boilers fired by coal and the other half using oil, whilst the same year the French constructed a submarine with oil-fired water-tube boilers. Despite the high steam pressure available from water-tube boilers, the Royal Navy made no move towards the adoption of quadruple expansion engines even for

A four-cylinder triple expansion engine of 6250ihp for the battleship HMS Triumph *of 1903 built by Vickers-Armstrong.*

its most powerful ships. Amongst the largest, and final, triple expansion engines to be fitted in British battleships were those provided for the *Duncan* class vessels completed in 1903–4. Each of the two engines could develop in excess of 9100ihp from a boiler pressure of 300psi; HP cylinders were 33.5in diameter, the IP (intermediate pressure) cylinders 54.5in diameter, but in order to keep dimensions within limits two 63in diameter LP cylinders were fitted to each.

Rotational speed of large engines rose to about 125rpm (revolutions per minute) but engines driving torpedo boat destroyers and gunboats operated at much higher speeds. Effective lubrication of bearings is a problem at high speeds and the torpedo boat destroyer HMS *Syren* of 1899 was provided with engines having enclosed crankcases and forced lubrication. With the turn of the century the age of the reciprocating engine was drawing to a close as the turbine offered the possibility of providing high power from a lighter and more compact unit. For naval purposes these were the main criteria but for merchant duties the reciprocating engine remained the prime source of propulsive power until the advent of geared turbines.

Advent of the steam turbine, 1900–1905

In 1899, soon after Parsons had demonstrated the advantage of the steam turbine with *Turbinia*, the Admiralty ordered that HMS *Viper*, one of a number of destroyers then building, be fitted with turbines. Other turbine driven destroyers quickly followed and in 1902 HMS *Eden* was given separate main and cruising turbines. As experience proved the advantage of the turbine its adoption for larger ships was inevitable and the 1905 decision to install turbines in the battleship HMS *Dreadnought* marked a new dawn in naval propulsion. The only fundamental changes from that time until the present day have been the introduction of gearing and the replacement of steam by a different working fluid in the gas turbine.

Why Britain as marine engineering leader?

Much of this chapter has dealt with engineering developments in the British fleet but this is not to denigrate the efforts of other nations.

For most of the period covered by this chapter the French and British had been fierce rivals whilst towards the end Germany would be at war with both of these nations. Other European countries also developed major steam fleets, as did America, from the 1880s. However, as far as engineering was concerned, Britain made the running for most of the nineteenth century. British shipyards and marine engineering workshops had built an enviable reputation for innovation and quality, reliable products which others could only copy. Whilst France and Germany had aspirations towards industrialisation the engineering flair of the British resulted in orders for commercial steamers from both of these nations and many others. The fact that Britain had a large and expanding mercantile fleet certainly resulted in innovation as shipyards and engine builders competed for orders. The rate at which main and auxiliary machinery developed during the latter half of the nineteenth century was unprecedented and has probably not been matched since. Such a large commercial shipping base helped support military work and many of the ideas developed for use in naval steamers were based upon mercantile practice.

It would have been unthinkable for France or Germany, or any other potential enemy for that matter, to have its warships constructed in Britain no matter how advanced its marine en-

gineering industry. The potential gravity of the situation was not lost on the rulers of such countries and steps were taken to develop home-based shipbuilding and marine engineering. In the granting of mail subsidies governments imposed conditions with respect to quality and in the 1880s it became necessary for any ship in receipt of a French government subsidy to be constructed under supervision. Whilst construction abroad was still allowed conditions were so restrictive that such adventures were prohibitive. A similar situation existed with respect to German express mail steamers and the final German express Atlantic mail liner constructed in Britain was *Lahn*, built for North German Lloyd by Fairfields on the Clyde in 1888.

No nation could develop a thriving and innovative shipbuilding or marine engineering industry on the basis of government orders alone; there would simply be insufficient work. Only extensive commercial operations could generate sufficient funds for development and in the nineteenth century Britain was able to command the major share of the world's shipbuilding orders. Other nations followed and copied, but lessons were learned and by the turn of the century Britain was no longer undisputed master of marine engineering practice.

Denis Griffiths

Bibliography

Compiled by Robert Gardiner, with the assistance of the contributors.

GENERAL

These works are the best available sources of basic data, either on steam warships generally, or on the ships of a specific navy, for the 1815–1905 period. In most respects, the second half of the period is better served than the first.

EDWARD C FISHER *et al* (eds), *Warship International* (Toledo, Ohio, quarterly since 1964).
From humble beginnings as a club magazine, '*WI* (not to be confused with *Warship* – see below) has become an important periodical for warship studies, publishing many major features. The early issues were particularly strong on nineteenth century subjects. The most relevant are listed in individual sections below.

SHIZUO FUKUI, *Japanese Naval Vessels Illustrated, 1869–1945. Vol 1: Battleships and Battlecruisers* (Tokyo 1974).
A magnificently complete collection of photographs; text and captions in Japanese but some data in English. The companion volume on cruisers is also relevant.

ROBERT GARDINER and EUGENE KOLESNIK (eds), *Conway's All the World's Fighting Ships 1860–1905* (London 1979).
A pioneering work listing all the major warships between the introduction of the ironclad and the *Dreadnought*, in considerable detail, although some minor craft and auxiliaries are excluded. The introductory essays to each navy are useful resumés of economic, political and technical developments. Work on the much needed 1815–1859 volume has been under way for some years but its publication has not yet been announced.

ERICH GRÖNER (updated by DIETER JUNG and MARTIN MAASS), *Die Deutschen Kriegsschiffe 1815–1945*, 8 vols (Munich and Koblenz 1982–).
The most comprehensive work on German warships, covering every craft of remotely military significance. Data rather than evaluation, but useful sections on handling and seaworthiness. Very difficult to use but being translated in a less abstruse form as *German Warships 1815–1945* (2 vols published to date, London 1990 and 1991).

WILLIAM HOVGAARD, *A Modern History of Warships* (London 1920; reprinted 1971).
Written by a prominent naval architect, this is probably the best of the older-style general introductions to warship development, with good summaries of machinery, weapons, armour, and even the 'novelties' of the time, the submarine and the aircraft.

FRED T JANE *et al* (eds), *Jane's Fighting Ships* (London, annually since 1898).
The best known naval reference work, but fairly thin on information in its early years; where available, modern studies supersede *Jane's* in every respect.

FRED T JANE, *The Imperial Russian Navy* (London 1899, 1904; reprinted 1983).
A journalistic contemporary survey of the ships, personnel and training of the Czarist navy, radically revised after its defeat at the hands of the Japanese.

——, *The Imperial Japanese Navy* (London 1904; reprinted 1984).
A companion volume to the above.

H JENTSCHURA, D JUNG and P MICKEL, *Warships of the Imperial Japanese Navy 1869–1945* (London 1977).
A well illustrated reference book on the characteristics of Japanese warships, including very small craft and auxiliaries.

A NANI and GIORGIO GIORGERINI, *Le Navi di Linea Italiane 1861–1961* (Rome 1962).
The official history of Italian battleships; well detailed but not very analytical.

——, *Gli Incrociatori Italiani 1861–1975* (Rome, 1975).
In the same series as the above, and the same reservations apply. Covers cruisers.

ANTONY PRESTON *et al* (eds), *Warship* (London, quarterly 1977–88, annually since then).
One of the two important periodicals in the field, this journal pioneered a more sophisticated approach to the study of warship history. Has published many significant articles, relevant titles being listed in specific sections below.

STEPHEN S ROBERTS, 'The Imperial Chinese Steam Navy, 1862–1895', *Warship International* XI/1 (1974).
An important article on an obscure and neglected force.

MYRON J SMITH, JR, *Battleships and Battle Cruisers, 1884–1984: A Bibliography and Chronology* (New York and London 1985).
A monumental listing of some 5500 published items relating to capital ships, including pre-dreadnoughts.

H W WILSON, *Battleships in Action*, 2 vols (London 1926; reprinted 1969).
There are few detailed accounts of the naval warfare of the later nineteenth century and this is probably the best. A revised and expanded version of *Ironclads in Action* (1896), although omitting some material, it covers the period from the introduction of armour to the First World War. Particularly useful for some of the more obscure conflicts like those in South America or the Sino-Japanese War.

INTRODUCTION

The nineteenth century naval technical revolution has, before now, never been considered in its entirety. In consequence the historical record is of variable quality. The books listed below under individual chapters all provide information on specific areas. Some cover naval policy in general, and these are often useful in gaining an insight into why certain technologies were pursued. This book attempts to reflect the latest thinking on warship development, and to place it in the proper historical context. In this respect it should be noted that political, international, economic, social and industrial history have a great deal to offer the serious student of warship design. It is of little consequence when or if any nation adopted new technology: what is important is *why*. American warship designs make little sense, unless they are examined alongside an atlas of the Atlantic Ocean, and a recollection that Washington DC was captured by the British in 1814. Similarly, the inability of France to compete with Britain as a seapower does not reflect some inherent defect in French decision-making, but a complex of factors from industrial weakness to the dominance of the land frontier in defence policy. Seapower has many uses, and individual nations develop strategic programmes to reflect their particular interests. In this respect the best introduction to the period will be found in a solid account of nineteenth century international relations, and pursued through national histories.

J C K DALY, *Russian Seapower and 'The Eastern Question'* (London 1991).
Limited in scope, but provides real insight into Russian naval policy and problems.

K J HAGAN, *In Peace and War* (Westport, Conn 1984).
Offers a series of solid essays on the nineteenth century American navies.

E H JENKINS, *A History of the French Navy* (London 1973).
Covers the period, but in no great detail.

PAUL KENNEDY, *The Rise and Fall of British Naval Mastery* (London 1976).
Remains the best introduction to the period for Britain. It is open to serious reservations, but has yet to be replaced.

D W MITCHELL, *A History of Russian and Soviet Seapower* (London 1974).
Little more than a bare chronology.

The Introduction of Steam

Published studies on this subject vary in quality and accuracy. Those listed below offer a variety of approaches to the major issues involved. Few are entirely given over to a study of the ships themselves. There is still no modern study of the introduction of steam into the Royal Navy, or of relations between the Navy and the civilian sector that provided machinery and often design expertise. Consequently many general histories merely repeat the antiquarian curiosities listed in contemporary accounts. The Brown, Canney and Roberts titles below are the best corrective to this approach.

General histories of steam engineering: Several works on the career of James Watt mention steamships, but there is, as yet nothing on the career of James Watt, Jr, an active steamship pioneer, and on the later history of Boulton & Watt as naval contractors. The papers of Maudslay, Son & Field were destroyed in 1900, and little more remains of the other Thames-side engineers. Among the other engineers to work with the navy, I K Brunel, despite the ridiculous account of his relations with the Admiralty in the 1840s provided by his son, and repeated by Rolt, made a major contribution to the successful introduction of the screw propeller.

Archival sources for the Royal Navy in this period are less full than might be expected, having been 'weeded' in haphazard fashion around 1900, at a time when early steamships were too recent to be of interest. Fortunately the draught collection at the National Maritime Museum is more complete.

C J BARTLETT, *Great Britain and Seapower: 1815– 1852* (Oxford 1963).
The classic study of naval policy in the period. The treatment of steam requires revision, but stands as a useful introduction.

D K BROWN, *Before the Ironclad: The Development of Ship Design, Propulsion and Armament in the Royal Navy, 1815–1860* (London 1990).
The modern account of the design and development of British warships in this period.

DONALD L CANNEY, *The Old Steam Navy: Frigates, Sloops, and Gunboats 1815–1885* (Annapolis, Maryland 1990).
The first part of what promises to be an excellent study of all steam warships built for the USN; the ironclad and torpedo boat section should be published in 1993.

ADMIRAL SIR P COLOMB, *Memoirs of Admiral Sir Astley Cooper Key* (London 1898).
Excellent biography of a pioneering steam officer, who rose to become First Sea Lord and exercise a major influence on design and procurement into the 1880s.

JOHN FINCHAM, *A History of Naval Architecture* (London 1851).
Despite his central role in the 1840s Fincham is an unreliable witness. The politics of naval construction in this troubled era leave many of his statements open to question.

BASIL GREENHILL and ANN GIFFARD, *The British Assault on Finland: A Forgotten Naval War* (London 1988).
The Baltic campaigns of 1854 and 1855; steam-powered coastal warfare.

C DE SAINT HUBERT, 'Early Spanish Steam Warships.' *Warship International* XX/4 (1983), XXI/1 (1984).

INTERNATIONAL COMMISSION FOR MILITARY HISTORY, *Proceedings of the Athens Conference 24–31 August 1985*.
Contains brief essays on the early steamships of several navies that provide the best, or in some cases the only, account in English.

ANDREW LAMBERT, *The last Sailing Battlefleet: Maintaining Naval Mastery 1815–1850* (London 1991).
The politics and tactics of the period in which the steam warship came of age. Includes work on the coastal warfare strategy of the Royal Navy.

SAMUEL E MORISON, *Old Bruin: Commodore Matthew C Perry* (Boston 1967).
One of the USN's pioneer steamship officers, who commanded during the Mexican War, and opened up Japan with his black ships.

ADMIRAL SIR C NAPIER, *The Navy* (London 1851).
This collection of letters contains several relating to Napier's work with steamships. However, the record is incomplete, and the texts have not been accurately transcribed.

STEPHEN S ROBERTS, 'The Introduction of Steam Technology into the French Navy: 1818–1852', unpublished PhD thesis, University of Chicago 1976.
A major contribution to any understanding of the period, based on the French archives.

CAPTAIN SIR JOHN ROSS, *A Treatise on Navigation by Steam: and an essay towards a System of Naval Tactics peculiar to Steam Navigation* (London 1828).
A worthy pioneering effort in the field by an officer on intelligence and some experience.

A W SKEMPTON, 'A History of the Steam Dredger', *Transactions of the Newcomen Society* 47 (19   ).
A solid study of the pioneer steamships.

L SONDHAUS, *The Habsburg Empire and the Sea: Austrian Naval Policy 1797–1866* (Louisiana 1989).
Contains a well researched discussion of the problems of minor seapowers in responding to steam.

H P SPRATT, *The Birth of the Steamboat* (London 1958).
A brief, well informed summary of early developments by the then Curator at the Science Museum.

J TANN (ed), *The Selected Papers of Boulton and Watt* (London 1981), Vol 1.
The limited coverage of steamships only hints at the riches that lie in this unique collection.

The Screw Propeller Warship

The lack of any solid sources for a life of Francis Pettit Smith has left modern scholarship with an enigma at the heart of any study of the screw propeller. The footnotes to this chapter indicate the fragmentary and widespread nature of the existing material. Ericsson, by contrast, left a major archive.

FRANZ BILZER, '*Kaiser*, Linienschiff und Kasemattschiff der k (u) k Kriegsmarine', *Marine – Gestern Heute* (1983).

W C CHURCH, *The Life of John Ericsson* (London 1891), 2 vols.

Standard apologist biography by his American champion. Helps to create the image of the engineer as high minded hero of science, although Ericsson himself was obsessed by money and far from universally successful.

ANDREW LAMBERT, *Battleships in Transition: the Creation of the Steam Battlefleet 1815–1850* (London 1984).
A study of naval policy and decision making on this critical issue.

——, 'The Royal Navy and the Introduction of the Screw Propeller, 1837–1847', in S FISHER (ed.), *Innovation in Shipping and Trade* (Exeter 1989).
A revisionist approach to the old myth that the Royal Navy obstructed or ignored technology in the first half of the nineteenth century.

——, *The Crimean War: British Grand Strategy against Russia 1853–1856* (Manchester 1990).
An assessment of the Crimean War as a world-wide conflict with Russia, in which steam-powered amphibious and naval forces played the critical role.

ANTONY PRESTON and JOHN MAJOR, *Send a Gunboat!* (London 1967).
The gunboat as a weapon and a symbol of Victorian naval policy. Does not give due weight to the intended role of coastal craft in a major war, but otherwise an excellent introduction.

Iron Hulls and Armour Plate

One of the few issues in this period to attract serious interest. There is a wide range of work, although few are based on archival work. From earlier sections, see also Bilzer, Brown, Church, Lambert (*Crimea*), Morison, Sondhaus, Spratt.

J P BAXTER, *The Introduction of the Ironclad Warship* (Cambridge, Mass 1933).
Still the basic text, although dated. Undervalues European experience and developments at the expense of American efforts; concludes with the *Monitor – Virginia* action.

J CHANTRIOT, 'La Frégate-cuirassée *la Gloire*', in *Marine et Technique au XIXᵉ Siècle* (Paris 1988).
A solid account of this pioneer ironclad.

ANDREW LAMBERT, *Warrior: The World's First Ironclad* (London 1987).
A study of the origins and reconstruction of the most important of the early ironclads.

JOHN H MABER, 'The Iron Screw Frigate *Greenock*', *Warship* 23 & 24 (1982).

THEODORE ROPP, *The Development of a Modern Navy: French Naval Policy 1871–1904* (Annapolis 1987).
Pioneering PhD thesis from the 1930s finally published. Some of the technical and ship design conclusions are at best of dubious value, but overall an impressive study.

F M WALKER, 'Precision Construction: Iron's contribution to Modern Shipbuilding', in *Metals in Shipbuilding*, papers of the Conference of the Historical Metallurgy Society (London 1990).
An introduction to the use of iron in the early nineteenth century.

THE AMERICAN CIVIL WAR

Although publications on the naval side of the war between the States are extensive, those dealing with technical aspects are quite limited, and heavily biased towards the ironclads, a trend set by Baxter (see above). The new multi-volume history of *The Old Steam Navy* by Canney has started well with his volume on frigates, sloops and gunboats (listed above) and another on ironclads is in prospect.

EDWIN C BEARSS, *Hardluck Ironclad: The Sinking and Salvage of the Cairo* (Baton Rouge, Louisiana 1980).

S B BEESE, *US Ironclad Monitor* (Newport News, Virginia 1936).

——, *CS Ironclad Virginia* (Newport News, Virginia 1937).
Mariners' Museum monographs with modelmaking data.

LESLIE S BRIGHT *et al*, *CSS Neuse: A Question of Iron and Time* (Raleigh, North Carolina 1981).

Dictionary of American Fighting Ships, 8 vols (Washington, DC 1965–72).
Brief summaries of the careers of each ship organised alphabetically.

TONY GIBBONS, *Warships and Naval Battles of the US Civil War* (London 1989).
Features rather garish colour artwork of the ships but useful resumé of information on each, including many of the more obscure craft.

FRANK L OWSLEY, *The CSS Florida: Her Building and Operations* (Tuscaloosa, Alabama 1985).

EDWARD M MILLER, *The USS Monitor: The Ship that Launched the Modern Navy* (Annapolis, Maryland 1979).
A detailed monograph on the ship; the bibliography listing some 200 items indicates how much attention this ship has received.

ERNEST W PETERKIN, *Drawings of the USS Monitor* (Washington, DC 1985).
A comprehensive portfolio of all surviving drawings relating to the ship and her fittings, with commentaries.

WILLIAM H ROBERTS, 'The Neglected Ironclad: A design and Constructional Analysis of the USS *New Ironsides*', *Warship International* XXVI/2 (1989).

PAUL H SILVERSTONE, *Warships of the Civil War Navies* (Annapolis, Maryland 1989).
An exhaustive listing of all ships of both sides, including those purchased or captured, plus the forces of the Revenue Cutter Service and the US Coast Survey. Probably the best available source of data.

WILLIAM N STILL, JR, *Iron Afloat: The Story of the Confederate Armorclads* (Columbia, South Carolina 1985).

——, *Confederate Shipbuilding* (Columbia, South Carolina 1987).

——, 'Technology Afloat', *Civil War Times Illustrated* XIV (November 1975).

DAVID M SULLIVAN, 'Phantom Fleet: the Confederacy's Unclaimed European-built Warships', *Warship International* XXIV/1 (1987).

CHARLES G SUMMERSELL, *CSS Alabama: Builder, Captain and Plans* (University, Alabama 1985).

STEPHEN C THOMPSON, 'The Design and Construction of USS *Monitor*', *Warship International* XXVII/3 (1990).

THE ERA OF UNCERTAINTY

Although the ships of this period are better covered than earlier vessels, reliable information is rare. Contemporary professional feuds, particularly over HMS *Captain* and her loss, generated a number of stories, at best only half true, which have been copied by later writers without question: for example, almost all references to stability are wrong. Very little original research has been done, reliance being placed on the fulsome press accounts of the day – there was little official secrecy, so technical reporting was far more comprehensive than it can be today, but that does not imply that it was accurate.

R M ANDERSON, 'The Rendel Gunboats', *Warship International* XIII/1 (1976).

ADMIRAL G A BALLARD, *The Black Battlefleet* (Lymington and Greenwich 1980).
Originally published as a series of articles in the Society for Nautical Research Journal *The Mariner's Mirror*, the material is based on official records and is more accurate than most. Excellent on seamanship and living conditions, of which the author had some experience as a young man, but weaker on technology.

K C BARNABY, *Some Ship Disasters and their Causes* (London 1968).
Includes trustworthy accounts of the losses of *Captain*, *Vanguard* and *Grosser Kürfurst*.

——, *The Institution of Naval Architects 1860–1960* (London 1960).
The centenary history of the INA, giving simple, readable accounts of the great debates. The Institution's *Transactions* contain many valuable papers by prominent naval architects, and since many naval officers were members, there were also articles on tactics. The discussions can be useful, but must be treated with caution since much nonsense was uttered, and some found its way into print.

DAVID K BROWN, 'Attack and Defence', *Warship* 24 (1982).
First of a series of articles concerned with British weapons trials against ships.

——, 'The Design of HMS *Inflexible*', *Warship* 15 (1980).

——, 'The Design and Loss of HMS *Captain*', *Warship Technology* 7 (1989).

—— and PHILIP PUGH, 'Ramming', *Warship 1990* (London 1990).
A cogently argued analysis of why ramming was never likely to be a successful fleet tactic, despite its popularity in the ironclad era.

J F CLARKE, 'Mild Steel and Shipbuilding – the Failure of Bessemer Steel', *Metals and the Sea*, papers of the Historical Metallurgy Society conference (London 1991).

BORIS V DRASHPIL, 'The Russian Rendels', *Warship International* XVII/2 (1980).

J W KING, *The Warships and Navies of the World* (Portsmouth 1880; reprinted London 1982).
A survey by the Chief Engineer of the US Navy, officially sponsored and based on a tour of the main European naval powers, but necessarily relying on published information as well. Interesting and generally accurate, though details need checking. An expanded version of *The Warships of Europe* (1878).

J LABAYLE-COUHAT, 'Evolution de Cuirassé 1865–1909', in *Marine et Technique au XIXᵉ Siècle* (Paris 1988).
One of a number of interesting papers in this collection on nineteenth century navies.

DR OSCAR PARKES, *British Battleships 1860–1950* (London 1956).
Long regarded as the standard work, it is primarily technical but included some background and details of principal foreign developments. Comprehensive and readable, but unreliable on some technology points.

EDWARD J REED, *Our Ironclad Ships* (London 1869).
A rare contemporary book by a leading designer. It is a work of self-justification, but is nevertheless one of the most reliable books available.

N A M RODGER, 'The Design of the *Inconstant*', *The Mariner's Mirror* 61/1 (1975).
The first of three important articles which are the only properly researched contributions to the understanding of British cruiser design in this period. The other two are 'British Belted Cruisers' in 64/1 (1978), and 'The First Light Cruisers' in 65/3 (1979).

——, 'The Dark Ages of the Admiralty', *The Mariner's Mirror* 61/4 (1975), 62/1 & 62/2 (1976).
A sympathetic survey of Admiralty administration and policy in the period 1869–1885, the so-called 'dark ages'; essential background.

DR C G ROFFEY, 'The Popoffkas', *Warship International* XI/3 (1974).
An analysis of the unique Russian circular ironclads.

GERALD WOOD *et al*, 'The Iron Clad Turret Ship *Huascar*', *Warship* 37 & 38 (1986).
An important account of this early Peruvian turret ship, captured by Chile in 1879, written by the team in charge of the ship's recent restoration as a museum ship.

WARSHIPS OF STEEL

Many works cited earlier are of relevance to this section, especially Hovgaard and Parkes, and the last parts of the articles by Rodger.

FRANK ABELSEN, 'The Gunboat *Tyr*', *Warship* 31 (1984).
A rare survivor, this Norwegian steel gunboat of 1887 is still afloat, albeit employed as a ferry.

SIR NATHANIEL BARNABY, *Naval Developments in the Century* (London 1904).
Written by a former Admiralty Director of Naval Construction, it contains a great deal of comparative data on technical progress in the hundred years preceding its publication. Concentrates on ship design but has some policy background.

THOMAS, EARL BRASSEY (ed), *The Naval Annual* (Portsmouth; annually from 1886).
'Brassey's' was the prototype naval yearbook, preceding 'Jane's' by over a decade, and preferable by dint of its discursive essays on the latest developments in ships, ordnance, armour, and important political events.

DR PETER BROOK, 'The Elswick Cruisers', *Warship International* VII/2 (1970), VIII/3 (1971), IX/3 (1972), X/3 (1973).

——, 'Armstrong Battleships built for Japan', *Warship International* XXII/3 (1985).

D K BROWN, *A Century of Naval Construction* (London 1983).
The centennial history of the Royal Corps of Naval Constructors, concentrating on later developments but with much of interest on the Victorian period.

R A BURT, 'The *Royal Sovereign* Class of 1889', *Warship* 14 & 15 (1980).

——, 'The Majestic Predreadnoughts', *Warship* 27 & 28 (1983).

ROSS GILLETT, 'The Story of HMS *Protector*', *Warship* 26 (1983).
The colonial gunboat (like an enlarged 'Rendel') built for South Australia in 1884.

JIRO ITANI *et al*, 'Sankeikan: Japan's Coast Defence Ships of the *Matsushima* Class', *Warship 1990* (London 1990).

KARL LAUTENSCHLAGER, 'A Majestic Revolution', *Warship* 25 & 26 (1983).
Argues that the British *Majestic* class was the true starting point for the modern battleship.

ANDRZEJ MACH, 'The Chinese Battleships', *Warship* 29 (1984).
The German-built turret ships of the *Ting Yuen* class of 1881.

ARTHUR J MARDER, *The Anatomy of British Seapower* (London 1940).
A detailed study of British naval policy and planning during 1880–1905, with particular reference to the rivalry with France.

BRYAN RANFT (ed), *Technical Change and British Naval Policy 1860–1939* (London 1977).
A series of essays by different hands but covering such diverse topics as trade protection policy 1860–1906, the introduction of the torpedo, the Admiralty and industry, and the evaluation of the lessons of the Russo-Japanese War.

CHRISTOPHER C WRIGHT, 'Impressive Ships: The Story of Her Majesty's Cruisers *Blake* and *Blenheim*', *Warship International* VII/1 (1970).

——, 'Cruisers of the Imperial Russian Navy', *Warship International* IX/1 (1972), XII/3 (1975), XIII/2 (1976), XIV/1 (1977).

GENE T ZIMMERMAN, 'Controversial Cruisers', *Warship International* XI/4 (1974), XII/1 (1975).
America's first modern cruisers, *Atlanta* and *Boston*.

THE PRE-DREADNOUGHT AGE

JOHN D ALDEN, *The American Steel Navy* (Annapolis, Maryland 1972).
History of US naval development 1883–1904, based around a fine collection of photographs. Covers ships, personnel, policy and operations, with drawings and particulars of all principal ships.

FRANCIS J ALLEN, 'The US Monitors', *Warship* 25 & 26 (1983).
The later coast defence ships completed in the 1890s.

——, 'The *Arkansas* Class Monitors', *Warship* 30 (1984).
The US Navy's last coast defence class.

R A BURT, 'The *Royal Sovereign* Class Battleships', *Warship* 34–36 (1985).

——, '*Minotaur*: Before the Battlecruiser', *Warship* 42 (1987).
The last conventional British armoured cruiser class.

——, 'The *Powerful* Class Cruisers of the Royal Navy', *Warship* 48 (1988).

——, *British Battleships 1889–1904* (London 1988).
Technical design history of classes from *Royal Sovereign* to *Lord Nelson*; strong on illustrations and data but weak on analysis.

J M DORWART, 'The Mongrel Fleet', *Warship International* XVII/2 (1980).
Covers US Navy acquisitions for the war with Spain in 1898, including auxiliaries.

C DE SAINT HUBERT and C A ZAFORTEZA, 'The Spanish Navy of 1898', *Warship International* XVII/1 & 2 (1980), XVIII/3 (1981), XXI/2 (1984).

ANDRZEJ JASKUŁA, '*Askold*', *Warship* 25 & 26 (1983).
The Russian protected cruiser of 1990.

KEITH MCBRIDE, 'The *Diadem* Class Cruisers of 1893', *Warship* 44 (1987).

——, 'The first County Class Cruisers of the Royal Navy', *Warship* 46 & 47 (1988).

——, 'The Dukes and the Warriors', *Warship International* XXVII/4 (1990).
British armoured cruiser classes analysed.

JOHN C REILLY and ROBERT L SCHEINA, *American Battleships 1886–1923* (Annapolis, Maryland 1980).
A technical history of US battleships from *Maine* to *Mississippi*, concentrating on the ships but with background detail on policy. Well illustrated with photographs and official plans.

CHRISTOPHER C WRIGHT and EDWARD C FISHER, JR, 'USS *Albany* and *New Orleans*', *Warship International* VIII/4 (1971).

UNDERWATER WARFARE AND THE TORPEDO BOAT

A general survey of the torpedo boats of this era with basic data is contained in *Conway's All the World's Fighting Ships 1860–1905* (see General section above). This includes what is so far the nearest approach to a full account of the development of torpedo craft in the Royal Navy (by David Lyon). A great deal was published in contemporary technical journals up to the beginning of the twentieth century when navies suddenly grew much more secretive. Good use of the published plans and details is made by Harald Fock in his history of the torpedo boat, *Schwarze Gesellen*. Though particularly from a German standpoint and with an emphasis on that country's craft and their organization, it does have an international coverage. However, it is weak on British developments and lacks the historical analysis necessary to evaluate the conflicting claims with which the contemporary literature is full and to place the technical developments in context.

Despite the large amount of contemporary printed material, histories (national or otherwise) of torpedo craft in this period are few and far between The French navy is well covered (in French) in Le Masson's classic which is wide ranging, based on detailed research in the French documents, and on very wide knowledge. It could perhaps give rather more prominence to developments outside France, but is the best national history of torpedo boats (and destroyers) yet available. The Italian Naval Historical Branch account of Italian TBs is rather more restricted to technical data and operational histories, but is also excellent. There is, unfortunately, no good comprehensive account of the vital American developments during and just after the Civil War, though Norman Friedman's *US Destroyers* (Annapolis & London 1982) is useful for the very end of this period. The same cannot be said for E J March's *British Destroyers* (London 1966). This poor book is at its nadir in its account of the first destroyers – full of errors of omission, interpretation and often of fact.

FRANK ABELSEN, 'The Torpedo Boat *Rap*', *Warship* 38 (1986).
The pioneer Thornycroft torpedo boat now preserved in Norway.

WOLF H BILLE, 'The Torpedo Vessels of the Imperial and Royal Austro-Hungarian Navy, 1875–1918', *Warship International* VIII/1 (1971).

PETER BROOK, 'Armstrong Torpedo Gunboats', *Warship International* XV/2 (1978).

DAVID K BROWN, 'The Torpedo Boat Destroyer Committee 1903', *Warship Technology* 2 & 3 (1987 and 1988).

BORIS V DRASHPIL, 'Surface Torpedo Craft of the Imperial Russian Navy', *Warship International* XIX/3 (1982), XXII/1 (1985).

G FIORAVANZO *et al*, *I Cacciatorpediniere Italiani* (Rome 1969).
Official history of Italian destroyers, from about 1900.

HARALD FOCK, *Schwarze Gesellen*, Vol 1 (Herford 1979).
German language history of the torpedo boat; first volume goes up to 1914.

I A GRANT, 'The Herreshoff Spar Torpedo Boats of 1878–1880', *Warship International* XIV/3 (1977).

HENRI LE MASSON, *Histoire du Torpilleur en France* (Paris 1963)
Fine study, in French, of France's torpedo forces.

PAOLO M POLLINA (ed), *Le Torpediniere Italiane* (Rome 1964, 1979).
Official history of Italian torpedo boats, with a brief overview of the development of torpedo craft generally.

PETER PRY and RICHARD ZEITLIN, 'Torpedo Boats: Secret Weapons of the South', *Warship International* XXI/4 (1984).
Details of Confederate torpedo craft during US Civil War.

EARLY SUBMARINES

FRANCIS J ALLEN, 'America's First Submarines', *Warship* 25 & 26 (1983)

RICHARD COMPTON-HALL, *Submarine Boats* (London 1983).
Probably the best single-volume account of the development of the submarine from early times to the end of the First World War.

ROBERT GARDINER (ed), *Conway's All the World's Fighting Ships 1906–1921* (London 1985).
Includes details of all early submarines of any fighting value (even those built before 1906, which were omitted from the 1860–1905 volume in this series).

NORMAN FRIEDMAN, *Submarine Design and Development* (London 1984).
A detailed survey of the development of submarine warfare showing the relationship between technology and tactics; concentrates on later periods, but the principles apply equally to early boats.

A N HARRISON, *The Development of HM Submarines 1901–30 (BR3043)*, Ministry of Defence (London 1979).
A comprehensive study of all the submarines built for the RN from the *Holland*s to the 1930s. Many appendices give detailed additional technical information on each specific class in addition to the abundant line diagrams.

JOHN M MABER, 'Nordenfelt Submarines', *Warship* 32 (1984).

NORMAN POLMAR and JURRIEN NOOT, *Submarines of the Russian and Soviet Navies 1718–1990* (Annapolis 1991).
The story of submarine development in Russia and the Soviet Union over a period of nearly 300 years, including good detail on early experiments.

ALEX ROLAND, *Underwater Warfare in the Age of Sail* (Bloomington, Indiana 1978).
Pretentious in style and approach but does summarise early developments.

MURRAY SUETER, *The Evolution of the Submarine Boat, Mine & Torpedo* (Portsmouth 1907).
A contemporary history of the development of the early submarines of the navies of the world.

MICHAEL WILSON, 'The First Submarines for the Royal Navy', *Warship* 24 (1982).

NAVAL ARMAMENTS AND ARMOUR

A good modern history of ordnance is lacking. Perhaps the best short accounts are the relevant chapters in Hovgaard and Baxter (listed above), but the sections on 'Armour Plates' and 'Ordnance' in the 11th edition of the *Encyclopaedia Britannica* (London 1910–11) can be recommended as the next level of sophistication. For those interested in real detail, the Admiralty Gun Manuals for 1880, 1887 and 1893 are more approachable than most textbooks.

F J ALLEN, 'USS *Vesuvius* and the Dynamite Gun', *Warship* 45 (1988).

N J M CAMPBELL, 'British Naval Guns 1880–1945', *Warship* 9–38 (1979–1986).
A series describing every Mark of every British naval gun down to 4in calibre.

J S COWIE, *Mines, Minelayers and Minelaying* (London 1949).
A classic account by a distinguished practitioner of mine warfare.

NORMAN FRIEDMAN, *US Naval Weapons* (London 1983).
More than just a catalogue of weapon systems since 1883, the book also gives an idea of technical and tactical concepts influencing developments.

H GARBETT, *Naval Gunnery: A Description and History of the Fighting Equipment of a Man of War* (London 1897).
An early history but now superseded in many details.

PETER HODGES, *The Big Gun: Battleship Main Armament 1860–1945* (London 1981).
Concentrates on gun mountings more than guns, and stronger on British developments than those of other navies.

ERNEST F SLAYMAKER, 'The Armament of HMS *Warrior*', *Warship* 37–39 (1986).

SPENCER TUCKER, *Arming the Fleet: US Navy Ordnance in the Muzzle-Loading Era* (Annapolis, Maryland 1989).
Although only relating to the early part of the period, it is good on the last generation of ML weapons, and the guns of the US Civil War in particular.

WARSHIP MACHINERY

There is no entirely satisfactory modern history of naval engineering in the nineteenth century. Probably the best short introduction is the chapter in Hovgaard (see General section above).

DONALD L CANNEY, 'The US Navy and the Steam Engine 1815–1870', *Warship 1989*.

GERHARD KOOP, 'The German Navies 1848–1870: Their Engines and Engineers', *Warship* 47 (1988).

E C SMITH, *A Short History of Marine Engineering* (Cambridge 1937).
The best available although not very detailed and lacking any sense of non-technological factors influencing developments.

Glossary of Terms and Abbreviations

Compiled by Robert Gardiner with the assistance of the contributors. This list assumes some knowledge of ships and does not include the most basic terminology. It also omits those words which are defined on the only occasions in which they occur in this book.

'A' tube. In a large built-up gun barrel constructed of concentric cylinders, the main inner tube was lettered 'A' and the next outer one 'B'.

Admiralty. The office responsible for the administration of the affairs of a navy, and in particular the Royal Navy. Originally headed by a Lord High Admiral, but for the period of this book his duties were discharged by a Board of Commissioners known as the Board of Admiralty, comprising a civilian First Lord, senior sea officers and a Civil Service secretariat.

AP. Armour piercing, usually of a projectile; designed to penetrate a ship's protective layer. Early AP ammunition was solid, but later developments, like Holzer shot (*qv*) and Palliser shell (*qv*) were hollow or included small bursting charges, eventually combined with a fuse that permitted sufficient delay to guarantee explosion after the shell had passed through the armour. From the late 1890s the addition of a mild steel cap improved penetration of face-hardened armour; the shell was then described as capped AP.

armour. Iron or steel plate added to the structure of a ship to protect the crew, the vital workings of the ship, or to preserve its buoyancy. Armour needed to be as hard as possible to resist penetration but would crack or shatter if not possessing a degree of ductility; thus armour development was a quest for the best compromise. The earliest protection was wood-backed wrought iron, but mild steel armour was tried from the late 1870s simultaneously with compound armour which combined a hard but brittle steel face with a ductile but tough iron backing. By about 1890 all-steel armour had proved superior, particularly with the introduction of the US Harvey face-hardening process, which could be further improved if alloyed with nickel. The final armour development of the century was 'Krupp cemented', an advanced form of face-hardened nickel-chromium steel soon adopted by most navies.

armourclad. Early term, synonymous with ironclad, for any vessel substantially protected with iron plates, principally on the vertical surfaces.

Armstrong. British engineering, ordnance and shipbuilding company founded by W G, later Lord, Armstrong (1810–1900) at Elswick on the Tyne. Armstrong's early achievements included advances in hydraulic machinery (the original product of the Elswick works), the first British breech-loading rifled ordnance, and eventually a shipbuilding yard whose designs included the famous Elswick cruisers (*qv*).

automobile torpedo. *See* torpedo.

Babcock & Wilcox. Water-tube boiler of the large-tube type; alongside the Yarrow large-tube pattern replaced the Belleville design (*qv*) in large British warships at the beginning of the twentieth century.

ball race. The bearings on which a gun mounting revolved; the larger turret and barbette weapons usually traversed on a roller path (*qv*) but some systems, such as the early Eads turret and some Krupp mountings, used ball bearings instead.

barbette. Originally an open-topped armoured enclosure inside which was a gun mounting, usually on some kind of turntable, which fired over the top of the barbette wall. In the 1890s an armoured hood was added, the whole assembly coming to be called a turret (*qv*).

barque. As understood in the nineteenth century, a vessel with three or more masts, square rigged on all but the mizzen, which set only fore and aft canvas. Any vessel, even steamers, carrying this arrangement were said to be barque rigged.

barquentine. A vessel with a full square rigged foremast but fore and aft rigged main and mizzen; later vessels had four or more masts, with only the foremast square rigged.

battleship. The most powerful unit of the fleet, suitable for fleet actions; descendants of the sailing 'line of battle ship'. Mid-century technical developments confounded many of the old categories of warship types – some early ironclads were referred to as frigates because they had only one covered gundeck, for example – but eventually a clear division between the battleship and the cruiser (*qv*) was re-established.

beakhead. In sailing warships the small platform at upper deck level forward of the forecastle, formed by an athwartship partition called the beakhead bulkhead. By the nineteenth century the hull planking was usually carried up to the top of the forecastle, and the beakhead disappeared.

Belleville boiler. A French large-tube design, the first water-tube boiler suitable for major warships, introduced in 1879, although employed in launches for some years previously. Was tried in the Royal Navy during the 1890s but found delicate, requiring careful operation, so was later superseded by Yarrow and Babcock & Wilcox types (*qv*).

Berdan torpedo. *See* torpedo.

Bessemer steel. The first commercially viable process for manufacturing steel on an industrial scale, demonstrated for the first time in 1856 by the British engineer Sir Henry Bessemer (1813–1898). Early steel lacked ductility, malleability and uniformity and was difficult to work, but the perfection of so-called mild steel by the open hearth process in the 1870s led to its rapid introduction as a warship building material.

Bilge keel. Narrow wing-like extensions along the midships underwater hull at about the turn of the bilge designed to dampen rolling.

bilge pump. A pump designed to extract water from the lowest recesses of the hull.

BL. Breech-loading or breech-loader (later bag-loading); gun with a removable breech block (*qv*) through which the projectile and propellant was loaded. As long as a good flash-proof seal could be contrived, it had a number of theoretical advantages over the muzzle-loader (*qv*) it replaced: the gun need not be run in for reloading (important as guns became longer); it might be reloaded at a wider range of angles of elevation and training; it was easier to protect the crew inside a turret or casemate; it promised faster, and once elongated shells were introduced, more accurate gunfire. Early BL guns were less reliable and more expensive than ML while barrel length was not required with early fast burning propellant. In later usage, it distinguished guns which used ammunition (*qv*), with the propellant charge in a fabric bag, from quick-firers (*qv*).

black powder. *See* propellant powder.

Blakely. British gun manufacturer; widely used on ships built for the Confederacy during the American Civil War.

blockship. Early British design for a low-powered screw steamer conversion of sailing warships; not intended to be truly seagoing, hence the 'blockship' (floating battery) designation. Applied to ships of the line and a few frigates.

Borden torpedo. *See* torpedo.

bp. Between perpendiculars, sometimes given as pp: modern, designer's measurement of length between stem post and rudder post, omitting the overhang of stem and stern structures, as opposed to length overall.

bracket frame. Probably devised by Nathaniel Barnaby and introduced in Edward Reed's ironclad HMS *Bellerophon* (laid down in 1863), the bracket frame system combined continuous deep longitudinals with transverse frames which consisted of inner and outer angle irons connected by a plate bracket. A skin of plating either side of the bracket frame produced a double bottom, the ensemble being both lighter and stronger than previous schemes.

breastwork. The built-up armoured section of an otherwise low freeboard turret ship on which the guns were mounted. The breastwork provided greater stability, gave the guns more freeboard, and protected the turning gear.

breech block. The piece of a BL (*qv*) gun which was removed to allow loading.

breech-loading. *See* BL.

Brennen torpedo. *See* torpedo.

Brig. A two masted vessel with square canvas on both fore and main masts, but with a gaff-headed fore and aft main sail. Nineteenth century naval brigs usually set the main from an auxiliary spencer mast, so were technically snows; some also had a spencer on the fore mast and could set square canvas from the crossjack on the main.

Broadwell ring. Steel ring used in early BL (*qv*) guns with a wedge breech, particularly Krupp, to seal the breech before firing; later Krupp guns, even the largest, used a metal cartridge case.

Brooke. The main pattern of Confederate naval gun, and the only type designed indigenously (by John M Brooke). The principal models were 10in and 11in smooth bores and 6.4in, 7in and 8in rifles.

Brooks mine. Confederate ground mine for riverine use. *See also* mine.

Brotherhood engine. A patent three-cylinder compressed air piston engine used in British Whitehead torpedoes from the 1880s; in its most advanced form it developed about 80–90hp at 950rpm with pressure in the air chamber of 100 atm. A more powerful four-cylinder engine was introduced by Brotherhood in the early years of the twentieth century.

Brown plate. A form of compound armour patented by the British John Brown company of Sheffield.

brown powder. *See* propellant powder.

built-up gun. One constructed of several tubes as opposed to one cast in a single piece. Generally does not include wire-wound guns.

calibre. The internal diameter of the bore of a gun, and consequently of the ammunition or shot fired from it. Barrel length was often quoted in 'calibres': *eg* a 12in/45cal would be 45 × 12in long, although the exact definition of internal length varied from navy to navy.

Cammell plate. A form of compound armour patented by the British Charles Cammell company of Sheffield.

capital ship. The largest and most powerful warship types; for the period of this book, effectively synonymous with battleship (*qv*).

capped AP shell. *See* AP.

carapace. The upper shell of a tortoise or crustacean; used by extension of the armoured covering of some ironclads.

casemate. A term from fortification meaning a heavily protected gun position; applied in early ironclads to the armoured box from inside which the main gun battery fired through a series of gunports. The term was revived towards the end of the end of the century when the secondary guns of many battleships and the main armament of cruisers were mounted in an open battery, firing through ports; a shell bursting inside this battery could kill the crews of several guns by blast and splinters. The casemate was then conceived as an armoured box, protected on all sides, and containing a single gun. It usually protruded from the side giving a degree of end on fire and a small shield was attached to the barrel protecting the gun port. The casemates were widely spaced for further protection which gave difficulties in ammunition supply. Most late nineteenth century ships had an ammunition passage running fore and aft which could pass flash and flood water and was a major, unrecognised hazard.

catcher. Some early craft designed to destroy torpedo boats (*qv*) were described as torpedo boat catchers. *See also* torpedo gunboat.

cellular layer. A double thickness water-tight and minutely subdivided layer designed to minimise the flooding caused by individual hits and so to preserve the buoyancy and stability of the ship, rather than to resist shellfire as with armour. Sometimes filled with buoyant material.

central citadel. An armoured redoubt amidships concentrating the armament and the ship's principal protection in one heavily defended block.

centre pivot mounting. An open mounting, sometimes with a gunshield, for medium and small calibre weapons developed in the 1880s in which the whole mounting revolved on a small diameter ring of rollers operating on a deck mounted pivot plate. An essential feature of the mounting was a system to absorb the recoil, first satisfactorily achieved by the Vavasseur mounting's hydraulic compressor brake; the slide which carried the gun was angled upwards so that gravity performed the run-out. Armstrong (*qv*) improved the system in the late 1880s, making the mounting more compact by devising a cradle that allowed recoil in the line of the gun's axis; the tall saddle or carriage between the pivot stand and the cradle was eventually replaced by a lighter pedestal, which became the standard mounting for smaller calibre guns from about 1890. In British mounting designations the two types were abbreviated to CP and P respectively.

centre-wheeler. Steamer with paddle wheel between a divided hull or hulls.

chambering. In muzzle-loading (*qv*) guns the breech end of the bore – the chamber, where the propellant charge was seated – was sometimes shaped or even of a different diameter from the rest of the bore. This was known as chambering; it was designed to make the charge more effective but had disadvantages and was not universally adopted.

chase guns. Those firing forward (bow chasers) or aft (stern chasers), used when chasing or being chased, as opposed to the broadside guns.

closed ashpit. *See* force draught.

closed stokehold. *See* forced draught.

coast defence ship. Relatively small vessel sacrificing range and seaworthiness to carry weapons and/or armour powerful enough to take on the enemy's strongest ships when fighting in home waters.

cofferdam. A water-tight double thickness bulkhead, usually employed as part of the protective scheme of a warship or to separate magazines from boiler rooms.

Coles turret. *See* turret.

composite construction. A ship with iron frames, beams, keel and, usually, deck stringers but wood planking on sides, bottom and deck. There were still well founded fears concerning the effect of shot on unarmoured iron plates and this construction was seen as a good compromise. The iron members tied the planks together, making them more effective in resisting bending forces and composite construction was normally used for smaller 'cruisers' which required copper sheathing against fouling which could not be applied directly to an iron hull. Such construction also used timber stocks and labour skills which were readily available. It went out when ductile steel became available.

compound armour. *See* armour.

compound engine. Machinery in which steam was expanded in at least two stages, in a high pressure cylinder and then a larger diameter low pressure one; eventually triple expansion (*qv*) became the norm, but quadruple expansion was also perfected, although not used in warships. Generally compounding refers to two-stage expansion.

condensate. The product of the liquification of steam in a condenser (*qv*).

condenser. The power and efficiency of an engine depends on the difference in pressure of the steam between inlet and exhaust. By condensing the exhaust steam to water, the pressure is dropped to near vacuum, raising efficiency. It was convenient and, when pure feed water was introduced, essential, to return the condensate to the feed tank by pump.

condenser air pump. A pump using air to move the condensate (*qv*) from the condenser to the boiler; usually driven off the main engine.

connecting rod. In a steam engine a bar transferring the thrust force on the piston to the crank (*qv*) of the output shaft. The connecting rod may attach directly to the piston or to its crosshead depending upon the type of engine.

conoidal propeller. Screw propeller with blades whose shape derived from the surface of a cone.

cordite. British 'smokeless propellant' (*qv*) based on nitro-glycerine and nitro-cellulose, introduced in 1895.

corvette. Originally a French term for small unrated cruising vessels with guns carried on the upper deck, equivalent to the British sloop. By the nineteenth century corvettes were usually regarded as intermediate vessels between frigates and sloops.

crank. Portion of an axle bent at right angles, used in an engine to convert reciprocating motion into rotary (or vice-versa).

Creusot steel. Steel produced by the open hearth Siemens Martin process. The first steel suitable for use in all-steel (as opposed to compound) armour, gradually perfected by the French Creusot works during the 1880s.

crosshead. In a steam engine the bar at the end the piston, sliding in straight guides to keep the motion of the piston true.

cruiser or cruising ship. Originally the term applied to any vessel on detached service but in the nineteenth century the meaning narrowed to ships not intended for duty in the battlefleet (*see* battleship), but designed specifically for scouting, commerce warfare, policing and showing the flag – previously the traditional roles of the frigate, corvette and sloop. Compared with battleships, cruisers were characterised by greater speed and endurance, but lighter armament and armour. Some were entirely unarmoured but by the end of the century, most were broadly divided into armoured cruisers (with vertical – side – armour) and protected cruisers which largely relied on an armoured deck to protect the vitals.

cylinder jackets. Casings around the cylinders of steam engines through which steam was passed in order to reduce power loss in the cylinders from cooling.

cylindrical boilers. Introduced from the late 1870s to withstand the greater steam pressures being demanded by triple expansion engines (*qv*). The so-called 'Scotch' type was the most popular.

Dahlgren guns. Ordnance designed by John Dahlgren, USN, characterised by their 'soda bottle' shape. Although he did design rifled guns he is best known for large calibre (10in, 11in and 15in) smooth bores, used by the North in the American Civil War.

De Bange obturation. *See* obturation.

despatch vessel. Fast, lightly armed craft designed to carry orders to commanders and foreign stations; the French equivalent was known as an *aviso*.

destroyer. Shortened form of 'torpedo boat destroyer', a Britsh designation introduced in the 1890s for a larger and more seaworthy opponent, initially to defend capital ships against torpedo boat attack but later usurping the role of the torpedo boat itself.

diving chamber. A floodable compartment allowing divers to leave or enter a submarine underwater.

division boat. German designation for a larger craft designed as a leader for torpedo boat flotillas; in effect, the German equivalent of early British destroyers (*qv*).

DNC. Director of Naval Construction, the head of the Royal Navy's design organisation in the later nineteenth century. *See also* Surveyor of the Navy.

Double-ender. American paddle gunboats of the Civil War era which had fine lines aft and a bow rudder to make them handy going astern (designed to give them the tactical advantage of not having to turn around in confined waters). They were not strictly identical fore and aft but their means of employment likened them to ferries which were.

driving band. External ring of soft metal (usually copper) at the base of a shell designed to engage the rifling (*qv*) and on firing to impart spin to the projectile.

drop keel. A keel plate or centreboard which could be lowered when beating into the wind to reduce leeway and raised when before the wind to minimise drag. Familiar from the modern sailing dinghy or shoal draught cruiser, the centreboard in its early form tended to be of the vertical daggerboard pattern rather than the pivotting type.

Eads turret. *See* turret.

Electric Boat Company. Early American submarine builder, taking over the patents established by the pioneer John Philip Holland in 1898; the company survives to this day building nuclear submarines at Groton, Connecticut, although now a division of General Dynamics.

Elswick cruiser. A type of small but heavily armed cruiser built at Armstrong's Elswick shipyard on the Tyne. One of the great British export successes of the late nineteenth century, the type evolved gradually from the Chilean *Esmeralda* of 1883 and served in many navies.

enclosed crankcase. An oil-tight structure around the piston/connecting rod/crankshaft mechanism of a reciprocating engine to facilitate the lubrication of bearings, etc.

engine. At this time it usually referred to a single-cylinder machine; those with two were referred to as 'engines' in the plural.

Ericsson turret. *See* turret.

feed pump. Pump moving feed water (*qv*) to the boiler.

feed water. Boiler water to be turned into steam. As pressures increased, feed water had to be extremely pure.

fire control. A system to direct the firing of weapons, by combining estimates of the target's speed, course and range with known details of own ship movements, expressed in terms of gun angles necessary to hit the target.

fire-tube boiler. *See* tubular boiler.

'flat-iron' gunboat. Nickname for small inshore steam gunboats, whose hull shape resembled an old style smoothing iron. The most common pattern mounted one large forward-firing gun, and were also known as Rendel gunboats after their originator, George Rendel of Armstrongs.

flue boiler. Early rectangular type in which hot furnace gases passed through the boiler water in the form of a few large square-section flues. Made from flat sheet, these boilers were vulnerable to collapse and this limited pressures to very low values.

flush deck. One without a break or step; later applied to ships with an open weather deck, lacking quarterdeck and forecastle structures above.

forced draught. A method of increasing the rate of combustion in the furnaces, and hence the efficiency of the boiler as a steam generator, using fans to increase the amount of air supplied to the boiler under pressure, usually for a short period only. Naval practice favoured a closed stokehold whereas the merchant service preferred a closed ashpit only.

forced lubrication. Oiling of an engine's bearings and pin joints under pressure.

fore topsail schooner. *See* schooner.

Fossano powder. *See* propellant powder.

Fourth Rate. In the Royal Navy's classification system for sailing ships, a vessel that carried between 50 and 60 guns. In the nineteenth century this applied to the largest frigates (*qv*), some of which were 'double-banked', that is having two complete tiers of guns.

Fretwell mine. Also known as the Singer type, Confederate contact mine. *See also* mine.

frigate. The cruising ship of the sailing navy, designed for scouting and commerce warfare. Originally frigates carried between 28 and 44 guns on a single gundeck, the forecastle and quarterdeck, but in the nineteenth century they became larger and more powerful, mounting up to 60 guns. When the quarterdeck and forecastle were joined to form a completely armed upper deck, the resulting frigates were described as 'double-banked'.

frigate stern. The traditional sail ship stern with a row of gallery lights (windows); fitted to some early ironclads and larger merchantmen.

Gardner. An early machine-gun of .45in calibre used by the Royal Navy in some numbers; there were two- and five-barrelled models.

gas check. Rimmed copper disc around the base of a shell which expanded into the rifling on firing; designed to reduce barrel wear from powder gases escaping past the projectile. Mostly used in rifled muzzle loaders.

Gatling. The first effective machine-gun, comprising a circle of ten barrels which revolved by hand crank into the firing position; fitted with a drum magazine feed. Invented by the American, R J Gatling, and first used in the mid 1860s.

Germaniawerft. German shipyard at Kiel which built warships from the 1880s; leased by Krupp in 1896 and taken over entirely in 1902.

GM. Naval architects' notation for metacentric height (*qv*).

Gorgon engine. Early form of direct-acting paddle engine, designed by Seaward and Capel, and first installed in HMS *Gorgon* in 1837. With two vertical cylinders positioned under the paddle shaft, it was remarkably compact and consequently popular with the Royal Navy, although the vibration set up by its short connecting rods caused problems in service.

guerre de course. War on trade.

gunboat. Large boat equipped to carry a small number of guns (often one only); originally little more than ship's boats, which were rowed or sailed, they tended to become larger and more seaworthy in the early nineteenth century, and eventually steam power was added. Their early employment as inshore craft was overshadowed by the later colonial policing role, although strictly speaking 'gunboat diplomacy' was usually carried out by larger vessels.

gunhouse. The enclosed covering over a gun mounting; strictly speaking, not synonymous

with turret (*qv*) but sometimes loosely employed as such.

gunshield. A vertical or near-vertical protective screen, sometimes of armour plate, for a gun; depending on thickness, designed to protect the crew and the mounting from shell splinters, small arms or just the effects of the weather.

gun-vessel. A British term intended to denote something larger and more seaworthy than a gunboat (at the cost of deeper draught) but not quite a sloop. They were always independent commands whereas in the steam era gunboats were originally organised as tenders to larger ships.

Harvey steel. *See* armour.

Herreschoff. Nathaniel Herreschoff (1848–1938) was one of the greatest American designers of yachts and fast powered craft. The family firm, The Herreschoff Manufacturing Co of Bristol, Rhode Island, built many of the US Navy's early torpedo boats and destroyers.

Herz horn. Detonating device for mines (*qv*) invented in 1868. It contained a glass phial of battery electrolyte, which when broken activated a battery, the electrical charge then exploding the mine.

hogging. Because the usual hull form of a ship is finer forward and aft than amidships, there is less buoyancy at the ends of the hull than in the centre. Accentuated when a wave crest is amidships, at sea this tends to make the hull droop at the ends and the midships area to arch; this condition is known as hogging and was far more of a problem in traditional wooden hulls that lacked longitudinal rigidity.

Holzer shot. Of French manufacture, the first reliable steel AP (*qv*) projectile; in service from about 1880.

Hotchkiss revolver. French anti-torpedo boat gun. The 37mm five-barrelled cannon was manufactured from the 1870s; a similar 47mm weapon was also used by a number of major navies.

Howell torpedo. *See* torpedo.

howitzer. Short barrelled gun designed to fire explosive shells at relatively high trajectories.

HP cylinder. High pressure cylinder; in a compound steam engine (*qv*), steam first entered a relatively small HP cylinder before expanding into one or more larger LP (low pressure) cylinders. Steam in triple and quadruple expansion engines passed through three and four stages respectively.

hydraulic disappearing mounting. A type of mounting in which the gun was loaded out of sight of the target behind a breastwork or barbette and raised on a hydraulically powered carriage to fire over the parapet; it then 'disappeared' again for reloading. The best known, the Moncrieff disappearing mounting, had considerable vogue in coast defence fortifications in the 1870s, but seagoing employment was minimal.

hydroplane. A fast hull type designed to skim over waves rather than through them.

INA. The Institution of Naval Architects; leading British professional body, established in 1860 and from 1960 accorded the honorific 'Royal' so now abbreviated to RINA.

indicated horsepower (ihp). A measure of the pressure and volume of steam within a cylinder, giving the power available within the

engine (1hp = 550 foot pounds per second). Once allowance has been made for power losses in friction, driving auxiliaries, etc, ihp may exceed output power (brake or shaft power) by as much as 25 per cent.

intermediate battery. Apart from their main weapons, battleships carried a secondary armament (*qv*) of smaller guns designed to destroy the unarmoured areas of their enemies, plus an anti-torpedo boat battery. The movement towards more firepower led to the short-lived introduction of an intermediate calibre between the main and the secondary; effective fire control of so many calibres proved impossible and the layout was rendered obsolete by the *Dreadnought*, which carried only main armament and anti-torpedo boat quick-firers.

interrupted screw breech. The breech end of the gun was manufactured with an internal screw thread whose circumference was broken by a radial pattern of flat 'interruptions'. The breech block had a similar mating pattern, but with the threads opposite the interruptions; on closing, the block's screw thread passed across the flat interruptions opposite, and a part turn engaged the two sets of thread, locking the breech. It was an improvement over early complete screw breeches where a several full turns were necessary to open or close the breech.

ironclad. *See* armourclad.

Jacobi mine. Russian mine with a horn-like detonator; when bent or broken by contact with a ship a glass tube of sulphuric acid inside the horn fractured, causing a violent chemical reaction which set off the mine's charge.

jet condenser. *See* condenser.

jeune école. A movement in the late nineteenth-century French navy led by Admiral Aube espousing radical ideas of fleet composition and tactics. Its proponents argued against traditional battlefleets in favour of large numbers of fast gunboats, torpedo boats and later submarines, coast defence craft and commerce warfare.

KC (Krupp cemented). *See* armour.

KNC (Krupp non cemented). *See* armour.

knee bow. The traditional sailing ship bow employed a curved cutwater ahead of the stem proper. This was known as the knee of the head and usually supported a figurehead. Some early iron ships continued this feature and were said to have a knee bow.

Krupp. German steel, ordnance and shipbuilding conglomerate, built up by Alfred Krupp (1812–1887). Based at Essen, the company has become best known as an armaments manufacturer, but its first successes were in the field of metallurgy and steelmaking, although heavy naval guns were one early expression of its technological excellence. Its later diversification depended greatly on the business acumen of Alfred's son Friedrich (1854–1902) and included the acquisiton of the Germaniawerft (*qv*) shipyard at Kiel.

Laird. John Laird (1805–1874) was an early pioneer of iron shipbuilding. The Birkenhead shipyard that bore his name was responsible for a number of epoch-making vessels, including the *Nemesis*, the world's first iron warship. The yard survived after amalgamation as Cammell-Laird, and then became part of the VSEL (Vickers) group.

large grain powder. *See* propellant powder.

Lay torpedo. *See* torpedo.

lines. In general usage, the shape of the ship's hull; by extension, from the waterlines, frame lines, etc on the builder's plans that define the shape of the ship.

LP cylinder. Low pressure cylinder. *See* HP cylinder.

magazine. Secure area for the stowage of propellant charges or fixed ammunition.

Maury gunboat. A type of simple woodenhulled steam gunboat proposed for the Confederate States Navy by Matthew Fontaine Maury in 1861. Fifteen were laid down but only two were completed.

Maxim gun. The first practical automatic machine-gun in which the action of firing itself drives the loading, firing and ejection of rounds. The gun was patented by Hiram S Maxim in 1884 but was not widely adopted until about 1890, the Royal Navy taking it up in 1892.

metacentric height (GM). A measure of the stability of a ship, defined as the distance between the centre of gravity and the transverse metacentre. The metacentre is the point of intersection between a vertical line drawn through the centre of gravity of the ship when upright, and a vertical line through the centre of buoyancy when heeled. The metacentre must be above the centre of gravity for the ship to have positive stability. The tendency of the ship to come upright when heeled through small angles – the righting moment – is a function of the metacentric height: large GM will mean a lot of initial stability, but also a quick rolling period, so a moderate value is usually preferred.

mine. Underwater explosive device, in early years sometimes described as a torpedo (*qv*). For the period of this book mines can be categorised by methods of detonation (contact mines set off by the target running into them; observation mines fired electrically by wire contact with a shore station), or by methods of laying (moored mines anchored to the bottom; ground mines lying on the seabed; or even floating mines). Influence mines set off remotely by magnetic, acoustic or pressure signatures, etc were twentieth-century innovations. *See also* Brooks, Fretwell, Herz horn, Jacobi, Singer.

ML. Muzzle-loading or muzzle-loader; a gun with a solid breech, loaded by inserting charge and projectile from the muzzle end.

MLR. Muzzle-loading rifle.

monitor. Low freeboard coast defence turret ship, named after the progenitor of the type USS *Monitor* of 1862. The name was revived in the First World War for coastal bombardment vessels of shallow draught, but otherwise bore little resemblance to the earlier type.

mortar. Very short gun intended to fire explosive or incendiary ammunition at high trajectories, usually for attack on land targets or stationary fleets, being too inaccurate for ship-to-ship engagements. In the sailing era these were carried by specially designed bomb vessels, and limited numbers of mortar vessels (usually small and sometimes steam powered) were employed as late as the American Civil War.

mosquito fleet. A journalistic description of small flotilla craft, torpedo boats, gunboats and the like, comparable in numbers and 'sting' to a swarm of mosquitos.

muzzle energy. The measure of the power of a gun developed on firing, expressed in foot tons.

muzzle-loader/muzzle-loading. *See* ML.

nhp. Nominal horsepower, an early calculation of power based on the geometry of the engine. The formula was 7 × area of piston × equivalent piston speed, the sum being divided by 33,000. Piston speed for paddle steamers was taken to be 129.7 × $(\text{stroke})^{1/3.35}$. Real power as expressed in Ihp (*qv*) was usually greater than nhp and diverged more as engines improved, reaching ratios as high as 3–4 times nhp.

nickel-steel. Alloy much employed in armour in the 1890s; offered some improvement over unalloyed steel but at the expense of easy working.

Niclausse. French water-tube boiler; an early large-tube type.

ninety-day gunboat. A class of small wooden steam gunboats built for the US Navy at the beginning of the Civil War; they were constructed very quickly, the first supposedly in 90 days.

nitro-cellulose. A chemical used in 'smokeless propellants' (*qv*).

nitro-glycerine. A chemical used in 'smokeless propellants' (*qv*).

Nordenfelt. Swedish inventor and entrepreneur Thorsten Nordenfelt, a pioneer of submarines, a widely used automatic gun, and an electric torpedo. *See also* Nordenfelt gun; torpedo.

Nordenfelt gun. A multi-barrel lever-cranked quick-firer of 1in calibre employed as an anti-torpedo boat gun from the 1870s. The barrels were disposed in a horizontal line, and although the Royal Navy preferred two- and four-barrelled versions, models with up to ten barrels existed.

Normand. Jacques-Augustin Normand (1839–1906), France's premier designer and builder of torpedo boats and destroyers. The Augustin-Normand shipyard was at Le Havre.

obturation. The sealing of the breech of a BL (*qv*) gun, particularly one with a screw breech. In the most common, De Bange, system, the mushroom head of the vent axial was driven back upon firing against a pad which was forced into a conical seating.

oscillating engine. Early form of steam engine in which the piston drove the crankshaft directly, obviating the need for a connecting rod (*qv*); in order to allow the rotary motion of the crank the cylinder was pivotted at or near the end furthest from the crankshaft and swung to and fro with the stroke of the piston.

Ordinary. Ships laid up were said to be in Ordinary, so called because the permanent establishment of the Royal Navy, including ships not in sea pay, was paid for out of the Ordinary estimate. Replaced in the later nineteenth century by the Reserve.

P^2 powder. A large grain black powder. *See* propellant powder.

Palliser shell. An AP (*qv*) shell of chilled iron developed by Sir William Palliser in 1863. It had no fuse but exploded on impact; Palliser shot was hollow, but shell contained a small bursting charge. Effective until the introduction of steel and compound armour (*qv*) in the 1880s.

Parrott. American gunfounder Robert P Parrott produced a family of rifled ordnance widely used by both the US Navy and the US Army during the Civil War. The smallest in calibre was a 10pdr but at the other end of the scale there were 100pdr (6.4in), 8in and 10in models; all were similar in appearance, with a plain, straight exterior profile and a pronounced wrought iron band around the breech.

pebble powder. *See* propellant powder.

pedestal mounting. *See* centre pivot mounting.

pendulum inertia pistol. A British method of detonating mines in which a horizontal lever was attached to the top of the mine; when the target ship hit the mine, the lever was moved relative to the mine case, triggering the explosion. The spring assembly in the pistol was far from safe and in service the mine proved both unreliable and dangerous to its users.

Penn trunk engine. A horizontal direct-acting engine for screw propulsion patented by John Penn & Co of Greenwich. The space restrictions on a horizontal engine – with a cylinder placed to one side of the propeller shaft, effectively only half the breadth of the ship – made it difficult to provide a long connecting rod. Penn's solution was to attach the connecting rod directly to the piston head inside a trunk of sufficient diameter to allow for the swing of the connecting rod. The trunk fitted through the piston head, moved with it, and was long enough to pass through the front and back cylinder covers. Along with the return connecting rod (*qv*) engine it was one of the most popular types of propulsion for early naval screw steamers.

periscope. Optical tube which uses lenses and prisms to transfer the user's line of sight to a different plane, allowing vision over or around solid objects, *eg* from inside a gun turret or conning tower or from a submerged submarine.

pivot gun. A weapon mounted on a slide carriage that was pivotted at its end or centre, allowing the gun to be fired on different bearings.

plough bow. An extreme form of ram bow configuration in which the point was extended a long way forward of the stemhead. Often carried, not for ramming, but to reduce wave-making resistance at high speed, and of light construction.

polygroove rifling. Rifling (*qv*) in the barrel of a gun consisting of multiple grooves.

pom-pom. First applied to the 1pdr of the Boer War, in a naval context it came to describe the Vickers 2pdr automatic; the nickname was supposedly derived from the sound of the gun in action.

Pook turtles. Nickname for the riverine ironclads built for the Federal forces in the US Civil War under the direction of the naval constructor Samuel Pook.

prismatic powder. *See* propellant powder.

propellant powder. Little improvement over traditional black powder (gunpowder) was noticeable before the 1860s when the increasing length of BL (*qv*) guns encouraged larger-grained pebble powder of increased density designed to burn more slowly and exert a more even pressure on the projectile for the whole length of its travel down the bore. This approach was further refined by Major Rodman of the US Army who, realizing the importance of the size and density of grains, perfected the prismatic powder of regular hexagonal pattern so widely used in the 1870s. Some very large grain types, like Italian Fossano powder, were developed but the 1880s saw the introduction of German brown powder, which was even more slow burning. From its colour it was sometimes known as cocoa powder, and an improved version was known in the Royal Navy as SBC (slow burning cocoa). It proved irregular in action due to sensitivity to the moisture content, and this hastened its replacement by 'smokeless' propellants (*qv*) in the 1890s.

QF. Quick-firing, or quick-firer. A medium or small calibre gun characterised by a rapid-acting system of breech operation, firing a brass cartridge and projectile that was either separate from or fixed to the cartridge case and was not too heavy to be loaded manually. Called rapid-fire (RF) guns in the US Navy.

ram. The beak or spur extension of the bow at or below the waterline intended to sink an opponent by deliberate collision (as with ancient galley tactics); by extension applied to ships in which the ram was the principal weapon of offence.

razée. From French; applied to a warship of the traditional wooden type structurally cut down to a lower rate, usually by the equivalent of a single gundeck. Thus a two-decker might be made a frigate, and by the loss of its forecastle and quarterdeck a frigate could be made into a sloop. A useful modification for ships regarded late in their careers as too small for the current standard; retaining their more powerful main batteries, they then became formidable additions to their new lower rating.

RBL. Rifled breech-loader (or -loading); applied to guns, usually early.

receiving ship. Any vessel, usually a superannuated hulk, serving as temporary accommodation for seamen before they were sent on active service.

redoubt. Fortification term implying small independently defensible position within a larger fortress; used of the section of an ironclad enclosed behind armour.

reciprocating engine. One in which the power was developed by a back-and-forth motion (such as a piston working in a cylinder) rather than a rotary motion like a turbine. The term usually implied a steam reciprocating engine.

rectangular boiler. Early form fabricated of flat plates and consequently less able to withstand higher pressures than the cylindrical (*qv*) or 'Scotch' type.

return connecting rod engine. An ingenious solution to the problem of the short connecting rod imposed on horizontal engines for screw ships (where the cylinder had to lie to one side of the propeller shaft and so was limited by the breadth of the ship). Perfected by Maudslays, this type of engine had two piston rods passing above and below the shaft, power being brought back to the crank from the joint crosshead (*qv*) by a 'returning' connecting rod. Usually called a back-acting engine in the USA.

RGF. Royal Gun Factory (Woolwich), a major producer of the Royal Navy's ordnance for much of the nineteenth century.

rifling. Spiral grooves along the inside of a barrel designed to impart spin to the projectile in order to increase accuracy. A rifled muzzle-loader was usually abbreviated to RML or MLR (muzzle-loading rifle), and a rifled breech-loader to RBL or BLR.

Risk Fleet. Refers to the German fleet built up under Admiral Tirpitz's direction from the 1890s. Tirpitz argued that the German navy might not be able to equal the Royal Navy in numbers but should be large enough so that war between the two powers would be regarded by Britain as too great a risk to her naval supremacy.

roller path or roller race. The track for a circuit of rollers acting as a bearing to carry a heavy revolving weight, typically a gun turret.

rpm. Revolutions per minute: a measurement of revolving speed, usually in an engine crankshaft or propeller.

sagging. The opposite of hogging (*qv*), in which the hull distorts by drooping amidships rather than at the extremities, particularly when the ends are both in wave crests with a trough amidships. Hogging was the main problem with sailing ships; the weight of engines amidships made sagging more serious in steamers.

SBC. Slow burning cocoa. *See* propellant powder.

Schichau. F Schichau of Elbing, a German naval shipbuilder, particularly associated with the development of the German torpedo boat and destroyer.

schooner. A fore and aft rigged vessel with at least two masts (a fore and a main, unlike a ketch or yawl which carried a main and a mizzen). Those setting square sails on topmasts were designated topsail schooners or fore topsail schooners if they had square canvas on the fore topmast only.

Schwartzkopf. German manufacturer of early self-propelled torpedoes.

Scotch boiler. *See* cylindrical boiler.

secondary armament. From the late 1860s naval guns became larger, requiring the thickest armour to resist their shot, which meant for reasons of weight and stability that not all the ship could be so protected; the largest guns were also slow firing, reducing the chances of scoring enough hits on an opponent to be decisive. In these circumstances a secondary armament of more, faster firing but smaller calibre guns seemed logical, in order to attack the undefended or poorly protected sections of the enemy ship. *See also* intermediate battery.

segmental engine. The invention of William Wright of the Connecticut firm of Woodruff and Beach, this machinery was radically different from the usual reciprocating engine in that the piston did not move back and forth in a straight line but swung through 60 degrees in a curved cylinder shaped like a segment of a circle. The curved piston rods from each cylinder head were joined to form a complete circle, with a connecting rod to the crankshaft. The geometry was such that the travel of the swinging piston was sufficient to provide one revolution of the crankshaft. The engine was only fitted to the US gunboat *Pequot* of 1863.

separate ammunition. Ammunition which was loaded in two stages, the projectile and the propellant charge. This system applied to all the largest guns but in the smaller calibres distinguished separate loading quick-firers (*qv*) from fixed ammunition ones which had the projectile and cartridge case fixed together, and stowed and loaded as one.

sheer draught. The traditional name for the lines plan of a ship, showing profile with bow and buttock lines, waterlines and sections.

ship rig. In the sailing era the ship or full rig was defined as the principal driving sails on all three masts being square (later a few four and one five masted full rigger were built, but the vast majority carried three masts; two square rigged masts made the vessel a brig). The lower sail on the mizzen usually comprised fore and aft canvas but as long as square sail was carried above it the vessel was still rated as a ship.

Siamese engine. A patent paddle engine designed by Maudslay, Son and Field in 1839; its principal feature was two identical cylinders per crank (hence the name, by analogy with Siamese twins).

side lever engine. Early form of paddle machinery, transferring motion from the piston (*qv*) to the paddle shaft via a low rocking beam and a series of levers. It was, in effect, the traditional beam engine with the beam in pieces alongside the cylinder.

side-wheeler. Steamer with paddles on the broadside rather than at the stern.

Sims-Edison torpedo. *See* torpedo.

Singer mine. *See* Fretwell mine.

sloop. As understood in the nineteenth century a small cruiser, below a frigate (*qv*) but above a gunboat (*qv*) in size and status. Paddle sloops often carried out fleet duties, but the later screw sloops were mainly used for colonial policing duties. *See also* corvette *and* gunvessel.

'smokeless' propellants. Replacement for old gunpowder-derived propellants, which on explosion were not entirely gasified, the remnant being given off as clouds of dense smoke. Powders were mechanical mixtures of inorganic substances whereas the new nitrocellulose and nitro-glycerine based propellants were chemical compounds of organic origin which burnt with little or no smoke. Introduced in the late 1880s.

smooth bore. An unrifled gun; the traditional form of naval cannon before the mid-nineteenth century.

snagboat. A river steamer fitted to remove obstacles, such as tree stumps, from the navigable channels.

spar torpedo. *See* torpedo.

spur ram. A separate underwater extension to the bow designed to hole an enemy by deliberate collision in combat. The ram shape was often used for later warships but without a separate spur.

steam frigate. A frigate (*qv*) with steam power, at first in the form of paddle, and then screw, propulsion. The first seagoing ironclads had only a single covered gundeck and were initially referred to as frigates.

steam sloop. A sloop (*qv*) with paddle or later screw propulsion.

steam turbine. A form of rotary engine in which power is generated by the action of steam on a series of rings of closely set blades alternately fixed and revolving. The perfection of the marine turbine is attributable to Sir Charles Parsons, his first practical success being dated to 1892.

stepped screw. *See* Welin block.

Stevens Battery. A pioneering but abortive design of 1843 for an armoured warship for the US Navy; the brainchild of Robert L Stevens of Hoboken, New Jersey.

stroke. In a reciprocating engine, a single complete movement of the piston or piston rod; also the management of the distance travelled by the piston or piston rod.

Surveyor of the Navy. In the Royal Navy the senior official charged with the design, construction and repair of the ships; it later became an administrative rather than an active design appointment, being replaced in the latter role by the DNC or Director of Naval Construction (*qv*). The title Surveyor was changed to Controller in the second half of the nineteenth century.

TBD. Torpedo boat destroyer; a British designation for an enlarged torpedo boat, originally designed to protect larger ships from torpedo attack, but eventually superseding its intended prey in offence as well as defence. With its designation shortened to 'destroyer', it became the prime fleet escort, with anti-submarine and eventually anti-aircraft duties added to its job description.

Thornycroft. Britain specialist builder of fast craft, particularly torpedo boats and destroyers. Founded by John I Thornycroft, initially at Chiswick on the Thames, the company built its larger and later vessels at Woolston, near Southampton, but continued to build small craft on the Thames at Hampton.

torpedo. Underwater explosive device; the term was originally applied to the mine (*qv*) but was later confined to what was originally called the 'locomotive' or 'automobile' torpedo, the self-propelled submerged device developed by Whitehead (*qv*) in 1866. The spar torpedo (an explosive charge on the end of a long pole) of the 1860s and 1870s was replaced by a variety of self-propelled types besides the Whitehead: the Lay design of the 1870s, driven by compressed carbon dioxide and wire guided; the US Howell of 1889 powered by a flywheel spun up before release; the Berdan or Borden with a rocket-propelled turbine; and the British Brennan coast defence weapon of the late 1880s which was driven by reeling in two wires off drums that span the propellers. There were also electric torpedoes powered through shore cables designed by Ericsson (about 1873), and the Sims-Edison of the 1880s, but Nordenfelt's design of about 1880 was battery powered.

torpedo boat. Small, fast craft derived from steam launches designed to carry out attacks on larger ships by means of the torpedo.

torpedo boat destroyer. *See* TBD.

torpedo cruiser. A cruiser (*qv*) whose principal mode of attack was the torpedo; probably optimised for speed. The type tended to lose ground as the far smaller torpedo boat (*qv*) became the favoured method of delivery the new weapon.

torpedo depot ship. A combination of base ship and carrier for small torpedo boats which could be launched by means of heavy duty davits. The depot ship not only maintained the boats and their weapons but could transport them to the scene of action, overcoming their inherent tactical defects of short range and minimal seaworthiness.

torpedo gunboat. An early attempt to produce a seaworthy counter to the torpedo boat (*qv*) and thus a precursor of the TBD (*qv*).

torpilleur de haut mer. French 'high seas torpedo boats'; seagoing vessels for fleet duties as opposed to the *defense mobile* type which were fit only for local defence.

trade cruiser. A cruiser (*qv*) optimised for commerce warfare; the design would tend to emphasise range and seaworthiness, the other characteristics depending on whether the ship was intended for the attack or defence of trade.

triple expansion engine. Machinery in which the steam is subject to three stages of expansion, driving in sequence a cylinder at high pressure, then a larger one at intermediate pressure, and finally the largest (sometimes two) at the low remaining pressure. Since the same amount of steam was made to do more work, it was far more economical than simple expansion engines and resulted in significantly increased range.

trunk engine. *See* Penn trunk engine.

trunnions. Short cylindrical extensions at right angles to the barrel of a gun used to retain it to its carriage or mounting; the trunnions formed the axis on which the gun was elevated and depressed. In mountings where the gun was supported by a cradle, the term was applicable to the cradle in the same way, thus cradle trunnions.

tubular boiler. One in which the boiler space was filled with tubes in order to increase the area of water exposed to heating. Initially the hot gases from the furnace passed through tubes in a body of water (the fire-tube pattern), but in the more efficient water-tube type water passed through the tubes which were surrounded by the hot gases, allowing for more rapid and efficient steam generation.

tumblehome. The curving-in of the ship's side above the waterline; this feature was common before about 1815 but was abandoned in later sailing ships, the resulting vessels being described as wall-sided. Tumblehome was occasionally employed on steam warships, usually to increase the possibilty of axial fire from sponsoned gun mountings, or to reduce the weight of the deck.

turret. Revolving armoured gunhouse. The principal early designs of the 1860s were the British Coles type, which traversed on a roller path below the weather deck; the US Ericsson turret, which was completely above deck and had to be jacked up to revolve on a spindle; and the American Eads turret, probably the most advanced of all with extensive use of steam power, but not widely favoured in the US Navy. In France Dupuy de Lôme introduced a turret that resembled the Coles type but was mounted over an armoured cylinder, anticipating the later barbette-turret, in which the open barbette (*qv*) style mounting was covered by an armoured gunhouse; in later usage turret usually meant this kind of mounting.

turret ram. An armoured warship combining the ram (*qv*) and a revolving gun turret (*qv*) as its principal weapons of attack.

turret ship. An armoured warship whose main armament was mounted in one or more turrets (*qv*).

turtle-backed. A forecastle arrangement designed to throw off water at speed – a fore deck with exaggerated camber (curving down from the centreline to the deck edge) sloping down to the stemhead. A common feature of early TBDs which were often called 'turtleback destroyers'.

two-decker. A ship with two complete gundecks plus upperworks; always the most common arrangement for line of battle ships. When frigates acquired a complete upper (spar) deck, they were described as double-banked rather than two-decked since they had no additional upperworks.

U-boat. A German submarine (from *Unterseeboot*).

Vavasseur mounting. One of the first forms of modern mountings for medium calibre BL guns, developed by J Vavasseur in Britain in the early 1880; open shielded guns on broadside or centre pivot mountings (*qv*). The slides were inclined upwards and backwards, so that recoil and run-out were aided by gravity.

vent-piece. Part of the breech of the early Armstrong BLs through which the firing mechanism operates.

Vickers. The British engineering, shipbuilding and aircraft manufacturing company of Vickers, Son and Maxim; shipbuilding mostly concentrated on large warships, was based at Barrow in Furness.

water-tight bulkhead. Solid athwartship partition capable of resisting the flooding of water from compartments on one side of it to the other. It might have apertures such as doors or scuttles but these had to be water-tight also when closed, whilst pipes and ventilator trunks would have valves to be closed. Any such device will leak after damage.

water-tube boiler. *See* tubular boiler.

wedge breech block. Breech closing mechanism using a laterally sliding wedge; sometimes vertically sliding.

Welin block. A patent breech block (*qv*) locked by a stepped pattern of screw threads.

wet gun-cotton. Chemical explosive. Nitrocellulose with about 15 per cent added water to increase safety.

White. J Samuel White, British ship- and boatbuilder of Cowes, Isle of Wight, specialising in fast small craft up to destroyer size.

Whitehead. Robert Whitehead (1823–1905), British engineer, perfector of the automobile torpedo while in Austrian service at Fiume. In the early years 'Whitehead' was virtually synonymous with torpedo (*qv*).

wire-winding. British method introduced in the 1890s of building up large gun barrels by winding steel strip under pressure round a tubular core; very strong for its weight but sometimes criticised for lack of longitudinal rigidity, or 'droop'.

Yarrow. British specialist builder of small fast craft, particularly associated with torpedo boats and destroyers. Founded by A F, later Sir Alfred, Yarrow (1842–1932), the yard was originally on the Thames at Poplar but moved to Scotstoun on the Clyde in 1907.

Index